A Century of Alpines

Jill Biehl
June 1992

A Century of Alpines

The Sixth International Rock Garden Plant Conference
Held at Warwick University, 6th–11th April 1991

Edited by Richard Bird

ISBN 0 9518517 0 5

© Copyright The Sixth International Rock Garden Plant Conference Report
First published 1991

Published by the Conference and stocked jointly by

The Alpine Garden Society   and   The Scottish Rock Garden Club
AGS Centre   21 Merchiston Park
Avon Bank   Edinburgh EH10 4PW
Pershore
Worcestershire WR10 3JP

Photoset by Rowland Phototypesetting Limited,
Bury St Edmunds, Suffolk
Colour origination and printing by Simmons Printers Limited, Chelmsford

Contents

Illustrations

Conference Committee

The Conference was jointly sponsored by the Alpine Garden Society and the Scottish Rock Garden

Committee

Jack Elliott (Chairman)
Ron MacBeath (Vice Chairman)
Jill Wennberg (Co-ordinator)
Ian Aitchison (Treasurer)
Mary Randall (Show Secretary)

Richard Bird
David Hazelgrove
Alexander Leven
Jo Stallard

Joan Stead
Evelyn Stevens
Henry Taylor
Michael Upward

Introduction

JACK ELLIOTT

The 1991 International Conference, 'A Century of Alpines', was sponsored jointly by the Alpine Garden Society and by the Scottish Rock Garden Club. This was the fifth conference arranged by our Society since the war, the first having been in 1951. The preliminary organisation began three years ago with a committee composed of equal numbers of members from each Society, who were joined for the Conference itself by many other helpers, essential for the smooth running of the Show, the publications stand, the plant stall, the lecture arrangements and the pre- and post-Conference tours, together with the garden visits, theatre visits and many 'behind the scenes' activities. All these helpers worked together to make the Conference a success and we thank them most sincerely.

Five hundred delegates arrived from all over the world, with sizeable parties from Canada, New Zealand, the USA, Czechoslovakia and most other countries of Europe, with other delegates from as far away as Peru, Japan and Australia. They heard fascinating thought-provoking presentations from lecturers of many nationalities. During the last decade more and more British lecturers have been invited to the USA, Canada and New Zealand, and this has been a reciprocal arrangement providing an invaluable interchange of knowledge and fellowship between alpine enthusiasts, culminating in this Conference. The programme was very full but we did not anticipate our visitors attending everything we had arranged. It was equally important that they should take advantage of a unique opportunity of meeting the lecturers, meeting growers from all over the world and seeing the astonishing display of plants at the Show.

The Show, with over 1500 plants exhibited, was the finest display of alpine plants ever staged, a remarkable demonstration of the skill of our growers today, a skill which seems to increase from conference to conference. The Show is described in detail later but it is worthy of note that it included a great number of plants never previously exhibited. The last ten years have seen a steady influx of new plants from the gardens of other countries and from seed collections from around the world, especially from the Andes, from North America, from Japan, China and the Himalayas, and from New Zealand. After so many years of botanical exploration it is remarkable that there are many areas from which new and exciting plants can still be introduced. I am sure that in 2001, and probably 2051, we will still be enjoying the challenge presented by new introductions and re-introductions.

Where will the new plants of the next decade come from? The alpine plants of South America are still little known but they have often proved difficult to grow. With the ever increasing skill of our growers and the increasing use of scientific methods, including micropropagation, Andean plants should become more popular. The same applies to the smaller plants of China and the Himalayas, a large proportion of which have, in the past, been lost after their first introduction. Thanks to our seed exchanges the plants of North America are becoming increasingly known and grown, but there is a great and comparatively untapped potential which must impress any visitors to the Rocky Mountains or to the cooler areas between the Rockies and the Pacific coast. New Zealand plants are becoming increasingly popular and the only obstacle to their increased use in gardens is the difficulty of obtaining freshly-collected seed which germinated without difficulty, whereas the seed which has been stored until the next 'seed exchange' often produces poor results.

Experts on all these potential sources of plants talked to us at Warwick and showed us slides of many alpines yet to be introduced, as well as of those already ornamenting our gardens. They have contributed full accounts to this Report, which can now be studied here in more detail. The Report also includes comprehensive articles on micropropagation, a technique which is likely to play an ever-increasing role in making rare plants available to us.

We were fortunate at the Conference to have a good attendance of nurserymen and a well-stocked Societies' plant stall, which gave delegates from home and overseas an opportunity of purchasing many uncommon plants.

Warwick University proved an excellent venue. The Lecture Hall and Show Hall were of ample size and the nurserymen's displays were all nearby. Accommodation was of a good standard, with an unusual number of en suite rooms for those who like a little more luxury than most universities provide. The staff of the University were most willing and helpful throughout and we are very grateful for all they did to make the event so successful.

Among all our enthusiastic Conference visitors there was already some discussion about possible venues for the interim International Conference in 1996, and even for 2001, occasions which all our visitors appeared to be looking forward to with enthusiasm. Perhaps the organisers of this Conference will be happy to leave any serious consideration of 2001 until they have enjoyed 1996, whether it be in Sweden or in Canada, two possible suggestions mentioned as alternatives to the USA. I am sure that wherever it is held, British visitors will support it in strength.

What Makes Alpines Tick? – A Century of Alpine Ecology

JOHN GOOD

'In nature there are neither rewards nor punishments; there are consequences.'
Robert G. Ingersoll (1833–1899).

Among the earth's terrestrial environments there is none more hostile or with fewer kinds of adapted plants than the tundras and barrens above and beyond the alpine and arctic timberlines. The plants which live there do so not from choice but as a result of their ability to survive in an environment so hostile that it excludes other species. The primary aim of this chapter is to investigate the nature of that environment and the ways in which alpine plants have managed to adapt to it. The knowledge so gained should help us to know our plants better and cultivate them more successfully.

While some plant species are endemic to the Arctic, and many more are restricted to the alpine regions of various mountain ranges, a relatively large group of common species are widespread and occur in both arctic and alpine tundra locations. Such taxa are commonly called 'arctic-alpine' species. Much of the ecological research on tundra plants has focused on these species rather than on plants which are limited to the Arctic or the mountains. This is because an understanding of their adaptive mechanisms can provide answers to questions concerning evolution within and migration between these similar, but different, low-temperature environments. Species have been chosen for study because of their interest to ecologists rather than their suitability as garden plants, so some unfamiliar names may crop up in this account. Nevertheless, the information that has been gained from study of these species can be applied to the species we wish to grow.

For the purposes of this account arctic and alpine plants are defined as those growing beyond or above the tree line (timberline in USA). Many alpine species also occur in meadows or open areas below the tree line, in some cases right down to sea level, and we can grow many of them in lowland gardens, but no non-alpine survives for long in the true alpine environment. Tree line is a relatively reliable guide to alpine environments in mountains in temperate or warmer regions where natural forest exists unaffected at its altitude limit by man. It cannot of course be used for mountains in very cold regions (the Arctic, Antarctica) where trees are not able to grow even at sea level, or where the tree line has been altered by man's activities.

Where there is a tree line it seems that regardless of the elevation at which it occurs, varying from as low as 300m (1000ft) in some New Zealand mountains to as high as 4300m (14,000ft) in the Himalaya it approximates very roughly to the elevation at which the mean air temperature for the warmest month is 10°C (50°F) (Swan 1967). In some way, probably by a temperature limitation of photosynthesis, leaf growth and wood production, this mean temperature value appears to reflect the limit for tree growth. Wood production is quite wasteful of energy and this probably explains the reduction in both size and number of woody plants with increasing altitude that we see in the alpine zone and with increasing latitude in the Arctic and Antarctic.

In the last analysis, what constitutes arctic or alpine conditions is always a matter of judgement. However, the effect of a forest on microclimate is so great as to make it quite different from open tundra, so that where the tree line exists it remains a useful general boundary between ecosystems (Billings & Mooney 1968). Most of what follows will, therefore, relate to alpine and arctic-alpine plants as so defined, although exceptions will be made to throw light on particular problems.

ARCTIC AND ALPINE ENVIRONMENTS

Arctic and alpine environments share important characteristics but also differ substantially. The factor that unites them more than any other is cold or cool summers. Cold winters occur in other regions, such as the great central continental plains of North America and Eurasia, but in these places the summers are hot. Places near the tree line in the Arctic and in the alpine zone of mountains have similar mean annual temperatures and snow cover duration but little else. The Arctic receives virtually no solar radiation for up to 6 months of the year and almost continual sunlight for the remainder. Alpine regions, on the other hand, experience regular diurnal and seasonal light regimes determined by their latitude and largely unaffected by altitude. The Arctic is no more windy than most mid-latitude regions, while many alpine sites experience extreme maximum and high mean wind speeds. Much of the Arctic receives little snowfall whereas some alpine areas have among the highest totals of the world.

Comparative studies have been made of the productivity of the vegetation at arctic and alpine tundra sites, in which the total amounts of leaves, stems, flowers, fruits and roots produced from measured plots of land were recorded. The results indicate that temperature is the primary limiting factor to plant growth and that the amount of vegetation produced from a given area of land in arctic and alpine tundra is in the same range as that for deserts. Air and soil temperatures are generally lower in the Arctic than in alpine environments but wind-chill in the mountains keeps the summer maximum temperatures low so that the end result in terms of productivity is generally similar.

It is necessary to stress the importance of cold temperatures in summer as the dominant feature of alpine environments because it is not always apparent on summer excursions to the mountains, when a relentless sun beats down on inadequately protected backs and thighs through a thin and cloudless atmosphere. Those with more experience will expect and be prepared for that sudden change from 'summer' to 'winter' as the clouds gather, the wind blows and the sudden shower of driving sleet chills to the bone. And even when the days are bright all through there is the near certainty of frosty nights. In a study of climate in fellfield (alpine meadow) and cushion communities in New Zealand it was shown that the mean annual air temperature was close to freezing. Over a five-year period of continuous recording the longest period without frost was thirteen days. During a full year on average only about 20% of the days were frost free while on 30% of days there was no thaw. These figures are typical and could be repeated for mountains around the world in both northern and southern hemispheres.

Temperatures in the soil are generally much less severe than those in the air, particularly when the ground is covered with deep snow. A snow covering several metres thick may cause a temperature difference between air and ground of as much as 30°C (Ylimaki, 1962 in Woodward 1987). Thus when the air temperature is 30°C below zero, a not uncommon occurrence in the Alps in winter when wind chill is a major factor, the plants will be comfy at or near freezing point. Plants growing in bare soil or rock, as on cliffs, ridges or windswept screes, experience much more violent temperature fluctuations. The most dramatic diurnal temperature fluctuations of all occur in high equatorial mountains where 'summer' comes by day and 'winter' by night, there being of course no true seasons, only in some cases drier and wetter periods. The huge differences between day and night temperatures have caused plants to develop special adaptations which are somewhat different from those required by species occurring on mountains in the higher latitudes.

In an open vegetation of isolated plants such as occurs in a scree or polar desert, solar radiation reaches the bare soil between the plants without hindrance and heat is equally easily radiated outwards. In closed vegetation the plant cover insulates against heat flow thus slowing soil thawing and freezing. As a result of these vegetational differences soil and lower level air temperatures are quite different between, for example, an open scree and a moist meadow or bog. In the case of the scree there are significant microclimate differences between the crowns of the plants and the open spaces between. This 'phytomicroclimate' is influenced by the density of the plant and by leaf shape, size, colour and pubescence. Tight cushions trap warm air more effectively than plants with more open structure. Small, tightly clustered, incurved leaves which are dark in colour retain more heat than those which are larger and more open in arrangement. Hairy leaves trap more air than glabrous leaves and slow down air movement so improving insulation within the crown of the plant.

In a study of cushions of *Diapensia lapponica* in Swedish Lapland it was shown (Fischer & Kuhn 1984) that under summer conditions with almost continual daylight but much reduced light intensity at night, the outer layers of the cushion warmed up considerably more than the air in the day, causing a steep temperature gradient towards the centre. At night these outer layers cooled off more than the air as they slowly transferred their heat inwards towards the centre of the cushion and outwards to the air. The diurnal temperature fluctuations in the parts of the cushion close to the surface considerably exceeded those in the soil, but further into the cushion the temperatures remained much more stable. This temperature stability, and the ability of the cushion to retain heat gained in the day which would be lost in a plant with a more open growth habit, is probably important in allowing cushion plants to withstand severe cold and survive in very exposed situations. Hence their predominance on cliffs, windswept ridges and open slopes where insulating snow cover is absent in winter. Some measurements in *Loiseleuria procumbens* showed the diurnal temperature fluctuations in this cushion-like dwarf shrub to be similar in type if less in degree than those of *Diapensia*.

The moisture regime varies considerably between arctic and alpine environments. Precipitation is generally much lower in the Arctic than on even dry mountains further south. Low precipitation in the high Arctic, together with the presence of permafrost which on relatively flat ground prevents downward movement of water, often results in such weak soil leaching that salts accumulate on or below the soil surface in amounts sufficient to restrict growth of all except salt-tolerant plants. This is just what happens in deserts where evapotranspiration exceeds precipitation and the similarity has led to various authors describing the high Arctic as 'cold-desert' (Stocker 1963). Such saline deserts are rare in alpine situations because rainfall is generally higher and where there is permafrost the water moves over it in summer through the thawed surface soil. However, there are examples of cold-desert in dry mountain ranges, as, for example, the eastern slopes of the high Andes in Argentina. Plants from such areas are likely to be able to grow satisfactorily in cultivation without the need for added salt; they are able to tolerate salt rather than needing it for their metabolism.

If there is more precipitation in a particular mountain habitat than there is water loss by evaporation from the vegetation and soils, the net result is a water surplus that in alpine climates in winter accumulates as snow and in summer leaches soils. If there is a net deficit at any time of year water is used from soil storage, providing of course that excess water has been stored in the soil and is available. While alpine environments are generally wetter than arctic ones there is a considerable variation between and within different mountain ranges. Humid climates in which precipitation exceeds water demand throughout the growing season are much more common than arid climates, which imply water shortages at certain times of the year. Mountain chains with generally humid climates include the Alps, most of Scandinavia, the Caucasus east to Dagestan, the Urals, many mountain areas of southern Siberia, coastally influenced Alaska, the Aleutians, the mountains of Japan, the New Zealand Alps. Areas with slight to severe summer drought include Transcaucasia, continental valleys of Scandinavia, Central Asia, southern Atlas, parts of the Andes and the western United States. Both Mediterranean and dry continental climates produce summer drought even though there may be considerable winter precipitation. Thus plants growing at 1700m on Mt. Rainier in the Cascades of the state of Washington are likely to suffer drought in July of each year despite a mean annual precipitation of 2963mm (118in). This is because only about 43mm (1.7in) of that precipitation occurs in July; 55mm (2.2in) short of potential evapotranspiration in that month.

In most mountain ranges there are rain shadow effects and in some cases these are extreme, resulting in huge differences in precipitation on the slopes facing towards and away from the prevailing wind. Thus the south-facing slopes of the central and eastern Himalaya receive considerable monsoon precipitation while the high Tibetan plateau to the north is very dry. In the Pyrenees the north facing slopes, especially at the west end of the range near the Atlantic are wet and cool in summer while the southern slopes, particularly at the Mediterranean end, are hot and dry.

Most alpine areas even in arid mountains show some water accumulation as snow that becomes suddenly and totally available with summer. Local spots may therefore have a humid climate suitable for plants which could not grow in these mountains otherwise. With the possible exception of the well-known effects of geology, which result in the restriction of some plants to acid or alkaline rocks and soils, the distribution of soil moisture has the most profound effects of any environmental factor in controlling local habitat conditions and vegetational gradients both in alpine and and arctic regions. All plants growing in these environments are of necessity adapted to low temperatures but some are better adapted to drought and extremes of temperature than others. These are the plants which occur on the ridges, rocks and open slopes where soil moisture status is likely to fluctuate wildly during the growing season. The threat is particularly severe in winter when the plants are exposed to physiological drought. Even though there is plenty of water in the soil the plants are unable to utilize it because it is frozen. Thus they are unable to replace the moisture which is lost through the evaporative action of wind and sun. Water stress becomes more severe as the winter goes on.

Plants adapted to these windswept ridges have low transpiration rates throughout the year compared with those of the meadows below snowbanks which remain green and moist throughout the growing season. An example of a drought tolerant species which grows on exposed ridges is the dwarf alpine azalea (*Loiseleuria procumbens*). In addition to having low transpiration rates it is able to take up surface meltwater late in the winter through shallow adventitious roots when most of the soil is frozen. In contrast Alpenrose (*Rhododendron ferrugineum*) is intolerant of drought. It generally occurs in depressions which become snowbeds in winter. If the snow melts earlier than usual in late winter the plants lose water rapidly and may be killed. It is a not uncommon sight in summer to see dead plants at the edges of former snowbanks. Similarly, stands of coniferous trees can often be found at the timberline with their upper crowns completely brown and dead above the snowline of the previous winter.

The importance of snowbeds in determining patterns in alpine vegetation illustrates the pronounced influence of microenvironments. Environmental heterogeneity at particular sites is generally greater in the mountains than in the Arctic tundra because of the greater variability in slope, aspect, topographic irregularity and soils which in turn are reflected in more diverse microclimates and soil nutrient and water status. The effects of microenvironment may be pronounced even over distances as small as a few centimetres. For example, small changes in microtopography make a marked difference to soil temperature, depth of thaw, wind effects, snow drifting and resultant protection to leaves, buds and stems. The microtopographic effect may be caused by a rock, a peat hummock or by another plant.

The microhabitats provided by existing plants in open vegetation are exploited by others. Seedlings of many species in high alpine communities tend to be found more often in or on the margin of established cushions or clumps of vegetation than in the unvegetated areas between. The shelter and warmth provided by the cushion are probably major reasons for this. Additionally, soil fertility is greater among than between plants due to the accumulation of plant remains and the trapping of blown soil and dust, while soil erosion is less of a problem. Foraging animals are less likely to find seed or seedlings among vegetation than they are in open situations. These factors combined often more than compensate for the greater competition for light, nutrients and water that the seedling must endure when trying to develop within established vegetation (Welden 1985). Very often the species which colonise existing cushions or mats of vegetation are more competitive than their hosts and eventually overwhelm them. Thus the mix of species changes as soil stability and fertility increase and the

1   *Werneria nubigena* has far-reaching underground stems which enable it to survive fire and grazing (see page 13)

2   Midday in the high Andes and roots of alpine plants remained encased in ice while the shoots receive high insolation (see page 25)

3   A selection of blue poppies, meconopsis (see page 35)

4   A white form of *Meconopsis horridula* (see page 36)

5   A good form of *Meconopsis wallichii* (see page 39)

6   Val d'Heas in the French Pyrenees (see page 45)

7   *Linum flavum* in the Spanish Pyrenees (see page 47)

vegetation cover becomes more dense. Very often it is possible to see a patchwork of ground in a small area on a mountain where all stages of colonisation from bare ground to complete vegetation cover are juxtaposed. In the better developed patches of vegetation stress tolerant species still occur, but only as subdominants in local patches of disturbed ground caused by the activities of animals or such factors as scree movement, soil slippage or rock falls.

As the vegetation becomes more stabilized the extreme stress tolerators, including the cushion plants, become less common. This is because of their poor competitive ability, which contrasts markedly with the extreme competitive ability of alpine meadow plants. In the garden we must either keep good and poor competitors apart or else keep a constant eye on the more rapacious species, acting when necessary to restrain them. Pot cultivation is one way of eliminating competition and partially explains why some of the more extreme stress tolerators can be grown so effectively to large sizes in pots. Plants which are adapted to withstand severe competition may grow satisfactorily in isolation but will tend to remain more 'in character' if grown in company. The alpine lawn is the most natural place in the alpine garden for these competitive plants. Here they can fight among themselves with little risk of losses provided that the real thugs are disciplined from time to time.

The difference between the quality of the light which alpine plants receive at high altitudes in the wild and that which they must put up with at low elevation in our gardens, is commonly believed to be a major factor in limiting our success with some of the more difficult species. It is often said that light intensities are higher in the mountains and that the light is richer in some parts of the spectrum, notably the ultraviolet (UV) and that this results in more congested growth and more flowers. Research has shown that light intensity does indeed generally increase with increasing altitude because of the reduction of dust and particulate pollutants in the atmosphere. Of course, the actual amount of light received will vary depending upon latitude and cloudiness; mountains with clear summer skies will receive more light energy than those where summer rainfall is high.

The situation regarding UV is rather complicated and even more affected by cloudiness. The UV received at ground level is a combination of the direct ('beam') UV coming straight from the sun, and that reflected back from the sky. While beam UV does increase with altitude, sky UV often decreases, especially in cloudy mountains. The net result is generally a slight increase in total UV with elevation (Caldwell 1968). In field experiments at 3500m in Colorado using UV filters it was found that UV exclusion had very little effect on alpine plants. In one species of *Trifolium* removal of UV *increased* flowering, but there were no significant effects in five other species. Also there were very few effects on growth. If UV were really important for maintaining alpine plants 'in character' and enhancing flowering then it would not be possible to grow good specimens under glass because UV is mostly screened out by this material. The great reduction in light intensity at sea level and especially in an overshaded alpine house or frame, or one with dirty glass, is much more likely to be the cause of etiolation (drawn-up growth) and poor flowering. The reason why some alpines (e.g. *Androsace alpina*, *Saxifraga stolitzkae*) are so susceptible to these two problems while closely related plants (*Androsace vandellii*, *Saxifraga georgei*) are not remains a mystery.

PLANT ADAPTATIONS TO ARCTIC AND ALPINE ENVIRONMENTS

Terrestrial plants of arctic and alpine regions are mainly flowering plants (angiosperms), bryophytes (mosses and liverworts), and lichens. Ferns are also represented but with fewer species. Bryophytes and lichens are able to persist at altitudes and in extremes of environment where no higher plants can grow. This is because of their ability, most marked in the lichens, to withstand prolonged and extreme desiccation. Mosses tend to dominate in and below snowbanks while lichens cling to the windswept, rocky barrens. Almost all the flowering plants are herbaceous perennials or very low shrubs; annuals and biennials are very rare. For example, on the Beartooth Plateau of Wyoming only 3 out of a total of 191 species of flowering plants were annuals (Johnson & Billings 1962). One or 2 per cent of annuals seems to be about the norm in these environments while in temperate ecosystems they may comprise considerably more. Some species which normally are annuals near timberline and are listed as annuals in floras may be represented by perennial forms at higher elevations. Thus it was found that in the Medicine Bow Mountains of Wyoming all plants of *Androsace septentrionalis* at 2000m (8500ft) elevation were annual, but at 3640m (12,000ft) at least 80% were perennial. Such ecotypic variation should cause judges at shows to pause before disqualifying a plant from consideration for a prize because the floras say it is an annual.

Annual and biennial plants are scarce in tundra environments principally because of the necessity for them to complete the whole life cycle from germination to seed production annually or biennially. Few can manage this generation after generation in the short, cold growing season. Perennial plants have the advantage that they do not need to reproduce every year. They can put all their efforts in the early years into vegetative growth and thereafter need only set seed occasionally to ensure that the species survives and that as individuals they contribute their genes to future generations. The different strategies of biennial and perennial species is exemplified by a study which was made of the reproductive biology of gentians in the White Mountains of California (Spira & Pollak 1986). The biennial species (*G. tenella*, *G. prostrata*) were characterised by the production of large numbers of fruits each containing many seeds. In contrast fruit and seed set were considerably less and yearly seed production relatively low in the perennial *G. newberryi*. Closer analysis revealed that the biennial species allocated much larger proportions of their resources to flower, fruit and seed production than the perennial. Also, while *G. newberryi* depended on cross-pollination, which was often unreliable, *G. tenella* and *G. prostrata* relied on the more dependable self-pollination mechanism.

Prostrate shrubs exhibit the permanence of perenniality to the highest degree of any alpine plants, generally living longer than herbaceous perennials. So powerful are the environmental factors controlling form in arctic and alpine plants that the dwarf tundra shrubs often resemble non-woody cushion plants very closely. Compare, for example, the shrub *Kelseya uniflora* with the herbaceous cushion plant *Silene acaulis*. Both are equally congested and have similar small narrow leaves and stemless flowers. These very congested dwarf shrubs often grow extremely slowly so they require very little energy input in the form of carbohydrate produced by photosynthesis to enable them to survive from year to year. This and other characteristics, notably their tolerance of extreme cold, enables such shrubs as *Cassiope tetragona* and *Salix arctica* to grow almost at the limit of vegetation in the Arctic; both species extend north of latitude 83° in northern Greenland (Holmen 1957).

Despite the benefits of the dwarf shrub habit the greatest number of vascular plants in arctic and alpine environments are herbaceous perennials. These are of three main kinds: grasses, leafy dicotyledons and cushion dicotyledons. A few monocotyledons with bulbs also occur and these tend to increase in relative importance in the flora of the hotter, drier mountain ranges further south where retirement below ground in summer is an effective means of combatting drought. Typically the dicotyledons have a deep primary root system with shoots proliferating near the soil surface and no clear main stem. A few species have underground storage organs such as swollen roots (e.g. *Lewisia* spp., *Weldenia candida*) or rhizomes (e.g. many gentians, campanulas and primulas) which are utilized in food storage.

At the altitudinal limit for vascular plants in the mountains there is a greater variety of form in the less harsh environment of the snowbeds than on the windswept ridges and rock outcrops. The snowbed vegetation typically comprises grasses, small herbs, cushion plants and dwarf shrubs such as *Salix herbacea*. On the exposed areas small-leaved dwarf rosette plants, moss-like or cushion plants predominate, with occasional grass tussocks. Such well-loved species as *Silene acaulis*, *Saxifraga oppositifolia* and *Dryas octopetala* are common in these most extreme environments. In an interesting study McGraw (1985) compared ecotypes of *Dryas octopetala* collected from open ridges and snowbeds. He found that when both types were grown under the same 'lush' conditions of high nutrients, high light and high water availability the snowbed plants were larger in all their parts. They also withstood competition from other plants of either ecotype better. The plants from the open habitat were particularly poorly equipped to cope with root competition. These differences show how the tendency already noted for stress tolerant plants to be intolerant of competition extend right down to the within-species level.

High on the rocky peaks where most of the ground remains exposed to the fierce cold in winter there are miniature 'snowbeds' in the crevices of the rocks which have a flora all their own. The snow provides winter shelter and a supply of water to plants of a remarkably soft nature such as *Ranunculus glacialis* which it is a surprise to find at such high elevations. These plants depend upon meltwater to a greater extent than do the cushion plants and montane grasses. In many cases though softer in appearance they reach higher elevations than do the moss-like or cushion plants, extending well up into the zone of permanent snow where their only associates are crustose lichens and a few moss tufts. *Ranunculus glacialis* reaches 4270m (13,900ft) on the Finsteraarhorn in the Alps, the highest recorded elevation for any flowering plant in Europe. A similar and interesting parallel case occurs in New Zealand where *R. grahamii*, also an unlikely looking candidate to hold records for growing at high elevations, exists in snow crannies well above the permanent snow as high as 2900m (9500ft) on Malte Brun. Only two other species of flowering plants (*Parahebe birleyi* and *Hebe haastii*) grow higher in the New Zealand mountains and both of these are snow cranny plants whose straggly appearance belies their survival capabilities.

Tropical mountain vegetation is much more complex than and quite different floristically from the arctic-alpine types described so far. Tropical alpines are often columnar or sub-arborescent in form with large woolly leaves which fold inwards over the growing crown during the freezing tropical nights and spread out to capture moisture and sunlight during the day. Some species have been shown to have antifreeze-like compounds in their cell sap which protect the tissues from rupture during the alternating freeze-thaw cycles that they must constantly endure.

One of the most characteristic features of arctic and alpine plants, which is uncommon in plants of less hostile environments, is the possession of pre-formed flower buds. Rather than forming their flowers on the current year's growth they are initiated early in the season of the year before flowering, or in some cases the season before that. These flower buds are usually well developed by the time the plant goes dormant late in the summer and are ready to develop rapidly to maturity when conditions for growth return in spring. The legendary speed with which soldanellas push up through the melting snow provides a classic demonstration of this phenomenon. This adaptation, which allows the longest possible period for seed set and ripening, has been found in most species in each of a wide range of unrelated alpine floras as far apart as Greenland (Sorenson 1941) and New Zealand (Mark 1970). The repeated independent evolution of this adaptation suggests that preformed flowers confer a considerable reproductive advantage on plants growing in cold environments. Unfortunately flowers formed in the autumn are often less of an advantage in our gardens. Sometimes they are particularly prone to the freeze-thaw of our typical winters and they are also meat and drink to slugs and snails. You, like me, may have suffered the severe frustration of finally achieving a good plant of soldanella stuffed with flower buds in the autumn only to find that those malevolent molluscs have done their worst ere spring.

Another reproductive characteristic of arctic and alpine plants is the tendency for vegetative reproduction to increase and sexual reproduction by seed to decrease with increasing hostility of the environment. This is because producing seed is costly in terms of energy and therefore wasteful unless there is a high chance that the seed will perpetuate the species. A comparison of the metabolic costs of producing a new grass shoot by sexual reproduction via a seed or by the growth of a new tiller, based on rough calculations of the energy required for inflorescence production, seed set seedling survival, etc., suggests that sexual reproduction in this instance is some 10,000 times more costly! A comment of Oleg Polunin's following a trip to the Karakoram Mountains is worth quoting. 'I doubt whether much seed was set in the year of my visit. I concluded that the main methods of propagation and dispersal were by snow and earth movements, the crumbling of cliffsides, the flow of snow-melt water carrying pockets of soil containing living fragments of plants from one place to another' (Polunin, *The World of Rock Plants*, p. 96). The fact that sexual seed reproduction occurs at all in difficult environments where energy is in short supply is testament to the considerable evolutionary advantages of the recombination of genes achieved by cross-fertilization.

The pressure to reproduce vegetatively in harsh environments is shown by the evolution of vegetative adaptations within species which probably originally were primarily seed producers. For example, *Oxyria digyna* (mountain sorrel), which is a widespread arctic-alpine species, is non-rhizomatous and reproduces by seed in the central Rocky Mountains but populations from harsher environments in northern Alaska reproduce mainly by rhizomes. Another adaptation is the production of bulbils, usually as modified branches in the leaf axils, but sometimes replacing some or all of the ordinary flowers in the inflorescence. In *Polygonum viviparum*, a common plant of the European and North American mountains, the proportion of the inflorescence given over to bulbil production increases with elevation until in the most hostile environments there may be no seeds produced at all. In some arctic and alpine grasses vivipary is common. This involves germination of the seeds and formation of small plants within the seed head. Vivipary has been shown to be an inherited character which is only triggered when the seed-bearing plants receive particular combinations of environmental factors which are associated with arctic or alpine environments. Chief among these factors seems to be cold temperatures at the time of seed set.

Many arctic-alpine plants exhibit apparently normal seed production but some or all of the seeds are produced without fertilization. This phenomenon is known as agamospermy. Some species are obligate agamosperms, so that all their seeds are always produced in this way, as for instance in the genera *Alchemilla* and *Antennaria*. The more common condition, however, is facultative agamospermy in which the seeds may be formed either by the normal sexual process or, in more severe environmental conditions, without fertilization. This is the situation in the genera *Ranunculus* and *Polygonum* among many others. More commonly facultative agamospermy is characterized by predominantly asexual reproduction, which is only occasionally replaced by the sexual process. This rare fertilization gives rise to an immense variability in morphology within the species, because every one of the offspring can reproduce agamospermically as clones for many generations and give rise to large populations of apparently stable types. This is typical of, among others, the grass genus *Poa* and the genera *Hieracium* and *Taraxacum* (dandelions) in the Asteraceae and can lead taxonomists and others erroneously to distinguish the different types as separate species or sub-species.

Where cross-pollination does occur in arctic and alpine plants it is likely to be by insects rather than wind. In the Caucasus 89% of species were shown to be insect pollinated, the remainder being pollinated by wind. A few species rely on more exotic pollinators. Thus *Penstemon newberryi* and *P. davidsonii* have both been shown to be pollinated by hummingbirds in the Sierra Nevada of California, while the metre high *Lupinus alopecuroides* of the Andes is also visited by these wondrous birds. It seems that long-tongued insects such as moths and butterflies can act as surrogate pollinators, at least for the penstemons, since both set good seed in North Wales where hummingbirds are as scarce as dragon's teeth!

The principal kinds of pollinating insects for plants in the high mountains are short-tongued bees, bumblebees (syn. humblebees), flies (Diptera), butterflies and moths (Lepidoptera). Bumblebees are more common at high altitude in the North Hemisphere mountains than any other kinds of bees. In many places they are the only bees present. They fly only during the day when air temperature is above 10°C. Under favourable conditions they have been found at up to 5,100m (17,000ft) in the Hindu Kush where they were pollinating, among other genera, *Oxytropis*, *Astragalus* and *Hedysarum*. Flies can work at lower temperatures and in dimmer light than bees or butterflies. Long-tubed flowers are usually pollinated by bumblebees or lepidoptera while small flat flowers, e.g. Cruciferae and Rosaceae, are mostly pollinated by flies.

The puzzling and, for our Antipodean friends, disappointing predominance of white or yellow flowers in the New Zealand alpine flora has been explained as being probably due to the kinds of insects, and hence the types of pollination, which predominate there (Mark & Adams 1973). Specialised pollinating insects are either lacking (long-tongued bees) or scarce (butterflies). Both these groups are attracted by bright colours. Insect pollination appears to be carried out largely and quite efficiently by flies, with beetles, moths and short-tongued bees playing smaller roles. The flowers are in fact well adapted for pollination by these types of insects, as of course they must be if the species which bear them are to survive. If there had been insects in New Zealand that favoured brightly coloured flowers then there can be little doubt that such flowers would have evolved to satisfy them.

An intriguing characteristic of the flowers of some arctic and alpine plants, which is shared with the very un-alpine sunflower, is 'suntracking'. Species such as *Dryas octopetala*, *Papaver radicatum* and *Ranunculus glacialis* keep their flowers facing the sun. This 'suntracking', together with the parabolic shape of their flowers, captures the maximum amount of energy from the sun and reflects it towards the centre of the flower. This has a dual effect: it creates a warm spot attractive to pollinators and increases the rates of growth and maturation of the seed (Crawford 1989). There is increasing evidence that the Arctic forms of arctic-alpine species usually have the largest flowers, but more information is needed for a wider range of species to confirm this. If large flowers prove to be the rule of Arctic ecotypes it may well be that this is because they enable them to have the best chance of trapping as much as possible of the available sunlight energy, thereby enhancing their chances of setting viable seed during the period of long summer days.

Another adaptation which enhances flower warming and hence increases the chances of successful seed set occurs in those species such as *Saussurea gossypiphora*, *Salix arctica* and *Eriophorum* spp. (cottongrass) in which the developing fruits are surrounded by insulating down. It has been shown in *Salix arctica* that the temperature in the catkin surrounded by translucent down is several degrees centrigrade higher than that of the surrounding atmosphere.

Alpine plants tend, as we all know, to have large, deep-delving root systems. In fact their root:shoot ratios are generally much higher than those of other plants (varying from about 2:1 to 6:1), compared to values of 1:1 or less for most plants from lower altitudes. The large root systems of arctic and alpine plants act mainly as carbohydrate stores, providing reservoirs of energy to tide the plants through the long winter and allow for the burst of growth which takes place in spring as soon as the snow and ice melts. It is this ability of alpine plants to grow quickly at low temperatures as soon as the snow melts, using stored food reserves, combined with their early flowering, which enables them to persist and grow in alpine environments.

The new stems and leaves produced during this spurt of growth utilise the sun's energy throughout the short season to manufacture carbohydrate. This food is required for seed development, flower bud production and the laying down of stored reserves in existing and new roots.

The message here for the cultivator of high alpines is that they depend almost exclusively upon stored food in their roots for their early spring growth. Thus it is inadvisable and unnecessary to repot and risk root loss at this time. Repotting at the traditional time, immediately after flowering when the plant is growing busily and building up its reserves for the following winter, makes ecological as well as gardening sense. It is essential that there is always plenty of water available to the roots at this state to mimic the snowmelt of the mountains; also abundant light for photosynthesis. Once the season's new growth has been made it is probably best to keep the plants rather dry until the following spring unless they are known to come from an alpine environment where there is abundant summer moisture. Keeping the soil on the dry side should help limit the amount of soft growth made late in the season which is vulnerable to disease and cold in winter. Such late-season growth would not occur in the mountains because the temperatures would be dropping rapidly with the return of winter.

The vulnerability of many high alpines to winter cold in cultivation, particularly when a cold snap comes suddenly after a mild autumn, should not surprise us. This does not necessarily indicate, as is often supposed, that the species is not hardy, more likely that the plants have not received a necessary hardening period before being frozen. In the mountains the hardening process is guaranteed as the temperature drops rapidly in autumn. Thus it was shown in a study of *Diapensia lapponica*, which is a drought-tolerant evergreen cushion plant, that frost tolerance was only $-5°C$ in September but increased rapidly during October and remained high until March when the maximum frost resistance was $-58°C$ (Junnila 1985). Subsequently dehardening took place and in the beginning of May the maximum frost resistance was only $-9°C$. The period of winter hardiness was associated with increased tolerance of water deficiency stress indicating that this species like many other alpines can survive with very little water in winter provided it is fully dormant.

The plants of tropical mountains, unlike those from the far north which we have just been describing, experience suitable conditions for growth during daytime throughout the year even though they are frozen at night. Rolfe found on a 'winter' trip to the Bolivian Andes (Rolfe, personal communication) that even at 4,000m+ (13,000ft) plants continued active growth. Night time temperatures dropped so sharply that streamsides and small waterfalls froze until quite late in the day. Even with their roots frozen solid, species such as *Gentianella salifolia* were in full bloom while there was an endless display of Asteraceae.

Realisation of the need for plants from the highest elevations in temperate mountains to receive a hardening period and then remain dormant throughout the winter if they are to feel at home has led to attempts to mimic these conditions in cultivation. The well-known developments along these lines at Kew, which include the provision of refrigerated plunge beds, have been described in various articles (e.g. Halliwell 1981) and there is no doubt that success has been achieved with some difficult species, but it is very difficult to mimic natural conditions precisely and to provide for the varied requirements of different species, especially if those needs are not fully understood. Furthermore, the cost of providing special facilities means that few amateur gardeners are ever likely to consider installing them. The best general advice for those growing high alpines in pots, troughs or other containers is to try and ensure that the soil is full of roots as winter approaches and to keep the soil only as moist as is necessary to keep the plants alive.

An environmental hazard sometimes posed to plants growing in areas with summer drought, to which they must adapt if they are to survive, is fire. This may be either natural or caused by man as a way of improving the quality of grazing lands. Plants which have taproots, rhizomes or other underground foodstores which can survive the fire and give rise to new rosettes will have a good chance of survival in such situations as will naturally weedy plants which take advantage of the short-lived open ground that the fire creates. In the northern Andes *Werneria nubigena* is a widespread species forming large patches in grassland by means of its spreading rhizomes. Rolfe reports (Rolfe, personal communication) that it was seldom well flowered except in areas where the farmers had set fire to the hillside several months previously. In such places it was one of the few plants to have re-established, probably because it was able quickly to send up a fresh batch of leaves to replace the old ones. It seemed to Rolfe that this species was actually favoured by fire, possibly because it gets too congested in established grassland. He also notes that a report from Peru indicates that this species grows best where the turf is tightly grazed by rabbits and suggests that this may also be because grazing induces a similar flush of new growth to that caused by fire. Local increase in soil fertility as a result of burning or dung deposition may also be important in favouring this species.

In addition to harsh environmental conditions high alpines have to cope with pest and disease attack. Pests come in many forms and sizes, ranging from insects to molluscs, small mammals such as voles and large herbivores such as chamois, llamas, sheep and cattle. While little is known of the depredations of the smaller pests on alpine plants it can be assumed that they take their toll and that the plants have evolved means of resisting their attacks. They can do this either by employing various defences (thick waxy cuticle, spines, stinging hairs, chemicals which are either toxic or make the leaves unpalatable) or they can use the energy that such defences would cost in greater growth. Many species compromise, putting some energy into defence mechanisms and the remainder into growth. Both small and large herbivores may be fooled by camouflage and so miss out on a potential meal. *Ranunculus parnassifolius* is almost invisible except when in flower on its native scree slopes, as is the rosulate violet, *Viola congesta*, in its cindery home in the Andes, while Dora Stafford discovered a new species of *Nototriche* in Peru by sitting on it and shuffling over to investigate the nature of her soft landing! (Rolfe, personal communication). Should the camouflage fail the violet has a thick taproot capable of regeneration if decapitated and Rolfe noted that those rosettes which had been browsed had new shoots coming from their mangled bases. He also points out that there is some confusion between etiolation of the rosettes in cultivation, leading to an uncompressed, loose shoot wholly atypical of plants in the wild, and the quite normal elongation of the rootstock (with the rosette perched on the end) which is normal.

Plants are certainly not free of disease in the mountains, as careful observation will show. Few cushions of plants such as androsaces or drabas in the wild are as perfect as the unblemished domes we see at the Shows. Nevertheless, plants are probably generally more susceptible to disease in the garden than in the wild. This enhanced vulnerability is due to various reasons. The range of disease causing organisms to which the plants are exposed are different. Just as many tribes of South American Indians have been wiped out by diseases such as measles to which they have no natural immunity, so plants brought into cultivation may have no natural defences against diseases which they would never encounter in the wild. Even if a plant has some potential resistance to a particular disease in the garden it may still not be able to respond because of the very different growing conditions in cultivation compared with in the wild. For these reasons it is often necessary to give our plants a helping hand by controlling pests and diseases. This is best done by providing growing conditions which encourage healthy growth but from time to time chemical assistance may be required.

PHYSIOLOGICAL ADAPTATIONS OF ARCTIC AND ALPINE PLANTS

Much of the resistance of alpine plants to the many adverse factors which have been described depends upon specific physiological adaptations.

1. Seed dormancy and germination
Contrary to what has often been thought and written, seed dormancy as a protective mechanism is not common in arctic and alpine plants. Seed may

often germinate slowly and unevenly but this has too commonly been taken to be due to a chilling requirement. Where dormancy does occur (about 40% of species) it is most commonly due to seed-coat inhibition and can be overcome by soaking or scarification. Various studies have shown that seed dormancy is more common among dominant and abundant species than in rarer ones. It has been suggested that this may be one of the reasons for their success.

It seems that dormancy in nature is mainly under environmental rather than physiological control. Seed usually matures too late in the season to find the right conditions of temperature and moisture over sufficient time for germination to occur. Optimum temperatures for germination are sufficiently high in most tested species (20–30°C) to ensure this. The most effective temperature regime for germination generally involves substantial diurnal temperature fluctuation – constant high temperatures are not as effective as the same temperature alternating with much lower night-time temperature. In the wild most germination generally takes place soon after snowmelt begins – as soon as daytime temperatures are high enough. In many species, however, some of the seeds will not germinate in the first season, or even perhaps in the second. This indicates variable degrees of dormancy, not necessarily related to chilling requirement, within seedlots. This is an adaptive mechanism which ensures that germination is spread over several seasons, so reducing the chances of complete failure which might occur if all the seedlings appeared in what turned out to be a particularly hostile season. This staggered germination is often retained under ideal germination conditions in cultivation. In a study of the germination of snow tussock grass (*Chionochloa rigida*) seed obtained from the New Zealand mountains Mark (1965) found that at 21°C in the dark only 31% had germinated after 50 days; 40% after 109 days while the last germination did not occur until almost 4 years later at which time 94% of the seed had germinated.

While the seeds of most high alpines do not require chilling to germinate this requirement is more common in species from lower elevations, including many which we include in our catholic definition of 'alpines' as far as the garden is concerned. In their case a chilling requirement is a defence against germination in autumn when conditions may be satisfactory but the chances of the resultant seedlings surviving the winter will be low. Provided the seed is sown at a time when several weeks of cold (not necessarily freezing) weather can be expected it is likely to receive the necessary chilling to ensure good germination. There is still no harm in the old practice of exposing ungerminated pans to cold temperatures; few seeds of alpines will be harmed by this and some may be stimulated to germinate.

2. Seedling establishment

Little is known about seedling establishment in the wild because it is very difficult to observe. Even seeds germinating early in the season have only a few weeks to develop a root system and produce enough carbohydrates to survive the winter. At the highest elevations seedling establishment may well be the most critical stage in the life cycle and may occur well in only occasional favourable summers when temperature and moisture are adequate for sufficient time. It is likely that in most species most effort in the early years goes to root production, energy being gradually transferred to shoot growth and flower and seed production.

The natural tendency of the alpine seedling to produce roots rather than shoots explains the surprisingly large root systems attached to tiny seedlings in our seed pans. It suggests that it is a good idea to sow the seed thinly and prick out the seedlings as soon as possible. That way they will be able to make all the root growth they can without competition for water and nutrients. Also, the risk of much of the root system being lost, as often occurs when seed is sown thickly and pricking out is delayed, will be eliminated. What is more, keeping the seedlings growing as fast as possible under the best possible growing conditions is the best way of getting them through the difficult establishment period.

3. Mineral nutrition

Very little is known about the mineral nutrition of alpine plants. Certainly in the wild the growth of many is likely to be limited by shortage of nutrients, especially nitrogen, but on the other hand too much nitrogen can often kill alpines. It seems that alpines, like most plants growing in depleted or skeletal soils are very efficient at retaining nutrients once they have acquired them. Large root systems have probably evolved partly as a means of obtaining nutrients from nutrient deficient soils. Nitrogen fixing plants are common in alpine meadows and probably play an important part in increasing the nitrogen status of these and other well developed plant communities. Perhaps surprisingly, very few high alpines are nitrogen fixers, maybe because they cannot spare the energy required to maintain the microorganisms which do the nitrogen fixing in the roots. The role of mycorrhizal fungi in supplying soil nutrients to the roots of plants, also in exchange for carbohydrates, is probably as important for alpines as it is for other plants, but insufficient information is available yet to determine whether this is so.

4. Photosynthesis and respiration

The key to successful adaptation to arctic and alpine environments is the development of a metabolic system which can capture, store and utilize energy at low temperatures and over short periods of time. The photosynthetic season for most alpines is only 6–10 weeks compared with, say, 40 weeks at sea level in temperate regions. Photosynthetic activity occurs throughout most of the snow-free period when the temperature during daylight exceeds $0°C$, or even when it is below freezing in the case of some species. Thus Moser (1970) and Pisek *et al.* (1967) found that *Ranunculus glacialis* and *Oxyria digyna* can carry on photosynthesis at temperatures as low as $-6°C$ while leaves of most temperate crop plants cease photosynthesis at about $+5°C$ or above. The reason for this is that *Ranunculus glacialis* and *Oxyria digyna* are capable of greater supercooling than plants of lower altitudes, i.e. their cell sap freezes at lower temperatures.

Photosynthesis is not uniform throughout the season. Net photosynthesis of shoots (the difference between the amount of CO_2 being fixed by photosynthesis and that being lost by the respiration of carbohydrate) is relatively low early in the season because of high respiratory rates associated with rapid growth and flowering immediately after snowmelt. However, many alpines have hollow young stems without pith and some of the CO_2 produced by respiration may be recycled by photosynthesis inside these hollow stems in rapidly growing plants, thus making up in part the photosynthetic deficit during early growth. Later in the season when shoot growth has largely ceased net photosynthesis increases and the carbohydrate produced is stored away in the shoots and especially the roots for use during the winter and in the following spring. Conservation of precious carbohydrate is enhanced by an adaptation which enables alpine plants to reduce their respiration rate sharply as temperature increases in summer.

A common phenomenon in alpines is the speeding up or telescoping of developmental processes in plants released from snow cover relatively late in the summer. Plants released from snow by early or mid-June take much longer to reach maturity and have a longer photosynthetic season than those of the same species released in mid-July. While these late plants grow faster in shorter periods of time, they are smaller and produce less dry matter.

FACTORS INFLUENCING THE ORIGIN AND PRESENT DISTRIBUTION OF ARCTIC AND ALPINE PLANTS

One of the most interesting aspects of the ecology of alpine plants which can only be touched on here because of the complexity of the factors involved concerns the origins of the species and the factors influencing their present distributions. The question of origins is particularly fraught with difficulties because of our hazy knowledge of the history of the earth and the continents and of past climates.

It is essential when thinking about evolution to try and think in terms of geological time, where millenia are as seconds in a person's life. When viewing our present mountains and their plants we should think of what we see as we do when we look at a snapshot of some moment in our own lives. The living things in the photograph, including ourselves, are as they are because of the evolutionary processes that have formed them over aeons of time. Just as we are the products of our ancestors back through the ages, and just as those ancestors originated from species quite different from ourselves, and living in different places, so did the present-day alpines evolve from others, often at a great distance in space and time.

The rate of evolution varies in time and place, depending to a great extent on the fitness of the species to the environment. Thus in any one mountain range at any given time some species will be relatively stable, having changed little in recent times, while others will be undergoing rapid evolutionary change.

The best evidence for the powers of evolution to create new genera and species in mountain environments is the high degree of endemism in the great mountain chains of the world. While certain genera and species are widely distributed and turn up in most mountain ranges in the northern hemisphere, most major mountain chains evolve many species and, if sufficiently isolated, genera of their own. Many of these endemic alpines have probably evolved from ordinary populations of lowland plants by natural selection (Love & Love 1974). A small percentage of plants of the lowlands have invaded the slopes of newly formed mountains and volcanoes as they have arisen, and adapted themselves to the new conditions as races of the species surrounding the mountains. Where time has been sufficient to extinguish the original lowland races, or to allow the more or less isolated highland races to develop into new species, the plants of the mountain group may have evolved into a distinct flora, many species of which may be unable to survive in the original climatic conditions if the mountains erode away. We have records of such extinct alpines only when they have been conserved as fossils. Others we know because they have been able to survive such changes by invading other alpine regions. Nobody will ever know how many alpine species have evolved and succumbed when their environmental conditions changed too quickly or too drastically for them to re-adapt.

The number of species shared between mountain chains depends partly, but not always as much as might be expected, on their proximity. New mountains which develop near to older mountains or such continuing and reliable sources of plants as the Arctic, may develop floras in which endemics form a rather low proportion of the species. New mountains which are isolated from others by distance or by habitats which are inhospitable to alpine plants will tend to develop a higher proportion of endemic genera and species. The distances over which sufficient isolation may occur for measurable variability to develop within a species can be surprisingy small. Thus in a study of *Erysimum* Sven Snogerup found that while populations growing on cliffs less than 500m apart were generally indistinguishable, those growing further apart than this were morphologically distinct (Rolfe, personal communication).

Plant geographers agree that the original arctic flora of perhaps 1500 species must have reached a largely circumpolar distribution prior to the onset of the Pleistocene glaciations which began 2–3 million years ago. As the climate deteriorated and the ice sheet and glaciers developed in the Arctic the areas occupied by most of the formerly circumpolar plants were so radically split that they never recovered, as is evident from the present distributions of numerous species, which have large breaks. When the glaciations began the tundra was pressed southward but was also isolated in pockets surrounded by the ice further north. Some of the plants that had become adapted to the mild arctic conditions of the Early Pliocene may not have kept the genetic plasticity which was required for a relatively fast dispersal away from the increasing cold and the shortening of the growing season, so they succumbed to natural selection without leaving a trace. Other species succeeded in escaping the glaciers either by dispersing south into the lowlands or mountains of the normally temperate zone, which became considerably cooler during the glaciations, or by occupying islands and coastlands surrounded but not overrun by the ice, while a few very hardy species were able to survive on ice-free nunataks surrounded by the inland ice (Love & Love 1974). The southern refugia were considerable in size, especially near the coasts of eastern and western North America, in central Alaska, central Europe, and eastern Siberia. These refugia were open southward for dispersal and allowed the movement of some northern species far south into the present lowlands of the temperate zone. Refugia were absent, or at least very restricted, south of the ice in the middle of the continents, because the glaciers prevented water runoff northwards and caused the formation of enormous lakes to the south that drowned the vegetation before it could succumb to the cold (Love 1959).

It should be pointed out that some of the arctic-alpines which at present are met with in southern mountains as well as in the Arctic may have had very complicated histories. In the case of species such as *Vaccinium gaultherioides, Dryas octopetala, Diapensia lapponica* and some others with mainly arctic distribution and isolated occurrences on mountains in the temperate zone, it is suggested that whereas American alpine populations may be the result of southward dispersal during the glaciations, the populations in central and southern Asiatic mountains are more likely to be relics from the period before the glaciations, probably the ancestors of the arctic and American populations.

It is often assumed that when the climate improved during the inter-glacials and after the most recent glaciation the arctic-alpines which then occupied many lowland areas retreated northward with the ice, and that they also found refuge in temperate mountains. It seems likely from our current knowledge that the plants which survived in the arctic refugia, including those on nunataks, were more important than those moving northwards with the glaciers in recolonising the northern tundra. Thus examination of variability in arctic and alpine races of a range of arctic-alpines in North America and Europe has shown that the races are genetically quite distinct (Crawford 1989). If there had been major immigration to the Arctic over so short a period as the 10,000 or less years since the ice retreated we would expect them to be similar. This suggests, then, that the alpine populations of arctic-alpine plants that we grow have in many cases been isolated in their mountain fastnesses for very long periods.

The Pleistocene glaciations were repeated several times. Each certainly caused the extinction of some species and it is likely that we now only have about half the species of arctic-alpines that were present before the glaciations began. The splitting up of the original circumpolar populations of the species which survived the ice into isolated populations led in some cases to differentiation and the development of plants with morphological differences that have warranted their recognition as species, subspecies or varieties. An example is provided by the complex of arctic-alpine poppy species which are similar but nevertheless distinct. This group includes *Papaver relictum*, *P. radicatum*, *P. kluanense* and *P. alpinum*.

Some disjunct distributions of alpines are extraordinary and difficult at first sight to explain. An example is the occurrence of a primula of the Farinosae group (*P. magellanica*) very similar to our own *P. farinosa* in the extreme south of South America and in the Falkland Islands, separated by thousands of miles from its nearest relative in North America. It used to be thought that this disjunct distribution indicated that primulas had formerly occurred throughout the Andes and that some climatic event(s) had led to their extinction there. Recent research has led to the rejection of this theory. This research has shown that it is not only the primulas which have this disjunct distribution. The flora of Tierra del Fuego *in toto* resembles that of the temperate mountains of North America more closely than it does that of any part of the Andes (Simpson & Todzia 1990). It is suggested that this is because of the relative similarity of their present climates. The extremely recent (in geological time) emergence of the Falkland Islands and the Tierra del Fuego area from ice cover suggests that it is very likely that most if not all the species currently found in this region immigrated recently. Simpson & Todzia consider that dispersal of many species to southern South America has been facilitated mainly by migrating birds, coming primarily from the mountains of western North America. While any one bird flying south on migration from North to South America may have an infinitesimally small chance of successfully distributing the seed of a particular plant species, if many birds do the trip over millennia there are almost certain to be occasional successes, which are all that are needed to set the colonisation process in motion.

There are many other equally fascinating and mostly unexplained disjunct distributions. For example, *Rhodothamnus chamaecistus* and *Kalmiopsis leachiana* are so similar as to be easily co fused on casual inspection and are sufficiently compatible genetically to be capable of forming hybrids in cultivation. Yet *Rhodothamnus* occurs only in Europe while *Kalmiopsis*

8   *Gagea soleirolii* in the Val d'Eyne (see page 47)

9   *Geum montanum* in Andorra (see page 46)

10 *Iris stenophylla* ssp. *allisonii*, the queen of the Junos (see page 49)

11   *Fritillaria collina* can be grown in the open rock garden (see page 50)

12   *Ranunculus haastii*, a New Zealand buttercup (see page 55)

13   *Haastia sinclairii*, an endemic species from New Zealand (see page 58)

14   *Leptinella dendyi*, formerly in the genus *Cotula*, is another New Zealand native (see page 58)

occurs only in the Columbia River Gorge of western North America. Did a common ancestor once occur throughout Eurasia and across the then land bridge which is now the Bering Sea? How long ago was the ancestral link, if it existed, broken, and why? These are questions which we may never be able to answer.

REFERENCES

Barry, R.G. & Ives, J.D. 1974. Introduction. In: *Arctic and Alpine Environments*, edited by J.D. Ives & R.G. Barry, 1–13. Methuen, London.

Billings, W.D. 1974. Arctic and alpine vegetation: plant adaptations to cold summer climates. In: *Arctic and Alpine Environments*, edited by J.D. Ives & R.G. Barry, 403–444. Methuen, London.

Billings, W.D. & Mooney, H.A. 1968. The ecology of arctic and alpine plants. *Biological Review*, **43**, 482–529.

Caldwell, 1968. Solar ultraviolet radiation as an ecological factor for alpine plants. *Ecological Monographs*, **38**, 243–268.

Crawford, R.M.M. 1989. *Studies in Plant Survival: Ecological Case Histories of Plant Adaptation to Adversity*. Blackwell Scientific Publications, Oxford.

Fischer, H. & Kuhn, H.W. 1984. Diurnal courses of temperatures in cushion plants. *Flora, Jena*, **175**, 117–134.

Halliwell, B. 1981. A new alpine house at Kew. *Quarterly Bulletin of the Alpine Garden Society*, **49**, 23–25.

Holmen, K. 1957. The vascular plants of Peary Land, North Greenland, *Meddr Gronland*, **124**, 1–149.

Johnson, P.L. & Billings, W.D. 1962. The alpine vegetation of the Beartooth Plateau in relation to cryopedogenic processes and patterns. *Ecological Monographs*, **32**, 105–135.

Junnila, S. 1985. Seasonal changes in cold hardiness of *Diapensia lapponica*. In: *Proceedings of the 4th Oikos Conference on Winter Ecology, Oulu, Finland, September 12–13, 1984*, 81–85.

Love, A. & Love, D. 1974. Origin and evolution of the arctic and alpine Floras. In: *Arctic and Alpine Environments*, edited by J.D. Ives & R.G. Barry, 571–603. Methuen, London.

Love, D. 1959. The postglacial development of the flora of Manitoba: a discussion. *Canadian Journal of Botany*, **37**, 547–585.

Major, J. & Bamberg, S.A. 1967. Comparison of some North American and Eurasian alpine ecosystems. In: *Arctic & Alpine Environments*, edited by H.E. Wright Jr. & W.H. Osburn, 89–118. Indiana University Press, Bloomington, Indiana.

Mark, A.F. 1965. Flowering, seeding and seedling establishment of narrow-leaved snow tussock, *Chionochloa rigida*. *New Zealand Journal of Botany*, **3**, 180–193.

Mark, A.F. 1970. Floral initiation and development in New Zealand alpine plants. *New Zealand Journal of Botany*, **8**, 381–451.

Mark, A.F. & Adams, N.M. 1973. *New Zealand Alpine Plants*. A.H. & A.W. Reed Ltd., Christchurch, New Zealand.

McGraw, J.B. 1985. Experimental ecology of *Dryas octopetala* ecotypes: relative response to competition. *New Phytologist*, **100**, 233–241.

Simpson, B.B. & Todzia, C.A. 1990. Patterns and processes in the development of the high Andean Flora. *American Journal of Botany*, 77, 1419–1432.

Sorenson, T. 1941. Temperature relations and phenology of the Northeast Greenland flowering plants. *Meddr Gronland.* 125, 1–305.

Spira, T.P. & Pollak, O.D. 1986. Comparative reproductive biology of alpine biennial and perennial gentians (*Gentiana*: Gentianaceae) in California. *American Journal of Botany*, 73, 39–47.

Stocker, O. 1963. Das dreidimensionale Schema der Vegetationsverteilung auf der Erde. *Bereits deutsch botanisches Gesellschaft*, 76, 168–178.

Swan, L.W. 1967. Alpine and Aeolian regions of the world. In: *Arctic & Alpine Environments*, edited by H.E. Wright Jr. & W.H. Osburn, 29–54. Indiana University Press, Bloomington, Indiana.

Troll, C. 1959. The relationship between climates and plant geography of the southern cold temperate zone and of the tropical high mountains. *Proceedings of the Royal Society of London, Series B*, 152, 529–532.

Welden, C. 1985. Structural pattern in alpine tundra vegetation. *American Journal of Botany*, 72, 120–134.

Woodward, F.I. 1987. *Climate and Plant Distribution*. Cambridge University Press, Cambridge.

Meconopsis

JAMES COBB

One of the key symbols in German literature and culture is 'the blue flower of Romanticism'. The early German romanticist Novalis wrote the following passage in his novel *Heinrich von Ofterdingen* . . . 'The higher he climbed, the more sparse the forest became. At length he reached a small meadow which lay on the slope of the mountain . . . Dark blue cliffs with bright veins arose in the distance. But what attracted him with great force was a tall, pale blue flower, which stood beside the spring and touched him with its broad glistening leaves.' Have meconopsis, like the dragon and the unicorn, become mythical organisms whose stupifying qualities so entranced the beholders in their native haunts that they wove them into far flung legend? Blue poppies are certainly fabled in the literal sense of being fabulous. They are of course not only blue but yellow, red, pink, white and most regal purple. A single bloom can be a stunning 28cm (11in) across or a whole plant an eight foot spire incandescent with hundreds of ruby chalices. They grow from the most inhospitable screes at 5800m (19,000ft) in the Himalayas where the petals seem carved from crystals of pale blue ice to red banners streaming in the chill wind on the dry cold plains of northern China. They are fabulous indeed.

Descending to the muddy plains of taxonomy we find a slightly awkward group very carefully researched by Taylor (1934) in a comprehensive monograph which is of a quality years before its time. *Meconopsis cambrica* was separated out from *Papaver* before the first Himalayan species were discovered. The basis of this was an elongated style and the lack of a stigmatic disc. At this point it should be remembered that pollination specificity with particular insect vectors has been a powerful driving force in the evolution of many families of flowering plants. Now both the taxonomic criteria for *Meconopsis* fall into this category and this makes for problems. Over and over again organisms have come up with identical solutions to the same problem independently. These are called analagous characteristics. Only when there is unequivocal evidence that they are derived from the same ontogenetic source (i.e. have the same developmental origins) can they be called homologous. They must however be homologous to be used in classification and here is the rub. Proof of homology is hard to come by and a poor plant fossil record is no help. Modern studies of genetic relatedness will probably be shown to be yet another complicating factor rather than the reverse. It is quite possible that

Meconopsis, as we know them, really are a non-homologous group but changing things will only be altering one opinion for another. The preoccupation of botanists with taxonomy would not matter if it only affected taxonomists but regretably we all, amateur gardeners included, require a name that unequivocally specifies the organism we perceive. All most of us require is that the name is unequivocal and not that it reflects the latest theory of an individual taxonomist. To most biologists taxonomy is a chore and it should be made less irritating and more user friendly. I only hope we can settle to leave reasonably well alone, as Taylor suggested, unless there are very substantial amounts of very different new field data.

There are nevertheless real problems over naming and nowhere is this better exemplified than with *Meconopsis horridula*. Taylor lumped a number of species into a single one. He did this after a careful examination of herbarium material from a great geographical range. He stated that all the different types can be shown to merge with complete gradation of form. One cannot therefore entirely satisfactorily define the extremes as species. The truth is probably that in an actively evolving species we cannot categorise the variation at all with our artificial criteria. However if you grow the coarse meaty purple variety with large leaves and distinctive purple spots at the base of the spines (old *M. rudis*), the dark blue yellow anthered form (old *M. racemosa*) or the exquisite basal scaped pale blue jewel from high screes, you would be loath to accept them as the same species. I should be equally unhappy to see them interbred to become a single homogeneous garden variety. We do need a solution to this problem if we are ever to know what we are receiving from the seed exchange. It would seem sensible to re-instate these extreme variations as subspecies, the first two on morphological grounds and the third on ecological grounds as discussed below.

Another problem species is the blue form of *M. napaulensis*. This produces sterile progeny when crossed with other colours and it grows quite differently and would probably be best re-instated as *M. wallichii* as it was before Taylor lumped it. The trouble is where does one stop with this juggling. One might also, on new evidence of the last few years, lump pink *M. sherriffii* in with the very variable yellow *M. integrifolia* with the justification that flower colour is not enough, but who would this help? Henderson used the scanning electron microscope to show the superficially very similar *M. taylori* and *M. regia* had very different pollen morphology. How valid is this criteria unless we understand its adaptive significance and again how valuable was it to split them? Whatever we decide it is vital to remember that we are largely dealing with 'gut feelings' and definitions as opposed to hard facts.

Another taxonomic problem that has great significance is that of physiological characteristics. A single species defined on morphological grounds may span a range from the high Rockies to the Californian coast and yet plants from the extremes require radically different growing conditions. In this case the ecotypes are validly recognised as subspecies. The high altitude ice-blue *M. horridula* presents a similar problem since it undoubtedly contains genes which are involved in the amazing ability to thrive and set seeds in such a seemingly hostile environment. I am not clear however how you produce a valid definition or a name for a distinct ecotype of a species that shows a common morphology. A programme to conserve these genes may be far more important than a programme to save an artificially rare species defined by some misunderstood morphological quirk. As conservationists we must recognise that the current taxonomic definition of some species may let us down. Many Himalayan plants may become extinct while we argue about their classical taxonomy. World computer data banks of threatened plants are no use to conservation if we have not studied the ecological identity and physiology of the plants.

Stores of viable seed are certainly a brief moment of respite providing we are absolutely confident that we can break their dormancy. There are real problems here since many desirable Himalayan genera produce large, store-rich seeds (*Meconopsis punicea* is an example) that are very difficult to germinate however fresh the seed. There is much to learn about seed dormancy in *Meconopsis* amongst others despite some good progress (see Thompson 1968, and subsequent work at Kew).

Good germination is of no value if we cannot grow the plants on to seed setting maturity. It may be necessary to be guardians of species in a more rigorous way than progress with National Plant Collections currently allows. Even with a very optimistic view of mankind there will be many decades of turmoil as developing countries strive to achieve a fraction of what we take for granted and the rampant consumerism of developed countries is tamed to be compatible with a self-renewing environment. We must ensure continuity of plant material so that brief catastrophies in the wild can be bridged.

This means science in the garden, gadgets in the greenhouse and growth cabinets in the parlour unless we are to leave everything to the currently underfunded professionals. It is no use nodding wisely and saying old So and So really knew how to grow *M. rarissima*. It is not just the gift of green fingers but dedicated attention to detail. What we want to know is what detail? Humidity of air in relation to temperature, susceptibility to fungus and fungicide, UV light levels? In fact a whole host of parameters that can be objectively measured and attempts made to control them. We owe our plants more than just being mere flower watchers. By all means ban scientifically grown plants from shows if shows are to be just an art. Not everybody, of course, wants to grow plants in this way but let's encourage those who do. Let's ask a few hard questions about what we are trying to achieve. One for the lovers of *Meconopsis* is 'should a largely monocarpic genus really be safeguarded in National Collections of the current form?'

Even the most unlikely species of *Meconopsis* are now regularly hybridising in garden situations and leading to widespread sterility. *M. gracilipes* has gone from cultivation in that way and *M. dhwojii* may follow if we do not act. We need collections of single species in separate locations (which is of course a bit tough on the particular grower).

Hybridisation and selection of garden strains needs some careful thought in such a classic genus. It would certainly be quite wrong not to select material that has high horticultural value as long as this is not done at the expense of eliminating true species in cultivation or reducing the gene pool. A real warning is necessary on hybridisation since cross fertilisation will take place between all the groups of the blue poppies. This means that *M. napaulensis* will hybridise with species like *M. horridula* as well as with *M. grandis*, unlikely though this may seem. It is in fact a relatively common occurrence and progeny are invariably sterile. If the resultant hybrid is polycarpic this may not matter since propagation can be asexual. Monocarpic progeny are however really useless unless a brilliant F1 hybrid can be repetitively produced. *M. latifolia* in my garden is now regularly hybridising with *M. napaulensis* and the sterile progeny are ugly. *M. latifolia* has rapidly changed from weed status to being in need of my care and protection.

There is however room to produce polycarpic evergreen hybrids based on *M. napaulensis* types crossed with *M. grandis* and the like. Potentially one should obtain all flower colours from the material available. One such yellow-flowered hybrid is the toughest constitutioned *Meconopsis* (bar *M. cambrica*) that I have come across though the flowers are poor. The dwarf crosses between *M. quintuplinervia* and *M. integrifolia* have great potential in producing such exquisite dwarfs as *M. × finlayorum*. *M. sherriffii* and *M. punicea* could be involved in producing a range of such plants but a highly polycarpic nature is a must based, presumably, on the exemplary behaviour of *M. quintuplinervia*.

An interesting phenomenon has recently appeared in the form of seed of *M. × sheldonii*. Until recently this largely seems to have been misnamed seed of *M. betonicifolia*. There is now large sized seed (*M. betonicifolia* is half the size) circulating under the name *M. × sheldonii*. I have flowered none of this yet but did some years ago find a single pod on an undoubted *M. × sheldonii*. I surmised this was a backcross probably with *M. betonicifolia* and called the progeny *M. × Kingsbarns* hybrids. These have three great qualities. First the progeny are exceptionally fertile, the seed germinates very well under all conditions. Second the seedlings are very easy to grow under indifferent conditions. Third, and above all, the progeny are extremely polycarpic; they rarely flower until the third year with up to ten rosettes. They are certainly the most likely 'grandis' type to succeed in areas of the world that have unsympathetic climates. They should be a nurseryman's dream as they are very amenable to potting, without flowering to death in the first season. How many will be brilliant plants is not yet clear but third generation plants are producing some pleasing variations and there should soon be plenty of seed. Whether the other *M. × sheldonii* on offer as seed will have similar qualities remains to be seen and whether the commercial seed of this hybrid recently offered is actually true again needs testing, since the particular company has been wrong with *Meconopsis* before!

Selecting strains is just as important since flower sizes are very variable. I have seen the number of flowers on a *M. napaulensis* scape vary between 1 to 19 between different plants and the height of this species vary between a dwarf 60cm (2ft) and 200cm (6.5ft) M M. *horridula*, *aculeata* and *latifolia* can be breath-taking shades of blue and equally thoroughly nasty. Careful hand cross pollination (most are largely self sterile) helps and after two or three generations the characters begin to be consistent. What we do need is some way of submitting precious hand-pollinated seed to the exchanges so that it is kept separate. At the same time it should not become what is exclusively sent out, thus diminishing the gene pool that might be so valuable to the selection of good strains under different growing conditions. It is exciting that so much wild seed is being collected from what seemed impossible places a few years ago. Nevertheless this seed is often 'snatched' rather than collected from marked plants selected while in flower. It would be a pity if the excitement of the 'wild' collection saw the burgeoning in our gardens of poor forms. *M. wallichii* is a case in point, it is the most enchanting pale duck egg blue at best but nearly all the recently collected forms have been a relatively poor mauve. We need advice here from the seed exchange managers.

A great deal has been written recently about growing these plants (see Cobb 1989). The over-riding need is really rich feeding, especially in areas prone to summer drought. If you have failed to grow *Meconopsis*, try again with the following recipe. Dig a hole 50cm (20in) deep and fill it with well decayed organic matter. Well-rotted cow dung, a really fibrous load from a good compost heap or something of this sort (not peat). Grow a noted polycarpic strain from seed (i.e. *M. × Kingsbarns* hybrid), pot on fast into a good rich compost and keep growing humid and coolish, in a shaded frame if necessary, until 15cm (6in) high by mid August and plant it into your hole. When they go dormant place a thick dried bracken cover (or onion sack with polystyrene beads in it) over if subject to more than −5°C in winter over a long period or a simple tent cloche in a really wet winter climate. They will emerge strongly in spring and a soaking with water will help, if available, in very dry spells. As the air temperature increases with summer and humidity drops they begin to look unhappy and become mildewed. Nevertheless the dung underneath should keep them growing to flower the following year. An established clump needs the dung renewing every three or four years.

All the species respond marvellously to some compost or manure dug into the soil before planting and will rapidly impoverish the soil. In areas where there is adequate summer rainfall and humidity however, it is perfectly possible to grow them in quite poor soil and feed them inorganically or with such crudity as chicken dung. The soil can be acid, alkaline or neutral. I suspect however, though absolute proof is lacking, that slightly acid soil is necessary for good blues in M. *grandis* and relatives but not for M. *horridula* and similar. Good rich soil from cradle to grave is the real answer. Perfection requires a wind sheltered glade that gives morning or evening sun but a little respite from high noon.

Basic principles include: if in doubt sow seed in autumn; give heat in spring; prick on early and grow fast, humid and rich; pot on late spring and plant out early to mid summer and keep growing. Over-winter in pots only if unavoidable or as spare plants and in this case pot on to a larger pot mid summer.

There are finally some difficult species and a little 'latest' advice is offered but I (at least) have much to learn.

M. *bella*. Until recently seed was available. It needs very humid seed compost (based on sphagnum). Very slow growing (1cm ($\frac{1}{2}$in) at 1 year old or worse). Avoid aphids but do not use insecticides and keep slugs away at all times. Not hardy once back in growth in spring and if you achieve the miracle, and they grow, they will need protection from fiercely cold winds when winter dormant. Probably not very difficult but it only needs one unguarded moment in at least four years to lose your plants. Has been flowered from seed recently in expert hands. I have consistently failed.

M. *delavayi*. At last it is back on offer as seed thanks to the tireless efforts in China of Kew and Edinburgh. Trotter grew this well and showed it came from root cuttings. Seed of other species from this part of China germinates with difficulty so beware of poor germination and sow at least some in autumn for frost stratification. Should be perennial and dividable. I suspect it is not too difficult to grow.

M. *discigera*. This was collected by the AGS expedition to Sikkim and at least one was flowered. Recent seed was collected by the Kew/Edinburgh expedition (KEKE nos.). Slow growing seedlings and difficult monocarpic mature plants. The risk period seems to be autumn when mildew attacks the old leaves and rots into the winter resting crown. One that flowered from seed grew under a dry hedge. An artificially enriched hole near a conifer is worth trying. Probably needs a tent cloche with open ends in winter.

M. *horridula*. High altitude forms have proved difficult. Recent KEKE seed has grown well (unlike the AGS expedition seed which germinated well and then faded away) and if it flowers in character this will be a great joy.

M. *lancifolia*. There are a number of purple flowered relatives of M.

horridula in areas of China now being visited. Care is needed with these since in the days of abundant Forrest seed no-one managed much with any of them. Nursing in an alpine house with a rich gritty mix would be where I would start.

M. punicea. Easy to grow and flower. It seems to be largely monocarpic (though it does not look it in growth). Seed needs stratifying and even then germination is poor. Produces little pollen and the deep flowers may need pollinating by hand.

M. sherriffii. Rare and becoming rarer. Indeed I fear it may soon be extinct in cultivation if some of us do not learn the trick soon. Tends to be a reluctant polycarpic type, subject to spring frost damage and a martyr to early autumn mildew (the time I have always lost mine). May be worth routinely spraying with an anti-mildew fungicide from mid-summer but exercise care since meconopsis dislike most chemicals. Decidedly needs cross pollination so if offered one plant, demand at least two! The only saving grace is that is been reported recently well north into China from the previous range in an area where there are now tourists so it may turn up (perhaps even mistaken in seed for *M. integrifolia*).

M. superba. The most likely of the evergreen rosette monocarpic species to need winter protection. Flower buds are not hardy in spring to frost. Currently there is plenty of seed of this species so grow twice as many plants as you wish to flower. This species may be worth trying in hotter climates.

Acknowledgements

I am especially indebted to Ron McBeath of R.B.G. Edinburgh and Peter Cox of Glendoick Nurseries for trusting me with such generous amounts of wild collected seed.

REFERENCES

Cobb, J.L.S. (1989) *Meconopsis*. Helm, London.

Taylor, G. (1934) *An account of the genus Meconopsis*. New Flora and Silva Ltd. London.

Thompson, P. (1968) 'Germination responses of *Meconopsis*'. *J. Roy. Hort. Soc.* 99:336.

Flowers of the High Pyrenees

CHRISTOPHER GREY-WILSON

The Pyrenees, which form the mountain barrier between France and Spain, offer a great variety to the walker, naturalist and plant-hunter; indeed all those who love high, wild places. These splendid and rugged mountains run for some 350km (219 miles) from west to east, a mountain range which starts from close to the Atlantic and stretches to the shores of the Mediterranean. Although far less well known than the Alps, the Pyrenees and the adjacent Picos de Europa to the west, in north-west Spain, harbour a wide range of exciting and colourful plants, quite a number of which are endemic, occurring nowhere else.

The Pyrenees do not flaunt a great panorama of snowy peaks and glaciers like the Alps, although much of the scenery is very beautiful, with high passes, jagged peaks, mountain lakes and deep wooded valleys. The highest peak, the Pico de Aneto rises to some 3404m (11,165ft) on the Spanish side of the frontier and in the middle of the range. The French side is more abrupt with steeper valleys and numerous points of access into the mountains; here an east-west highway, the Routes des Pyrenees, winds its way through the foothills, occasionally climbing over a high pass, often blocked by snow until the late spring. The Spanish side, in contrast, is more gentle with long ridges dipping southwards into northern Spain, some for more than a hundred miles. Here the roads are fewer, generally rougher and access to the higher mountains less easy, but this should not deter the traveller, for each side has much to offer.

The flora of the Pyrenees consists primarily of rich associations of herbaceous plants at the lower and middle elevations and an equally rich array of alpine plants higher up. Although these mountains contain many familiar species which can be found in the Alps and other parts of Europe, others are restricted to the region (including the neighbouring mountains of northern Spain). Interestingly, some of these endemics are confined to the western part of the range, whilst others are only to be found in the east. The reason for this is almost certainly one of climate. The western part of the range has a higher rainfall and a milder climate which is influenced by the proximity of the Atlantic Ocean, with rainfall possible at almost any time of the year. The east, however, is more extreme and, with the influence of the Mediterranean, most rain falls during the winter and the summers are hotter. This has enabled Mediterranean species to creep up the flanks of the mountains, especially on the Spanish side, thus offering a rich assortment of species, including typical Mediterranean shrubs such as *Cistus* species and lavender, *Lavandula angustifolia*.

The Pyrenees have few large towns, although there are many places to stay in the numerous smaller towns and villages, and, for the hardier there are many camp sites, especially in the larger valleys. I am often asked when is the best time to go to see the flowers, to which there is no straight answer. Indeed any time from April to late July can prove rewarding depending on what you want to see and how high you want to climb. In April and May the lower valleys and meadows are alive with colour whilst on the other hand, spring does not reach the high meadows above the tree line until late June or July and, even then, areas can still be under snow, as they can in any great mountain range. However, if I had to chose a time I would say un-hesitatingly June or early July, for it is during this period that the visitor is most likely to see the largest range of plants in flower.

There are many sites that one can visit on both sides of the frontier, although I will only explore two main ones.

For those visiting the Pyrenees for the first time there is no better centre than Gavarnie in the central French Pyrenees. The small town is dominated by the great Cirque de Gavarnie, said to be the largest cirque in Europe, whose great rock walls soar in enormous cliffs which form a characteristic amphitheatre; here several narrow waterfalls plunge down the cliffs. From Gavarnie the visitor can take a different walk each day for a week or more. Throughout the summer months a stream of coaches travel up from the pilgrimage town of Lourdes to the north and the tourists and pilgrims, who mostly come only for the day, are ushered up the track to the cirque by strings of jolly muleteers and robust, if somewhat smelly, mules. To avoid them an early start before mid-morning is necessary!

The meadows around the town are cut for hay in midsummer and grazed afterwards but, before this, they are very colourful. In the spring daffodils, *Narcissus pseudonarcissus* subsp. *abscissus*, abound on the slopes, followed later on in early summer by deep blue irises, *Iris xiphioides*, a Pyrenean speciality. In some places colonies of another endemic, *Fritillaria pyrenaica*, are to be seen. Normally the lantern flowers are a dark purplish mahogany with yellowish green, but the diligent hunter may also see the charming all-yellow form. The rockier meadows harbour several delightful small bulbs amongst which the charming and delicate, blue *Brimeura amethystina* (formerly *Hyacinthus amethystinus*) is restricted to the central Pyrenees, and the delightful little, sweetly scented, daffodil, *Narcissus requienii*, with its small-cupped flowers, are the most notable. Here also, another Pyrenean speciality, *Viola cornuta*, abounds in the spring. Usually with violet or lilac, but occasionally white, flowers, this species is familiar in our gardens and extremely reliable.

The walk into the cirque itself is very rewarding scenically but many of the flowers have long since been removed by the visitors. However, the agile of foot can still see much by clambering up the steeper slopes and ledges close to the cirque walls. Here you may chance upon a tuft of edelweiss, *Leontopodium alpinum*, Pyrenean columbine, *Aquilegia pyrenaica*, or cushions of white *Androsace villosa*. But on the wet walls where water drips throughout the summer the great speciality is the rare and little known butterwort, *Pinguicula longifolia*, which like other species in the genus, catches small insects on its sticky, fly-paper, leaves. In the gravels which abound in the area a common harebell, *Campanula cochleariifolia*, in various shades of blue or white, is easy to spot, as is the alpine cress, *Hutchinsia alpina*.

On a hot summers' day one may be lucky enough to catch a glimpse of griffon vultures or lammergeiers circling in a warm thermal high overhead. They come from across the border, just to the south, where the Ordessa National Park, one of the most beautiful in Spain, is located – one can in fact walk across the mountains from Gavarnie, although a new road today over the Port de Gavarnie, makes the journey a lot simpler.

To the south-west of Gavarnie a track climbs ever upwards towards the Breche de Roland. The scenery is generally very dry, with few trees or bushes and with exposed pale, bleached limestone all around. In the spring the limestone pockets are full of colourful herbs and occasionally spring gentians, *Gentiana verna*, the deepest of blue forms. Here it is the cliffs that attract the eye and the walker will be rewarded with two more Pyrenean endemics, *Ramonda myconi* and the extraordinary *Saxifraga longifolia*. The former is related to the African violet and forms dark green, leathery leaf rosettes which nestle in deep rock crevices. The flowers, which appear in June or July, are blue or violet. *Saxifraga longifolia* makes a large lime-encrusted rosette of numerous narrow leaves which gradually gains size over a number of years. Eventually the rosettes elongate into a huge panicle of white flowers arching out from the cliffs. The plant is monocarpic, dying after flowering and seeding; in some years few plants flower, whilst in others thousands are to be seen, like flocks of snowy sheep over the rocks – one of the floristic wonders of these mountains. On the rocky slopes at these heights you may be lucky enough to come upon the curious Pyrenean yam, *Borderea pyrenaica* (syn. *Dioscorea pyrenaica*), whose cousins are the tropical yams. This extremely rare plant has an underground tuber and small heart-shaped leaves; the rather insignificant greenish flowers are borne in racemes or clusters, the male and female on different plants. This is no plant for the show bench, but a tiny wonder for the botanist to delight in.

The Val d'Ossoue, to the immediate west of Gavarnie has a fairly new road which leads up the base of the Vignemale, the third highest mountain in the Pyrenees. This splendid sheltered valley, which is a haven for butterflies and other insects, deserves careful exploration. Here you are likely to see the Pyrenean form of the spurge laurel, *Daphne laureola* var. *philippi* which forms a spreading and suckering bush, the dwarf form of *Rosa pendulina*, scarcely 30cm (12in) tall, with large cupped flowers of deep pink, and the charming Pyrenean honeysuckle, *Lonicera pyrenaica*, a shrubby species. The rocky banks everywhere are alive with yellow or white rockroses, *Helianthemum nummularium*, *H. canum* and *H. apeninnium*, *Erinus alpinus*, *Scutellaria alpina*, and two pink-flowered legumes, *Astragalus monspessulanus* and *Trifolium alpinum*, besides many other species. This is a long walk but every foot is worthwhile. If time permits, and you are not too tired, a climb high onto the limestone shoulders of the Vignemale is well worthwhile and you may be rewarded by spotting cushions of pink *Androsace ciliata*.

Another superb outing is to take the road east above the town of Gedre (just north of Gavarnie) which runs along the Val d'Heas. This eventually leads to another cirque, the Cirque de Troumouse, the only place where I have spotted chamois in the Pyrenees. In the spring, snow banks are frequent along the way and a search amongst the meadow snowfields may reveal spring crocuses, *Crocus vernus*, in white or purple and the daintiest of all alpines, *Soldanella alpina*, whose tiny fringed blue bells never fail to delight. The cirque itself is noted for a very fine form of *Geranium cinereum*, var. *roseum*, with large pale blooms etched with pink veins, the dwarf form of *Daphne cneorum* known as var. *pygmaea*, which is wonderfully scented (unbelievably slow-growing in cultivation) and, on shaded wet cliffs, colonies of *Primula hirsuta*; but there are many other treasures here as well.

The principality of Andorra in the eastern Pyrenees offers an interesting contrast to Gavarnie, for it mostly lies on the southern, drier side of the main divide. The usual approach is along the French highway which leads dramatically into Andorra over the Envalira Pass. Here in early summer the high slopes are heavily scented with bright yellow Pyrenean broom, *Sarothamnus purgans*, and the meadows dotted with yellow patches of *Pulsatilla alpina* subsp. *apiifolia*, oxlips, *Primula elatior*, and vivid blue trumpet gentians *Gentiana acaulis*. These last, one of the great glories of the pass, used to, before the advent of the modern highway, occur in thousands but have been tragically reduced by senseless digging by ill-informed and selfish tourists – the likelihood is that few, if any, survive the transition from highland meadow to lowland garden.

You can drive right through Andorra in under an hour and into Spain and many do, pausing only in the dreadful capital town, Andorra la Vella, to buy duty-free items. But to do so is a great pity for it is in the delightful side valleys, where the pretty little Andorran villages still exist, that one can still see this country as it once was.

In the spring the valley meadows are thick with *Narcissus poeticus* whose familiar pheasant's-eye blooms fill the air with scent. Occasionally one may come across a far rarer sight, a meadow full of wild tulips, *Tulipa australis*, yellow with a reddish purple reverse. These same meadows, like those throughout the Pyrenees, are mostly unaffected by weedkillers and are full of colourful herbs, yellow daisies, *Arnica montana*, columbines, *Aquilegia vulgaris*, and the fluffy lilac and yellow *Thalictrum aquilegifolium* as well as purple *Adenostyles alliariae*, a plant closely related to our own native butterbur. In mid-summer these same meadows are cut for hay.

A delightful walk in central Andorra is to follow the path along the Val d'Incles with its flowery meadows and wooded slopes. After about 3km the path steepens across rocky defiles whose grassy dells are full of pale yellow daffodils, *Narcissus pseudonarcissus* subsp. *pallidiflorus*, as well as many of the plants already mentioned including the trumpet gentians, yellow pulsatillas and soldanellas. Higher still, amongst snow patches in June, crocuses are still to be found in flower as well as *Hepatica nobilis*, always white-flowered here, and with its characteristic three-lobed leaves. Rarer are the patches of pink *Androsace carnea* subsp. *laggeri*, nestling amongst the grassy tussocks with *Viola palustris*.

Perhaps the most rewarding walk in Andorra for flowers and mountain tranquility is to take the road north from Andorra la Vella to Ordino and El Serrat and on to the head of the valley, just below the French frontier. A longish walk in early and mid summer takes one across rocky meadows full of white buttercups, *Ranunculus pyrenaeus* and sparkling brooks edged with pink *Primula integrifolia* in a variety of hues, as well as bold patches of bright yellow *Geum montanum*. Here, if you catch the season just right, there is a breathtaking display of gentians – five species can be distinguished: *Gentiana verna* and *G. acaulis*, a smaller trumpet gentian with dumpy flowers and rounded leaves, *G. alpina*, the brilliant small blue stars of the annual *G. nivalis*, the snow gentian, and, perhaps most exciting of all, the Pyrenean gentian, *G. pyrenaica*, which is readily distinguished by its violet-blue flowers which appear to have ten, rather than the usual five, petals. Here I once found a pure white form of the Pyrenean gentian. This last species is confined to the eastern Pyrenees, but despite its name it is also found in Turkey – an extraordinary distribution for a fascinating species.

The walk eventually leads to the blue lakes of Tristaina at about 2100m (6,900ft) altitude where thickets of pink alpenrose, *Rhododendron ferrugineum* abound. Pyrenean gentians are common here, including occasional pale forms. In June *Erythronium dens-canis* and *Hepatica nobilis* frequent the lush turf. On the poorer rockier slopes the exquisite spring pasque flower, *Pulsatilla vernalis*, forms small colonies and, clasping the rocks, deep pink mats of *Silene acaulis*, the moss campion as well as several saxifrages; *S. moschata* and *S. paniculata* being the most frequent. A search of the cliffs and larger boulders will probably reveal small dense grey cushions, studded in small white flowers if the time is right, of *Androsace vandellii*, but they can be easily overlooked.

Head south from Andorra towards the Spanish frontier and the altitude lowers and the climate becomes warmer and drier. The plant associations here become very different and more typically Spanish or Mediterranean.

The spiny Pyrenean eryngo, *Eryngium bourgatii*, with its metallic-blue flowerheads is common along the road verges, together with a bright yellow flax, *Linum flavum*, which opens its blooms to the sun. One plant, easily mistaken for a rush, sports surprising blue flowers in the late spring and early summer, *Aphyllanthes monspeliensis*. On the old walls and bridges close to Spain grows a charming snapdragon, *Antirrhinum molle*, with white and yellow flowers and the softest of grey leaves.

For a special excursion leave Andorra and head further east in France to the Val d'Eyne. There is no road along this small valley but it is a wholly delightful walk through woodland and follows a bubbling stream, lined by colonies of yellow Pyrenean lilies, *Lilium pyrenaicum*, beautiful, but foully scented, and clumps of blue columbines, *Aquilegia vulgaris*. Higher up the valley steepens and the trees thin. The rocky side streams sport extensive colonies of stout leafy, white-flowered *Saxifraga aquatica*, which, as the name suggest, grows in the running waters. There are many plants to be seen here growing on the grassy slopes including wild tulips, tiny starry yellow gageas, *Gagea soleirolii* and *Linum alpinum*, whose large satiny flowers vie with the sky for blueness. However, the great joy here must be the colonies of yellow *Adonis pyrenaica*, like a large multi-petalled buttercup with ferny leaves. This species, which is confined to the eastern Pyrenees and the Maritime Alps, is becoming increasingly rare. Higher up the valley on the frontier crags can be found various buttercups, *Ranunculus pyrenaeus* in drifts, *R. glacialis* and wonderful forms of *R. parnassifolius*, with large-cupped, white flowers veined with rose-pink. Scattered here and there will be seen a fine candytuft, *Iberis spathulata*, with its shiny, rather succulent, spoon-shaped leaves and domes of tightly packed pink flowers. One of the alpine poppies, *Papaver rhaeticum*, is also a denizen of these heights.

Of course there are many more delightful places to visit in these mountains. One could write pages on the Val d'Aran or the Col de Tormalet or the spectacular views from the Col d'Aubisque or the magnificent grandeur of the Ordessa National Park inside Spain, but the real thrill is to go to these mountains and to explore them for oneself and to find those hidden corners where few others seem to venture.

Development of tourism and town expansion in many parts of the Pyrenees in recent years has had a marked effect on some valleys and threatens the wild life. Yet there is still much to be seen and enjoyed in these splendid mountains where there is a great range of flowers, birds, insects and other animals. Today there are a number of national parks, both on the French and the Spanish sides, created to protect the wildlife and to preserve the unique scenery of this wilderness region. The flowers are there for all to enjoy, even outside the parks, and to pick or dig them is not to be condoned. Left alone they will remain for succeeding generations to marvel at.

Bulbous, Cormous, Tuberous and Rhizomatous Plants for Rock Garden and Alpine House

ERICH PASCHE

As bulbous plants are spread all over the world it is a difficult task to select only some out of the gigantic bulb kingdom to write about. It is not my intention to report only about extreme rarities, as not all members of the societies are specialists. Good growing 'simple' plants give much more pleasure than half-dead rarenesses, and are often under-valued.

Collecting bulbs is a fascinating matter, and, once infected, one cannot stop it. In comparison with non-bulbous plants, most of the bulbous plants have the great advantage of being dormant during summer. One can leave them alone for a couple of weeks and travel for holidays during this time, as nearly no or only little care is necessary to keep them alive. This could lead to the assumption that bulbs are plants for intelligent, lazy people. But that is not so.

I started with a small frame for crocuses, when I began collecting bulbs more than twenty years ago. The frame was replaced later on by two glasshouses of a size of 5 × 2.75m (16 × 9ft) in which I now cultivate most of my bulbs. As we have a precipitation of 1200mm up to 2000mm (47–78in) in our region per year, controlled cultivation methods are necessary to save the bulbs from drowning. Under glasshouse conditions the bulbs are also better protected against other inclemencies of the weather, as well as against slugs, snails, birds etc.

The crocuses are still amongst my favourites, as they represent excellent plants for the alpine house and rock garden. They are neat dwarfs, and the flowering season is a very long one, beginning in July/August with *Crocus scharojanii* from north-east Turkey and the Caucasus, where it grows in alpine turf, and ending with the bi-coloured *Crocus scardicus* from southern Yugoslavian and Albanian mountains. Both are best cultivated outside in a humus-rich gritty soil. Under the same conditions will thrive *C. kosaninii* and *C. vallicola*, as well as its Caucasian relative, the extremely rare lilac *C. autranii*.

Another species suitable for outdoor cultivation is *Crocus biflorus* ssp. *pulchricolor*. I found some nice colour forms in north-western Turkey, also

48

some hybrids with *C. chrysanthus* of a distinct bronze tint. They are all still in existence after ten years.

Crocus baytopiorum attracted much attention just after its description in 1974 because of its unusual turquoise-blue colour. In Turkey we saw it growing in scree among *Pinus nigra* ssp. *pallasiana* together with *Fritillaria carica* ssp. *serpenticola*, *Muscari macrocarpum* and many other geophytes. A well-drained, sunny spot in the rock garden will suit it best.

All species belonging to the 'Saffron-Group', i.e. *Crocus asumaniae*, *C. pallasii* and its subspecies, *C. cartwrightianus*, the gorgeous *C. moabiticus* from Jordan and *C. oreocreticus* are best kept under glass, and do not get any water while dormant. The same applies to *Crocus boulosii* from the Gebel Achdar area in Libya and its closest relative *Crocus veneris* from Cyprus, *C. cambessedesii*, *C. candidus*, *C. adanensis*, *C. sieheanus* and the very widespread *C. cancellatus* with its edible corms of a hazelnut like taste.

An occasional watering is advisable for *Crocus abantensis*, *C. gilanicus*, *C. sieberi* and its subspecies, *C. reticulatus* and further species.

Because of the high precipitation in our region I did not try any of the Scorpiris (Juno) outside, as all these originate from hot, dry areas, with an extension from Spain to Central Asia. Some are real jewels, especially those belonging to the Persica-Group, such as *Iris persica* itself, which shows a great colour variation, as does *I. galatica*, which bears sometimes lovely purple forms, hence the synonym *I. purpurea*. I would elect *I. stenophylla* and the sub-species *allisonii* as the queen of the Junos. But the species from Central Asia are also splendid figures, i.e. *Iris nicolai* and the related *Iris rosenbachiana* and *I. baldschuanica*. These are low growing, compact plants of great beauty, presenting no difficulties in a very well-drained calcareous soil. Other short-stemmed species from Middle Asia which are worth growing are *I. maracandica*, *I. parvula* and *I. kuschakewiczii*.

Some are taller growing, but not less beautiful, i.e. *Iris vicaria*, *I. warleyensis*, *I. orchioides* (the true one), *I. kopetdaghensis* and the tricky *I. aitchisonii* from the rocky hillsides in Pakistan, of which the yellow form flowers every year with me in February. Another garden-worthy species is *Iris aucheri* from the Near East. In south-east Turkey we saw a location with thousands of flowering plants in all colour shadings from pure white, all tints of blue to dark violet. It grew in a field with deep clay, flooded in spring, but bone dry during summer.

A smaller yellow flowering Juno-Iris from eastern Turkey and the Caucasus is *Iris caucasica*, only 10–15cm (4–6in) high, but unfortunately very susceptible to virus infection.

Another fascinating group of Iris are those belonging to the Sub-genus Hermodactyloides, better known as Reticulatas. All are choice plants which will succeed in a sunny, well-drained spot. The best for planting in the open are *Iris danfordiae*, *I. histrioides*, *I. reticulata* and *I. winogradowii*. *I. kolpakowskiana*, *I. pamphylica* and *I. vartanii* should be grown in a frame or glasshouse, the latter frost free. *I. pamphylica* is regarded as a difficult species. I grow it successfully in pots in pure sand. In its natural habitat (southern Turkey) *I. pamphylica* grows on limestone in light pine-woods, at the edges of fields, and often takes refuge in thorny shrubs, which protect it against cattle, but unfortunately not against commercial collectors.

The Oncocyclus-Iris belong to the most sensational irises of all. But, alas, like many other *Iris* species, too, they are very susceptible to virus diseases, usually caused by aphids which must be controlled continuously. I use 20cm (8in) pots for planting, and plunge these into black ash to guarantee a free root run. Besides that, black ash has very good draining and thermic qualities. All Oncos are kept in a glasshouse, where no hard frosts can harm the plants. Watering should not start before November, after a hot dry summer rest. *Iris sari* is one of the easiest in cultivation. But especially nice is the very variable *Iris iberica* ssp. *elegantissima* and the splendid *I. paradoxa* var. *choschab*, which we met abundantly growing in mountain steppes of eastern Turkey. There we also found a very attractive hybrid *Iris barnumae* × *paradoxa*.

Iris masia, a species with swollen leaf bases from south-eastern Turkey, Syria and Iraq can be grown in the same way as the Oncos and Junos.

A plant from the damp, partly subtropical regions near the Black Sea of north-eastern Turkey and adjacent USSR is *Iris lazica*. The flowers resemble those of *Iris unguicularis*, but the leaves are broader, shiny and bow-shaped, overhanging, not stiff as in the latter. Besides that, *I. lazica* has quite a different ecology. A good spot for it is in the light shade under the stages of an alpine house, where it should be kept moist the year round, whereas *I. unguicularis* likes a drying off period in summer.

There are also lots of decorative species worth growing in the rock garden, i.e. *Iris schachtii*, *I. reichenbachii*, *I. suaveolens*, *I. taochia*, *I. douglasiana*, *I. kerneriana* and *I. ruthenica* to name only some. But one of the most robust and free flowering ones is *Iris pallida* ssp. *cengialtii*.

Fritillaries enjoy great popularity among bulb collectors and alpine gardeners. Many of the 100 species or so are destined for the rock garden, e.g. *Fritillaria michailovskyi*, *F. caucasica*, *F. eduardii*, *F. collina*. *F. latifolia* and others and make a great display in spring. Most of the nearly 80 species I cultivate are kept under glass, as some like an extensive dry period during summer, for example those belonging to the Rhinopetalum group, i.e. *Fritillaria ariana*, *F. bucharica*, *F. gibbosa* and *F. stenanthera*, but also many of the North American species.

Fritillaria alburyana, *F. crassifolia* and its subspecies, *F. minima*, *F. minuta* and others should get a shower now and then during summer.

Fritillaries under glass get easily burnt by spring sun. A slight shading is advisable.

Fritillaria, *Lilium*, *Nomocharis* and *Notholirion* are closely related genera. In nature lilies often grow at wood edges or on clearings, shaded for some hours during the day. One can find them also on steep, stony alpine slopes or in sunny meadows, where scree or grass keeps the ground cool. All these habitats are always perfectly drained. This factor has to be taken into account when growing lilies. The best way is to encompass the bulbs with coarse grit, black ash or other drainage material when planting them. The sharp drainage materials are also avoided by mice, slugs and snails. Most of the lilies as well as *Nomocharis* and *Notholirion* I cultivate under glass in lattice pots, plunged in Lecaton, which is a burnt, ball-shaped clay, normally used for hydroponics. In this medium the plants build up a very good root system.

Most of the tulips I grow in containers, which are plunged in the garden. After having faded away they are stored under the stages and get a warm dry summer rest until October. One of my favourites is *Tulipa montana* (= *wilsoniana*) with its brilliant red flowers.

Among the colchicums, *Colchicum speciosum* is one of the hardiest and finest. In 1984 I brought back from Turkey some nice colour forms, including a pure white one, which do well under a carpet of *Fragaria nubicola*, an invasive species from Himalaya and western China. *Colchicum cilicicum* and the spring flowering *C. szovitsii* are not as hardy as the former. The leaves are sometimes damaged by late frosts, and should be covered after cold nights with spruce branches. *C. troodii*, the yellow spring-flowering *C. luteum*, *C. hungaricum* and all *Merendera* species are best grown under the protection of a frame or alpine house, giving plenty of air to prevent botrytis.

Under deciduous trees and shrubs exist ideal circumstances for planting a wide range of bulbs, e.g. most *Galanthus*, *Erythronium*, *Trillium* and *Scilla* species, *Narcissus cyclamineus*, *Cyclamen coum*, *C. cilicium* etc. *Geranium macrostylum* thrives excellently with us under *Gleditsia triacanthos*, which do not begin to sprout before the *Geranium* has flowered.

Every year the cyclamen get a slight covering of a mixture of leaf-mould and pine needles (50:50) with an added fertilizer, to which the plants respond very positive. Until now I have not been courageous enough to try *Cyclamen pseudibericum* and *C. trochopteranthum* in our climate outside. But these thrive and grow well under the glasshouse stages. *Cyclamen persicum* and *C. rohlfsianum* are grown frost free and kept hot and dry between May and September.

A frost free corner is also necessary for *Narcissus serotinus*, *Leucojum valentinum*, *Scilla lingulata* var. *ciliolata*, as well as some Californian and South African bulbs, such as *Dichelostemma ida-maja*, *Antholyza ringens*, *Sparaxis elegans*, *Geissorhiza tulbaghensis* and many more. They all like a summer baking phase, which is also indicated for some Moroccan and Spanish narcissi, e.g. *Narcissus cantabricus*, and for *Allium falcifolium* and *A. schubertii*, and *Sternbergia* species. Furthermore *Sternbergia* should get a feeding at every watering to flower well.

Corydalis are getting more and more popular among alpine gardeners, and the tuberous ones of this very large genus are normally in the limelight. Many of these come from Central Asian mountains, from Iran, Turkey etc., where they get a dry summer rest period. Two of the finest of the tuberous group are *Corydalis popovii* and *Corydalis schanginii* ssp. *ainii*. A very good drained soil is essential for both.

In contrast with these, *C. cashmeriana* likes peat bed conditions in a cool spot of the garden. It can flower twice a year in a fascinating brilliant blue colour.

Dicentra is related to *Corydalis*, as both belong to the poppy family (Papaveraceae). *Dicentra peregrina* is a marvellous species, which will succeed best in a gritty soil. I have not been very successful yet, but I have seen a lot of superb plants in the Botanical Garden at Gothenburg.

A warmth loving plant is *Anemone coronaria* from the Mediterranean. With its red, blue or white flowers it colonizes abandoned fields, field edges, clearings of pine woods or wall crevices. We also find it on grassy slopes associated with *Leontice leontopetalum*, a nice member of the Berberis family. Both will grow best under the shelter of an alpine-house.

Eminium rauwolfii inhabits hot dry areas in southern Turkey and Syria, where it grows in stony situations. In cultivation I find all eminiums difficult to flower, though I do feed them regularly and give them a thorough baking during summer.

In contrast to *Eminium*, *Arisarum vulgare* is a free flowering aroid. It grows best when not pot bound in a frost-free spot of an alpine house or frame. The same applies to *Arum creticum*, which, in our part of the continent, I prefer to grow in a big pot under glass rather than outside. It is kept completely dry from June to September. The yellow or white spathes appear in April. This species is surely one of the best of all arums.

A further species, *Arum italicum*, is not only worth growing because of its sometimes white nerved leaves, but also for the very decorative infructescences, which enhance the autumn garden.

Two other aroids from China are recommended for the alpine garden: *Arisaema candidissimum* and *A. consanguineum*. The pinkish, white striped spathes of *A. candidissimum* are more conspicuous than the red-brown ones with white stripes of *A. consanguineum*. But the latter has more elegant leaves, divided in 10–20 small-pointed leaflets. A deep planting (20cm; 8in) is advisable to keep the tubers from the frost.

Among the roscoeas cultivated in gardens, *Roscoea humeana* is one of the finest species. The rather large purple flowers appear from May to July. As it is a plant of the summer rainfall areas in China, a deep planting in a peat bed suits it best.

In 1974 I got a rhizome of *Cypripedium formosanum* with a single 'nose' from Paul Christian in Wrexham. I planted it in a 10cm (4in) clay pot and repotted it at two year intervals, using a well-drained soil consisting mainly of organic materials (leafmould, pine needles, sphagnum moss etc.). In the meantime I learned that the soil should be more mineral, as the roots are then less attacked by pests (? eelworms) and stay white and healthy. The soil surface is covered with Lecathon to keep the rhizomes well aerated.

In May 1983 it flowered with 16 blossoms. Now it is in a 35cm (14in) pot and has more than forty stems. I am looking forward to next May.

From spring till autumn the plant can be plunged in a half-shady spot in the open, feeding it three to five times at three week intervals with a highly soluble liquid fertilizer, poor in nitrogen, but rich in potassium.

Cypripedium acaule is short living with me and I lost all the plants I had. But this nice species is certainly worth every effort to keep it in cultivation, as are so many other 'bulbs', too, I think.

New Zealand Alpines in the Wild

PAT HALL

New Zealand consists of three main islands, North Island, South Island, and Stewart Island. It is about 2000km (1250 miles) long, and 256km (160 miles) wide at its broadest point. It lies between latitudes 34° and 47° south, which equates in the northern hemisphere to Berne in Switzerland and Casablanca in Morocco. Or, in America, to Seattle and Los Angeles. In area it is very similar to the British Isles.

Most of the mountain regions occur in the South Island, along with a high proportion of the alpine plant species. The North Island contains recent volcanic mountains of erodable ash and scoria, and also greywacke mountains. The greywacke continues into the South Island. These rocks are easily shattered by frost, resulting in vast scree areas, especially on the eastern slopes of the main divide. Further south in Central Otago, the mountains are mainly schist. On these windswept plateaux soil is frozen for up to six months of the year, and air frosts may occur in mid summer. These rigorous conditions permit the existence of mainly dwarfed cushion and mat-forming plants. Still further south, in Fiordland and Stewart Island the mountains are granite and gneiss. There are also granite mountains in North Westland and North-west Nelson. Scattered among these rock types are very important areas of limestone and marble, especially in North Canterbury and North-west Nelson, where alpine plants are typical and plentiful.

At one stage in the country's very early development, the north-western corner of the South Island was joined to Fiordland, but with the movement of the Pacific and Indo-Australian Tectonic Plates, it slowly moved to its present position, and so we have many of the same plants in the two areas.

The climate varies from sub-tropical in the north, to sub-antarctic in the south. The prevailing wind is westerly. The South Island mountains run almost north/south, so the weather, coming in from the Tasman Sea, strikes the mountains, dropping large quantities of rain and snow on the western and southern slopes, and giving much drier weather in the east.

Originally most of the land was forested, now native forest covers only about 40%, and this mainly in the South Island. On the central ranges, beech forest reaches a height of about 1200m (4000ft). The beech species reaching the highest altitude is *Nothofagus solandri* var. *cliffortioides*, or mountain beech, and in good seasons its flower is impressive. Above the treeline are herbfields and tussock grasslands, which in New Zealand are dominated by long-lived large tussock grasses and associated large herbs. Above that, the fellfields, the barren slopes and loose screes, and topping all, perpetual snow. On the eastern side the greywacke ranges have vast, almost barren screes and shingle slips, often from summit to the valley floor, caused firstly by the nature of the rock, and secondly by the low rainfall, which results in less luxuriant stabilising growth.

The snowline also varies from north to south. There is very little permanent snow in the North Island, but it is quite extensive above 2200m in the South Island.

Sandwiched between evergreen forest and perpetual snow is 'the cream of New Zealand vegetation'. Into this narrow strip are crowded hundreds of alpine plant species, and there is an amazing and highly attractive diversity of plant form in this alpine landscape. A very large proportion of alpine plant species, about 90%, are endemic to New Zealand, although only about 10 of the 130 alpine genera are. A few are cosmopolitan, and others shared with other southern hemisphere lands. About one fifth of the species have yet to be named, and there are undoubtedly more waiting to be discovered.

True, there is a lack of spectacular colour: the flowers are mostly white or yellow. On closer inspection, an appreciable number are marked with mauve or yellow, and of course there are the exceptions. The likely reason for the predominence of white flowers is the scarcity of specialised pollinating insects, especially the long-tongued bees and butterflies. Insect pollination seems to be carried out largely by flies, and to a lesser extent by short-tongued bees, moths and beetles. White petals are usually associated with short-tubed flowers which are best suited to the insects available. There is, however, a variety of colour in the profusion of fruits. The main flowering time is late spring and early summer, November to January, and fruits ripen throughout summer and autumn.

Let us consider the families and genera of the plants.

The podocarp family
Most of New Zealand's conifers are forest trees, but three of them, one each from the genera *Phyllocladus*, *Podocarpus* and *Lepidothamnus* reach the alpine zone as shrubs. They are usually unisexual and can be found up to an altitude of about 1600m. Only the pollen is produced in typical cones. The seed is either surrounded by a cup-shaped aril or is seated on a fleshy scale or stalk.

Ranunculaceae – the buttercup family
Genus *Ranunculus* is common throughout the temperate regions of the world. Of the 45 New Zealand species about half are alpine. They vary in size, habitat and foliage but are immediately recognised by their flower.

Brassicaceae or Cruciferae – the cress or mustard family
Genus *Notothlaspi* is endemic to New Zealand. Of its three species, all are alpine, one is a scree plant.

Scree plants
These have many common characteristics. They are never abundant, and easily missed in their vegetative form, if you are not searching for them. Most species are glaucous, often tinged with purple. Most are succulent, and rhizomatous, the underground stems creeping down the mountain slope to a more stable accumulation of silt below the stones. The shoots are annual or biennial, and die after flowering, being renewed from the rhizome the next season. *Cardamine* – A large genus of about 120 species from temperate regions. Of about 30 native species only a few are alpine. Most prefer moist sites. Most are still unnamed.

Droseraceae – the sundew family
Genus *Drosera* is widespread, many species are Australian. There are six native species. Droseras are insectivorous plants. They attract small flying insects and ants onto their leaves where they are trapped by tentacles and held against sticky plates. Small glands on the leaves secrete enzymes which are injected into the insect within minutes, and it is digested as if by an external stomach, providing the plant with nitrogen which is lacking in their boggy niche.

Caryophyllaceae – the chickweed family
Colobanthus is a southern hemisphere genus. Most of our native species are alpine. They are separated into two habit groups, cushion and tufted. They have no petals, and vary from 4 to 5 sepals. Genus *Stellaria* is worldwide. Two of the five native species reach the alpine zone. One is a scree plant, the other prefers rocky well-drained sites.

Geraniaceae
Geranium, often called cranesbill, is a widespread genus of some 300 species with only seven of them native.

Polygonaceae – the buckwheat family
Genus *Muehlenbeckia* is found in South America and Australasia. Of the six native species five are trailing plants, one of them reaching the alpine zone.

Portulacaceae – the portulaca family
Genus *Neopaxia* consists solely of four or five Australasian species. It is also known as *Montia* or *Claytonia*.

Oxalidaceae
Oxalis is a widespread genus of about 800 species, found from lowland to

alpine regions. It spreads by creeping rhizomes. There are five native species.

Onagraceae – the evening primrose
Epilobium, meaning flower on top of pod, known as willowherb, is a large genus from temperate regions and present throughout New Zealand in a variety of habitats. There are about 50 native species.

Thymelaeaceae – the daphne family
Genus *Pimelia* is the native daphne. A group of about 80 shrubs, chiefly Australasian. About half of the 20 natives reach the alpine zone. *Kellaria* or *Drapetes*, is a small southern genus, centred in New Zealand. All nine species reach the alpine zone. Their whipcord growth form is very suited to withstand both the force and the drying action of the wind.

Euphorbiaceae – the euphorbia family
Oreoporanthera is a small Australasian genus, the single native species is alpine and confined to marble outcrops in well-lit areas, only in North-west Nelson.

Rosaceae – the rose family
Genus *Acaena*, meaning thorn, and referring to the spines on most of the fruit. A large southern hemisphere genus. Only a few of the 18 native species reach the alpine zone.
Geum, a widespread genus, most of the natives are alpine, some are aromatic.

Apiaceae or Umbelliferae – the carrot family
This is cosmopolitan but mainly temperate. Most are pungent and have a stout taproot. They extend from subalpine to high alpine. The family contains the genera *Anisotome*, *Gingidia*, *Schizeilema*, *Lignocarpa* and *Aciphylla*. *Aciphylla* is often referred to as speargrass or wild spaniard, because of its swordlike leaves. It is a distinctive and important genus with over 40 species, most reaching the alpine zone. They vary from plants 1m (3ft) tall with 3m (10ft) flower spikes down to the pigmy speargrass only 30cm (12in) high.

Epicaceae – the heath family
Gaultheria, is a large widespread genus. About half the natives are alpine, and often called snowberry. *Pernettya*, a southern hemisphere genus. All three natives are alpine. These two look very similar and hybridise freely. *Pentachondra*. A small Australasian genus, the only native species being alpine. The immature fruit of one season ripen in the next, giving flowers and fruit together. *Leucopogon*, *Cyathodes* or *Styphelia*, a genus of Malasia

and Australasia. There are 5 native species. *Dracophyllum*. A genus of Australasia and New Caledonia. Sometimes called the dragon or grass tree. About half of the 27 native species reach the alpine zone and vary from a tree 13m (43ft) high down to a cushion plant in bogs.

Rubiaceae – the coffee or madder family
Coprosma is a genus of about 100 species in Pacific and Malaysian regions. Of the 52 native species only a few reach the alpine zone. Male and female flowers are borne on separate plants, but it is the fruit which is prominent and covers a wide range of colours.

Asteraceae or Compositae – the daisy family
Celmisia is a very large genus of about 60 species mainly from New Zealand, with a few species in Australia. Most of them reach the alpine zone and they are by far the most plentiful of our alpine plants. Their flower heads are distinctive and rather uniform, but there is a remarkable assortment of vegetative form. Most are found only in the South Island. *Abrotanella* is a South American and Australasian genus. All of the 10 native species reach the alpine zone and most have a small almost moss-like habit. *Leptinella*, formerly included in *Cotula*, is a very widespread genus with 28 native species, only a few reach the alpine zone. It is sometimes called the cup flower because of the hollow in which the florets sit. *Raoulia* is a large, predominently New Zealand group of plants found only in the South Island. Most are mat plants, others cushion plants which are called vegetable sheep because at a distance they look like sheep on the mountainside. *Haastia* is an endemic genus of 5 species, all of them alpine, some also vegetable sheep. *Leucogenes* contains only 4 alpine species, 2 still unnamed, all are endemic to New Zealand. Commonly called the New Zealand eidelweiss. *Helichrysum* is a large widespread genus with 9 native species mostly alpine and varying from herb to shrub. None of them are true *Helichrysum*, they will be put in other genera. *Craspedia* is an Australasian genus. Of about 40 native species a number reach the alpine zone. They are often called woollyheads. Most are still unnamed. *Brachyglottis* and *Dolichoglottis* used to be called *Senecio*, which is a large cosmopolitan genus. *Brachyglottis* varies from a herb to a shrub, while *Dolichoglottis* has only 2 species and is commonly called the snow marguerite, living in permanently wet areas.

Gentianaceae
Gentiana, in a broad sense, is a widespread genus typically alpine, which flowers mainly in late summer and autumn. Native flowers are mainly white.

Campanulaceae – the bell flower
Wahlenbergia is a widely distributed genus particularly in the southern hemisphere. Of the 7 native species, one is a scree plant.

Donatiaceae – cushion plants
Cushion growth is the alpine heat trap. The dense foliage absorbs and conserves the sun's heat. *Donatia* is a subantarctic genus, found also in Tasmania and South America.

Stylidiaceae – the stylidium family
Phyllachne, also subantarctic, is another cushion plant. Both species are alpine. *Oreostylidium* contains a single endemic species, found in the alpine zone. *Forstera* is a small genus from South America, Tasmania and New Zealand. There are 7 native species, all alpine.

Lobeliaceae
Lobelia is a widespread genus. Only 3 are native, 2 are alpine, one of these being a scree plant. *Pratia*, a small genus from Asia, South America and Australasia. There are 12 native species, all creeping and rooting herbs.

Boraginaceae – the borage family
Myosotis, the forget-me-not, from temperate regions. Of about 50 New Zealand species, most are alpine, many as yet unnamed. There are more species in New Zealand than in any other country.

Lentibulariaceae – the bladderwort family
Utricularia, a widespread genus of insectivorous plants, frequenting peat bogs and tarns where they trap insects in their underwater bladders.

Scrophulariaceae – the figwort family
Genus *Euphrasia*, called the eyebright, is a semi-parasitic plant from temperate regions. *Ourisia*, the mountain foxglove, is a small genus from South America and Australasia. *Chionohebe*, or *Pygmea* is a genus of 6 native species, 2 of which extend to Australia. All are confined to high altitude areas of the South Island. *Parahebe*, has about 35 species. (It is going to be split up when some will go to *Chionohebe*.) They are found in New Zealand, Australia and New Guinea, and cover a wide altitudinal range, from lowland to high alpine. *Hebe*, is the largest part of a group of southern genera related to *Veronica*. It is almost exclusively a New Zealand genus with about 100 species, 2 of which are also found in southern South America, and one further species which is confined to Rapa Island, near Pitcairn Island in the south eastern Pacific. About half reach the alpine zone. They are varied, but recognised by the neat four-ranked arrangement of their leaves. They are at present being revised by Dr. Phil Garnock-Jones at the Botany Institute, D.S.I.R. Land Resources.

Liliaceae – the lily family
Astelia is a Pacific Ocean genus, centred in New Zealand. All plants are

unisexual. There are over 20 native species, about half reaching the alpine zone. *Bulbinella* is a genus of about 20 species in South Africa and new Zealand, 6 of them being native.

Agavaceae
Phormium, or flax is a genus of 2 New Zealand species, one also in Norfolk Island. Only one reaches the alpine zone.

Orchidaceae – the orchid
This family contains over 100 native species. Most are ground orchids, and only a very few reach the alpine zone.

My thanks to Mr. A.P. Druce for checking and corrections.

Alpines of Bulgaria and Romania

JAROSLAV KAZBAL

B otany pastures of heaven beyond the so-called socialist paradise being
for peculiar, and pecunary, reasons so distant from us as the moon is to
the rest of mankind, we, Czech and Slovak alpine enthusiasts, have had to
frequent, in bygone years, mountains of Bulgaria and Romania in the
Balkans. Thus we have become acquainted with its floral abundance.
Everybody knows that a pretty girl can be found in a poor remote village as
well as in some rich, gorgeous city. The same goes for beauty in nature. The
creative nature of Nature, contrary to people, is indiscriminate; she loves all
her children equally and in the process of natural selection wisely decorated
the mountains of the world with her jewels.

If I may say so, the alpine plants of Bulgaria and Romania were in no
respect last in the queue when beauty was distributed. Let us look at some of
them.

When I saw the golden glare of *Alyssum cuneifolium* var. *pirinicum* for the
first time it was in the greyness of a marble, stony desert near a receding
overhang at the very top of Mount Vichren (Vichren meaning windswept),
just short of 3000m (10,000ft). I got the impression of the personification
of 'magic circles' with the flowers beginning to open in outer, peripheral
rings first, then slowly filling-in the whole inflorescence. It charmed me so
that I never missed a chance of going back. Ever since 1975 I make the
pilgrimage to the Pirin mountain range, just for the sake of seeing the same
single species. But there are, of course, others too.

One of the silvermost edelweis I know of is *Leontopodium alpinum* ssp.
pirinicum. Brooch-like, densely hairy-leaved, it has a small stature which,
importantly for rock gardeners, stays so on lowland rockeries, where it is
also floriferous.

Another gem which grows there, at about 2500m (8200ft) elevation, is
Saxifraga oppositifolia in its uniformly six-petalled form. There is a whole
colony of it. What a memorable sight!

In the highest reaches of the marble part of the Northern Pirin range
grows a delicate members of the *Saxifraga*, *S. spruneri*, whose small, but
old, buns resemble *Androsace helvetica*. They fill the fissures of stones faces or
crouch under big boulders that protect them from the midday scorching
sun. Another member of this section, *S. ferdinandi-coburgi*, its flowers, in all
possible shapes and shades of golden yellow, spread over large cushions can
be found everywhere, along with the wine-red *S. sempervivum* f. *stenophylla*.

In association with *Viola grisebachiana*, which ornaments drying grasses on south exposed slopes, grows the single-headed *Centaurea actarovii*. It is only up to 5cm (2in) tall, its noble flowers, about 4cm (1.5in) in diameter, seated in rosettes of felty leaves that look as if tailored from cobwebs.

These and many other fine plants of great horticultural value, such as *Genista subcapitata*, *G. depressa moesiaca*, *Globularia meridionalis*, *Daphne oleoides*, *D. velenovskyi*, *Gentiana verna*, *G. dschimilensis*, *Androsace villosa* var. *arachnoidea*, *Helianthemum*, *Primula* and one of the most variable of *Dianthus*, *D. microlepsis*, in all shades of pink, rose and white are framed by these mountains.

Many nice alpines grow in Romanian mountains. I present here but two. First is my find of the white form of *Primula minima*, its portrait in captivity was published in the AGS *Bulletin* Vol. 57, no. 2, page 131. The second is the *Eritrichium jankae* from the stony outcrops of Bucegi Mountains.

For the omission of geographical and other details, I do apologise. It was on purpose as I dislike didactic traveller's stories. 'Have fun and travel' is the much better and active philosophy of rock gardening. Only personal study of where and how plants grow in their natural habitats can help us to simulate conditions for cultivating them in our gardens.

A True-to-life Approach to Alpines

DUNCAN LOWE

At the heart of what I am about to present lies my own long-sustained desire to grow mountain plants as closely as possible to their natural character and behaviour. I use the term 'mountain plants' to separate from the massed and varied inhabitants of rock gardens, those species which we regard as true alpines, as it is upon these that I wish to concentrate. The mountain flanks, screes and crags where they reside are almost, but not quite, unique habitats. There are parallels in the wilderness approaching the polar latitudes, but in both instances the prevailing conditions are very far removed from those where we make our gardens.

To maintain these highly specialised plants in cultivation we have developed methods, treatments and aids to provide them with as many as is practicable of the natural habitat features. The results still fall sadly short of reproducing authentic terrain and fail almost entirely to offer climates and seasons bearing any resemblance to those which the plants experience and have evolved over millennia to accept as 'normal'.

At times the lengths to which we go in striving to create the 'right conditions' culminate in what can only be described as successful eyesores. Is there anything less evocative of the summer mountains than an alpine house bench, or a brick-built plunge bed capped by an aluminium penthouse? Whilst there are sound arguments in defence of such devices and horticultural triumphs to support them, it is difficult to ignore their ugliness and many growers much prefer to see and enjoy their plants in more kindly settings. These sensitive souls will be pleased to know that it is both possible and practicable to grow choice, difficult and rare alpines in reasonable replicas of their true dwelling places. What is more, with just a few exceptions, plants given the 'natural' treatment can often equal in quality those raised in purely functional contrivances.

'True-to-life cultivation' was perhaps an over-statement as a title, but it serves well enough to give the theme for what is to follow. For the purposes of cultivation the plants can be put into two distinct categories:

(a) Those which respond best to the closest approximation of their natural growing places.
(b) Those which languish or even die when given simulated homes, but respond to strange alternatives.

A few examples will illustrate what is involved and provide a basis for discussion.

In the first category is *Saxifraga caesia*, widely distributed through the European mountain chains and invariably found on sunny limestone rocks and rubble. It is obviously equipped to cope with torrid conditions and periods of drought, judging by the nature of the places and substances in which it chooses to live. The logical reaction of the cultivator is to provide a stony cranny or scree which enjoys plenty of sunshine and *voila!*, the saxifrage grows and blooms just as it should.

Saxifraga retusa is another truly saxatile species, favouring similar crevices, in granite or schist and is closely comparable to *S. caesia*, but in cultivation its needs are quite different. Given a similar fissure or scree it may persist and even put up the odd flower from time to time, but it will be clearly displeased with what has been provided. Take the same specimen and plant it in a well-drained pocket of gritty, fibrous soil and its behaviour is transformed. New growth thrusts outwards to build a dense healthy mat which is generously clothed in jostling flowers every spring. Unlike *S. caesia*, however, it will strongly resent any hint of parching at its roots.

There are quite a few examples of such contrasts in cultivation. The raoulias of New Zealand inhabit piles of rock debris in nature, where there is scant presence of humus in their perches, yet by accident it was discovered that the best mixture (in the UK) for pot-grown subjects is an ericaceous compost with a little grit added! Again this is an instance of a rock-dwelling plant responding to a completely different rooting medium when in exile; and it occurs frequently enough to be an accepted but puzzling phenomenon. The ultimate example is provided when two totally unrelated plants share the same cleft in a mountain cliff or boulder, yet react to cultivation in extremes. *Eritrichium nanum* and *Saxifraga squarrosa*, co-habiting in a tiny pocket, might suggest that what is good for one must be equally acceptable to the other when the grower tries to please them, but not so. The saxifrage is an amenable species, quite content in the open rock garden but the eritrichium's dislike of garden culture is notorious and even the most sophisticated growing conditions and care sustain the plant in a weary state for only a short time. This frustrating disparity has never been convincingly explained.

Accepting such oddities of behaviour, we can still pursue the realistic housing of our plants and in doing so, often introduce beneficial features and agencies, intentionally or otherwise. Dedicated and enthusiastic growers of alpines have now more or less abandoned the traditional rock garden constructions as the principal location for the plant collection. Scree beds, raised beds, troughs and other containers feature strongly in today's alpine gardening. And it must be said that although those earlier terraced piles of stone blocks and soil were supposed to reproduce a 'natural outcrop', they rarely did. The few masterpieces of simulation, built with great skill and at considerable cost, were impressive and inspiring, but generally failed to meet even the basic needs of mountain plants. Their role was much more

15   *Alyssum cuneifolium* var. *pirinicum* on Mount Vichren in the Pirin
Mountains, Bulgaria (see page 61)

16   *Saxifraga retusa* growing happily in a pocket in the rock garden
     (see page 64)

17   *Edraianthus serpyllifolia* in an artificial crevice in a rock garden
     (see page 64)

18 Part of Mike and Polly Stone's garden at Askival (see page 70)

19 *Shortia soldanelloides* sow themselves around at Askival (see page 75)

20   A well-stocked peat bed from which to choose plants for showing (see page 77)

21   *Cassiope* 'Beatrice Lilley' in peak condition (see page 78)

as a focal point in the created landscape than a place specially prepared for growing.

Inevitably the swing to functionalism has been taken to extremes by some. Stark, rectangular enclosures, filled with zealously proportioned mixtures and set about with frameworks and automated care systems, have proved their potency in producing hitherto ungrowable rarities. Take heart all those of you who cannot live with these horticultural laboratories – you will not miss out on very much.

Scree beds are one of the simplest and most productive elements of the alpine garden. Consisting for the most part of stone chippings, they can be laid directly over previously well-weeded ground and do not have to look like the base for a railway track or a misplaced part of the driveway. Some patience and a willingness to hunt for interesting materials can improve the end result, both visually and for the welfare of the plants.

Builders gravel is excellent for the bulk of the scree, but as a finished surface it is wanting. The stones are deliberately graded to a uniform size and so have little resemblance to the rough and tumble of a natural scree. There is no difficulty in correcting this shortcoming; it can be done 'cosmetically' by just skinning the surface with more oddly assorted and realistic material. The quantity required is no more than about 5% of the amount used to form the bed; a few bucketfuls will cover a large area and it thus becomes feasible to make a special collection of surfacing stones. In size they can range from that of a biscuit at the top end, to that of a pea at the other limit, with all the intermediates included. Generally speaking, flakes or angular shards of stone produce the most authentic look to the finished work, but where such are difficult to obtain a pleasing alternative makes use of river bed or sea shore pebbles. Particularly where rounded boulders or cobbles feature in the rockwork, shingle can be used to good effect and functions almost as well as the sharper chippings and shards.

Even when given an irregular, realistic surface, a scree can still present a somewhat bland appearance and is greatly improved by incorporating just a few much larger chunks of matching or complementary stone. The setting of these can provide an opportunity to create crevices, about which more will be said shortly.

Screes often take the form of raised beds in the garden and the approach to surfacing is identical to that already described. Many raised beds, however, are filled with a richer, compromise mixture to cater for a larger range of plants, often a roughly half and half amalgam of stone chippings or gravel and a peat/soil blend. To give the plants the essential well-drained, quick-drying surface on which to sit or sprawl, the bed is usually 'top-dressed' with pure gravel or chippings, which do the job, but can have a very strong hint of the cemetery about them. In addition, because of the underlying moist mixture, the top dressing is more vulnerable to invasion by mosses and other low forms of plant life, which can quickly impair the effectiveness

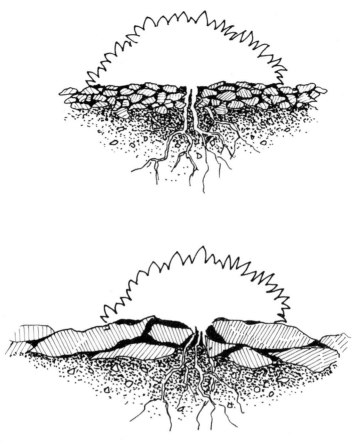

Fig. 1

of the surfacing. A final layer containing a good proportion of larger stones, as recommended for finishing ground-level screes, not only enlivens the appearance of the surface, but is also more resistant to infiltration by creeping weeds and forms a superior seating for the plants. This last benefit is due to larger air spaces in the randomly sized final layer, giving improved ventilation and drainage, so important in the winter months.

Like the scree, the raised 'soil mixture' bed can be given added character and usefulness by incorporating a few rocks, not deeply embedded in the root-run, as gardening tradition would have it, but sunk only just enough to give them stability. Their placing is best done prior to the top-dressing, to ease the contriving of crevices, for which two or more rocks are selected to achieve a rough match in the shapes of their adjoining faces. With the rocks mated and firmly based, the intended occupants can be planted as the 'crevices' are filled with soil mixture. The elevated and superbly drained

66

Fig. 2

growing places created by this simple method closely approach in character the true rock fissure, and beneath lies a virtually unlimited, moisture-retentive, root-run.

My initial experiments with artificial crevices of this type produced very rewarding results and I have yet to find a better means of satisfying some of the more difficult saxatile species. A good example is *Androsace alpina*, which, in relation to most aretian androsaces in cultivation, requires rather more sustenance and root freedom, whilst demanding the same excellence of drainage and aeration in the growing medium. My best results were achieved with a plant grown in a raised bed containing the 50/50 mixture, its cushion cradled between two flakes of rock. In this simulated habitat it asks only for a pane of glass to keep off the winter rain and is in all other respects an open-garden plant.

Encouraged by the success with a none-too-easy androsace I gave similar treatment to other plants generally regarded as needing alpine house conditions and very few failed to respond positively. Examples of these are:

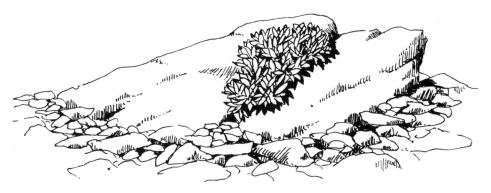

Fig. 3

Physoplexis comosa, *Dionysia aretioides*, *Asperula suberosa* and *Petrocallis pyrenaica*. There was also an improvement in the vigour and character of other rather less demanding plants when provided with a sham crevice; *Daphne arbuscula* behaves much more naturally and *Edraianthus serpyllifolius* is nowhere better than in its counterfeit cleft.

On a much smaller scale the same technique can be applied to pot-grown alpines. Take for instance *Saxifraga florulenta*, which in my conditions really needs a portable growing crevice in order to be given the benefits of an outdoor life in the growing season and indoor comforts whilst dormant. Carefully chosen stones cap the soil mixture in the pot and give the plant a platform to substitute for the granite cliff face of its natural haunts. By this means the 'neck' between root crown and foliage is held clear of the moist pot filling and is well supplied with ventilation to ward off rot, to which it is so vulnerable. For setting up in such a manner the plant must be trained from infancy, the seedling being given deeper than normal top-dressing in its first pot to discourage root branching near the surface. At the next potting-on the first stones are introduced and carefully wedged beneath the rosette, persuading the development of a long, clean neck. At each subsequent repotting the stones are progressively increased in size to improve the realism of the rock anchorage. It is useful, at this point, to compare the conventional top-dressing with the capping just described. The usual material employed in the great majority of pot-grown alpines is gravel, similar in size to that used for the bases of fish tanks or the finer path-making grades. There are specific horticultural gravels but these are really only cleaned and bagged versions of builders' materials. The most common shortcoming in their use is over-economy in the amount applied. All too often the dressing is sparingly sprinkled on the soil surface in the manner of cake decoration and is just enough to hide the soil. To be properly effective

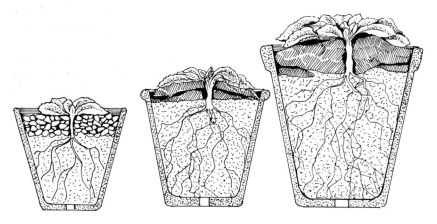

Fig. 4

the top-dressing should be at least a finger's thickness in depth, yet even with this generous layer the essential properties of drainage and aeration gradually decline and after a year at most a complete renewal is usually necessary. The need arises from the infiltration of liverworts and mosses and the mysterious rise of soil into the gravel. Flakes of stone do not suffer such deterioration; they are unable to settle and compact like gravels and offer far less hospitality to unwelcome growths, thus they sustain their assets indefinitely.

Not all saxatile plants can be grown on what is essentially a slab of stone, for some of them like to put down roots from their stems as they spread. Raoulias, mat-forming androsaces and many saxifrages, are just a few of the types which behave so. Others, like campanulas, need to send out runners just beneath the ground to send up shoots in their exploitation of suitable growing places. In both cases it is necessary to revert to the gravel topping but even so, a few miniature rocks inserted will cause them to creep around in a more interesting and typical manner. Nothing has yet been said of those mountain-dwellers favouring the short, wiry turf that climbs just as high as any of the flowering plants – but what can be done to reproduce that delicately balanced association in the garden?

From my own failures the answer to the question is – little or nothing. I have tried! Using dwarf grasses of excellent pedigree has been quite unsuccessful; the grass either refused to grow in the same places as the plant or, conversely, overwhelmed it. Authentic mountain grasses and sedges behaved in the same way. I have even teased out and nurtured grassy fragments from plants collected at great heights in the Himalaya, but to no avail. The problem seems quite clear; taken from their native haunts and given strange new soils, pests and climates, the plant and the grass no longer keep their ancient truce. The natural balance is lost as one adapts better than the other and eventually prevails. The result of the contest speaks for itself – there is either a plant surrounded by several whisps of dead grass, or a lusty clump of blades and no plant, (with the potential of a new weed for the garden!).

Translating a predominantly visual presentation into a written article has had its difficulties, but I hope that what I have produced here has been enough to stimulate the imagination and provide sufficient for the mind's eye.

By Loch Ness, Naturally?

MIKE AND POLLY STONE

At a major international gathering such as this, there will be talks on many aspects of alpine gardening. My wife and I are not botanists, intrepid explorers of remote and exotic mountain ranges, nor specialists in a particular genus or type of cultivation. We are just gardeners, and as such our remit was to give you a brief glimpse of our garden at Askival.

The late Bobby Masterton, who had more influence on us in the early days than any other single gardener, once observed that it was easy to make any garden look good in photographs. Bobby was replying to a compliment given at the conclusion of a lecture he had given on his superb woodland garden near Aberfeldy; and he did have a point. We all tend to photograph our successes, and given adequate lead-in time should be able to construct a worthwhile slide lecture. To write an interesting paper on one's own garden is quite another matter. It is all too easy to fall into the same boring trap as authors of travelogues: 'We walked up the path from so and so, and here we saw A, B and C.' The garden equivalent would be 'in such and such a bed we planted X, Y and Z, and they all do well!' So if one is to avoid a tedious catalogue of plant names, what is the alternative?

It is our intention in this paper to attempt to explain our garden philosophy, the thinking behind the way we garden, what we are trying to achieve, and how it relates to the current world of alpine gardening.

The title perhaps makes as good a starting point as any.

The word 'natural', like 'organic', is a much over-used one nowadays; it can mean almost anything, or virtually nothing, according to context. There is no doubt that all gardens are artificial in the sense of being man-made, but then so is much of the rest of the planet. Very little of Scotland is truly natural, except possibly parts of the seashore and the alpine zone. The Great Wood of Caledon is reduced to a few scattered remnants; but it is not too late, a little fencing and regeneration is immediate. Man is not the only animal to modify his environment! Ecologically speaking there is no need to separate man; after all we are closer to the chimpanzee than the chimp is to the gorilla. The real difference was suggested by the famous anthropologist Richard Leakey, 'Alone among the animals, man knows he's an animal, that's the cross he has to bear.' One of the ways we have found of lightening this burden, is the contemplation of the beauty of plants, in particular those tenacious alpines which have conquered the hostile environment of the high places.

While accepting that no garden can be completely natural, we should like to adopt an Orwellian approach – some gardens are more natural than others. A geometrical design executed in bedding plants is scarcely a recreation of nature, but we should not scoff too loudly, as we have our own version: the alpine show. We are well aware of, and accept, that they have an educational and advertising function, and, above all serve as a social occasion, bringing like-minded people together. Like everything else in life, they do have their down-side, in particular the influence they have on the way plants are grown and presented. There is little doubt that some alpine plant forms are completely un-suited aesthetically to pot cultivation. Two groups spring immediately to mind, the taller bulbs, and prostrate spreading shrubs such as *Epigaea repens* or *Daphne blagayana*. We well remember a specimen of the latter, poor thing, folded up like an umbrella and potted in a drain-pipe! I think they call them long toms. Did it ever return safely to the garden we wonder?

The trouble with the taller bulbs is not solely that they can look faintly ridiculous standing to attention evenly spaced in a pot, or alternatively flopping over some artfully contrived support, but in that it is all too easy crossing the arbitrary boundary into the sort of flamboyant florist's flowers my Mother used to pot up in bulb fibre for Christmas decorations. On one occasion at a spring show, I recall discussing a pan of *Fritillaria michaelovskyi* with my fellow judges. They wished to mark it down as it obviously comprised several seedling clones, whereas I actually enjoyed the diversity. The slight variations in height and in the proportions of the yellow and brown zones the corollas made a welcome change from the regiments of commercial tulip cultivars we had just been examining.

It might be thought that the cushion is an ideal plant form for pots, but even here we have a tiny axe to grind. While we can appreciate all the skill and dedication necessary over many years to produce a perfect hemisphere uniformly covered in bloom, we must confess to finding these humps squatting smugly in the centres of their pans rather boring. Many growers have confessed to us privately that they agree with this heresy. Evidence that we are not alone comes from the trend to present cushion plants on, and over rocks.

Before leaving shows and their ramifications, we must consider the alpine house, for the two are irrevocably intertwined in the basic culture of alpine gardening. The newcomer might be forgiven for gaining the impression from a show that the house is the place for the rare and interesting, the garden for the more ordinary 'rock plants'. If we have one single aim in our presentation at the 'Sixth International' it is to refute this suggestion. Typical of comments one reads are those of M. Northway in the A.G.S. *Bulletin* (Vol. 36, page 75) Writing of *Draba polytricha*, he asks 'Who wants to stoop over badly-grown specimens in a March snow-storm when perfection is so readily achieved in the alpine house?' We would dispute that any plant can ever be perfect, it's really a matter of individual taste, whether one prefers the symmetry of a 'spirograph' pattern or an artist's free-hand drawing. Up here at Askival, *D. polytricha* flowers in April, its tight cushions hugging rocks in our winter-covered troughs.

At this point one should perhaps pause and consider where the increasing sophistication of alpine houses may lead. The specialist grower may have his climate-controlled alpine room, such phytotrons already exist in research establishments. Really effective systemic fungicides may one day control diseases or the plants genetically engineered, and insects will be excluded. But where is the fun, the excitement of anticipation, the hopes dashed, or the subtle variations from season to season?

Before leaving this question I hope I might be permitted a current analogy to stress the distinction betwen growing for show and gardening. Consider concerts by Madonna, and Tina Turner. The former is a carefully contrived and constructed package whose prime purpose is to sell the 'product'; the latter a genuine live performance, real musicians doing their own thing, fronted by the Grand Dame of Rock, clearly enjoying herself!

At the other extreme from the alpine house we have the school of so-called 'natural rock gardening' advocated by Symons-Jeune and others. Rock, and its placement, is all, plants are merely decorations added later. Quite apart from their drawbacks as homes for plants, these rock-piles are inappropriate on two further counts. They can look incongruous in today's small gardens many miles from their native strata, no glacial erratics these; and they are very poor conservation. Tearing up an entire limestone pavement in the name of art is far more destructive to the environment than collecting a fern or two from the clints. Plants regenerate, rocks do not, at least within a human time-scale.

In truth a better adjective to describe these landscape rock gardens would be 'artificial' in the sense of a substitute for the real thing: like artificial flowers or an artificial ski-slope. A friend who once lived on the other side of the Glen, had a real rock outcrop in her garden. Nothing would grow on it save a semi-bonzai larch which had sown itself into a crack. Our troughs, raised beds, and terracing make no pretence; they are man-made solutions to our problems in cultivating a wide range of 'alpines' here in the Scottish Highlands. In them we try to tread a middle way, between the rock arranger and the alpine house, i.e. between art and artifice.

The view from our garden south-westwards down the Great Glen is dominated by the bulk of Ben Tee. Although only some 900m (3000ft) high, the climate up on top is truly alpine, treeline is at around 600m (2000ft). Contrast this with the Alps or the Rockies where the timberlines are several times higher. As one moves north, so the climate zones descend until alpines are found at sea-level, as for example at the North Cape. Our garden climate is very roughly equivalent to the meadow zone in the Alps. Here alpines can occur lower than normal in habitats where competition is reduced, thin turf over rock, on boulders, or in riverside gravels, like the *Saxifraga oppositifolia* near Drumochter (400m; 1300ft).

In our garden we aim to provide similar living space free of competition by more robust and aggressive lowland species, i.e. we weed the latter out! Our site lies one mile from the south end of Loch Ness, on steeply undulating glacial-fluvial deposits. The thin skin of stoney, acid top-soil varied from less than 10cm (4in) on top of the humps, to around 30cm (12in) in some of the hollows. In the twenty years since we started the garden our primary effort has always been towards enriching and thickening this fragile soil. Only the hollows have been dug in the usual way, and then only to one fork's depth.

Over much of the garden we have simply killed out the weeds and built our beds on top with no further preparation. Dwarf walls of boulder stones are used to construct terraces and raised beds. We are very fortunate in having ready access to an inexhaustable supply of stones from ruined drystane dykes around the village. Our use of stones in this way has nothing to do with the traditional rock garden as landscape, we employ them because they are free for the asking, durable and maintenance free. As it has turned out, all our hard landscaping using the same kind of split boulders for all the disparate beds, has acted as a unifying theme in the garden. To infill these beds we have completely stripped all the top-soil from the trough and frame areas, augmenting it with brought in peat and chippings, and our own leaf-mould.

Over the years we have experimented with various soil mixtures, but now grow all our plants in one of three bed-types. The ground level herbaceous beds in the hollows get all available compost from the heaps, Ericaceous terraces are bulked up with peat and leafmould, and the screes get chippings. Plants have shown their disdain for our modifications by, for example, wide mats of *Saxifraga paniculata* self-sowing into the meconopsis beds, while the meconopsis have moved themselves to the unimproved stony rose borders.

In spite of all our efforts our soil still dries out at the drop of a hat! Although our rainfall is from 1000 – 1500mm (39 – 60in) per annum, too much of this falls in the winter months. After 10 dry days in summer we have to start watering. Just as important as actual precipitation, is air humidity. One look at the mosses, lichens and ferns spreading themselves around Askival should leave the visitor in no doubt on that score. Remember that many true alpines detest a hot dry atmosphere!

Another advantage bestowed upon us is the Highland winter, longer and colder than other parts of the British Isles. While frosts of more than a couple of weeks duration are rare, the temperature remains in the range 3–5°C for much of the winter, giving alpines a proper dormancy. The various environmental factors are summarised in Fig. 1.

As our plant collection has expanded over the years, so the time available to cultivate each individual species has decreased. Thus, by necessity, has evolved our minimum interference approach to gardening, helped by our greater awareness of the suitability of our garden environment for the majority of alpines.

In recent years this trend has been reinforced by our visits to see alpines at home in the mountains. After our first visit, (we said) in the 'Stone Column' (published in the SRGC's *The Rock Garden*) that we would not be changing any of our cultivation methods as a result of our alpine holiday. For reasons given at the time, we still stand by this statement, but there have been two other consequences. Knowledge of how plants really look in the wild has made us far less clinical in our approach. We are more tolerant of imperfections, we allow plants to mingle as they will, and are less fussy about the odd patch of annual weeds, or moss in cushion-plants and peat beds alike. Secondly we have a more relaxed view of taxonomy, never an exact science. Neither can our labels be totally accurate, nomenclature is often a matter of opinion; would that some visitors realised this!

While the reasons for an alpine gardener to seek out a particular plant are many, and occasionally defy logic, two traits are discernable: the collecting

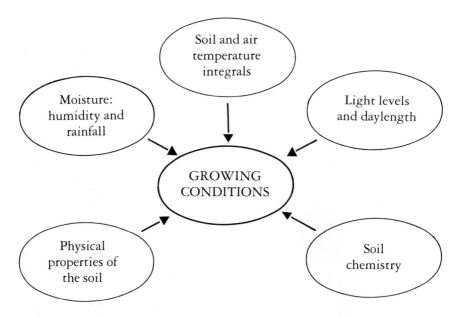

N.B. 1. Average temperatures govern plant growth; peaks and troughs are only important as possibly damaging.
    2. Recent research indicates that the physical nature of a soil is more important than its precise chemistry.

Fig. 1

instinct and the acceptance of a challenge. We ourselves are not completely immune, I have tried in the past to acquire all the verna gentians, and we raised *Pyxidanthera barbulata* from seed simply to prove it was possible. We like to think that these are the exceptions. We would never seek out all the species of *Fritillaria*, only those which we consider have a good chance of succeeding outside in our bulb borders, or would we accept any *Dionysia*, no matter how rare, as all have failed here.

When the opportunity arises to acquire a new plant, be it seed-list, catalogue or proffered gift, we always ask ourselves whether it us likely to grow at Askival, without continuous attention. If the answer is no, then ours is thanks, but no thanks. We have found that the mountains of the world afford many beautiful alpines which will grow relatively easily here. We do not agonise over those which won't. We are aware that this is diametrically opposed to the standard advice given in much alpine literature – acquire the plant first, then find out how to grow it, by applying various recipes etc. To this we answer: a collection of cosetted rarities does not a garden make!

Outwith the world of alpines many modern styles of gardening regard plants as expendable furnishing subjects (how I hate that word). As soon as flowers fade, or cropping ceases, out they come and the space is replanted. We are at the other extreme, we hate to disturb any plant once it is established. We only take up a plant if it is obviously going back, and in need of division and replanting, or is threatened with overgrowing by a more vigorous neighbour. Following a particular request we will take a piece off one of our garden plants, if possible, but we should far rather give away a potted plant from the frames.

Our minimum disturbance ethic has two important side-effects, it reduces the weeding by bringing less seed to the surface, and paradoxically increases the number of plants which maintain themselves by self-sowing. Species as diverse as *Fritillaria caucasica*, *Lewisia tweedii*, *Paraquilegia grandiflora*, *Androsace vandellii* and *Shortia soldanelloides* have all propagated themselves in this way. Not a few have taken things too far and almost become weeds, *Aquilegia bertolonii* in the trough area, *Soldanella carpatica* in one of the raised Ericaceous beds, or *Primula denticulata* anywhere.

As far as intentional propagation goes, we always prefer seed, very rarely taking cuttings. If a plant is going to fail, it generally does so during the first winter in the seed-pan; this natural selection ensuring a steady flow of the best adapted young vigorous plants for the garden. We have never suffered from 'clonal fixation' – the endless search for the best form. What constitutes a good form is entirely a matter of personal taste, we feel one should accept natural variation as part of life's rich pattern. Clonal fixation is perhaps encouraged by shows: it is very easy to rationalize being beaten by thinking that the prize winner had a better form, not that they are a more skilled grower. The current awards system to plants also encourages the application of unnecessary clonal names, even when the species hardly varies, or is short-lived!

While on the subject of seed propagation we sometimes worry about the ethics of repeatedly reintroducing plants as wild-collected seed, when they will not maintain themselves in cultivation. *Primula obliqua* is an example. This is an aspect of conservation which has yet to be adequately considered.

We have no alpine house, nor do we ever intend building one; all our propagation is in cold frames, the plastic lights merely serving to prevent the water-logging of pots in winter. We use only plastic pots, not plunged for lack of time. It is essential that they are not crocked, so that the compost therein is in capillary contact with the sand bed upon which they stand.

At this point of obvious deviation from the traditional practices of the alpine gardener, we should like to make a plea in favour of the open-mind. Always ask yourself why you are growing something in a certain way. If the answer is simply that you like doing it that way then no further discussion is either necessary or, indeed, desirable. If, however, you have no strong feelings in favour of, say, clay pots, then natural curiosity should be allowed to play its part. Is this really the simplest or most satisfying way of growing this plant? What we have tried to explain here is how we apply these principles in our garden.

Our plants associate together as naturally as we can contrive, natural pictures within their artificial frames of bed or trough. This is the antithesis of the old landscape rock garden, which were extremely unnatural and labour intensive in detail, all mown grass paths, clipped edges, and controlled artful planting – within a supposed natural framework.

Although we often call ourselves growers, we don't grow plants, they grow themselves. All we do is to try and provide conditions within their tolerance for growth. As Eric Clapton says, 'Plant your love and let it grow, let it blossom, let it grow. . . .'

Preparation Pays Dividends

HAROLD McBRIDE

Stories abound of exhibitors lifting plants out of the garden on the evening prior to a major Alpine Show, and low and behold on show day the plant sits in an honoured position bedecked with Farrar Medal or Forest Medal honours! While such a feat may well be possible, particularly with ericaceae or peat bed plants, I would suggest that the chances of winning a major honour on the show bench, are greatly enhanced if some more careful planning goes into the plant's preparation in the six to eight weeks prior to the exhibition date.

At this early stage it is often quite possible to assess which are your most promising plants. It is often quite easy to see which plants are healthy and well budded. Experience will tell you if the plant is at the correct stage of development (of course this will vary from plant to plant) to reach flowering peak around the date of the show. While this knowledge concerning the pace of the plant's flowering development is very important, weather conditions can seriously affect your calculations, obviously high temperatures and abundant sunshine in the weeks prior to the show will accelerate the flowering development, whereas dull, cold weather will hold progress back.

If the plant has been lifted from the open garden, potted up and placed in a plunge frame, some control can be exerted on its development, regular examination will disclose if the all important flower buds are progressing in a satisfactory manner, if not, the plant should be given a spell in the south side of the alpine house. If on the other hand the buds are opening too quickly, a cool-shaded, well-ventilated position may slow up progress for a few days.

Care is required when keeping plants such as *Rhododendron* in the alpine house, some pale-pink-flowering species such as *R. pemakoense* when kept under glass can fade very quickly to an unnatural white. Such a plant will of course be 'marked down' by the judges. Ericaceous plants in pans will require copious amounts of water at this time, and benefit from regular spraying with tepid water.

In Ireland we suffer from false springs, with perhaps 7–10 days of very mild spring-like weather, quite often followed by cold east winds and late spring frosts which can destroy the flowering potential of Ericaceae and indeed many other plants in a single night. If the potential exhibition plants are housed in a cold frame during the crucial six weeks prior to the show, it is quite easy to provide them with a frost-proof cover when low temperatures are expected.

Ericaceous plants, such as *Cassiope* or *Phyllodoce*, dislike very high temperatures when close to flowering peak, and will react to such treatment by dropping their flowers. Some years ago I exhibited at a show where the plants were benched on the evening prior to judging. The show hall was centrally heated and overnight all windows were closed for security reasons, on returning to the exhibition just prior to judging I was amazed to find my *Phyllodoce* and *Cassiope* had shed 50% of their flowers overnight, indeed the plants concerned were perhaps fortunate to survive this ordeal.

It is quite possible to lift asiatic primulas from the open garden and exhibit them immediately with reasonable success, however quite often primulas can suffer foliage damage from slugs etc, which spoils them for serious exhibition, and so I feel it is also much better to keep them potted up in a plunge frame for several weeks prior to the show, where the exhibitor has more control over their environment.

It is also possible to lift foliage plants from the open garden and pot them up just prior to exhibition, this is particularly the case with shallow rooted plants which are grown in a peat bed situation. Those excellent 'silver' foliaged plants from Australasia, *Leocogones leontopodium* and *L. grandiceps*, and *Celmisia longifolia* and *C. hookeri* enjoy our moist north west Irish climate. These plants lift quite easily and make excellent entrants for the silver-foliaged classes.

Many plants however hate root disturbance. Such plants can be grown in pots sunk in the peat bed or scree and they can then be lifted at will with minimal risk of damage to the plant concerned. If the pot has become very dirty from its stay in the ground is it usually quite possible to transfer the plant to a clean pot of similar dimensions without any root disturbance. This works well with a number of plants which thrive in the open garden and hate alpine house or even cold frame conditions, e.g. *Rhodohypoxis baurii*. They can become very 'drawn up' in the alpine house but when grown out of doors produce the correct balance of leaf and flowers.

Remember no matter which technique you adopt, I suggest 'lack of preparation' will most likely be 'preparation for failure'.

Showing Bulbs

DAVID MOWLE

G rowing for showing seems a rather loaded title for our symposium. I grow entirely for fun and to increase my all too scanty knowledge of the plants which inhabit the mountain ranges of the world. I started with the alpines of Scotland, as I knew those best, and remember struggling to keep *Salix reticulata* in a small pan as healthy as I knew it on the Scottish Bens. I planted it out in desperation and it has grown beautifully and delighted me ever since.

My aim now is to grow uncommon plants in pots to determine their needs, so that I can attempt to grow them in the open garden with a greater chance of success. Where my experience with a plant in a pot suggests that it will not be growable outdoors, my interest in it quickly fades, and it is usually passed on to a more dedicated potgrower! I confess that in trying plants outdoors a certain amount of cheating in the way of pieces of glass is allowed in the initial stages.

I fell in love with the bulbous plants before I realised the extent to which they add an extra dimension to the raised alpine bed. The wish to include the vertical growth of most bulbous plants among the mats and cushions of the alpine bed has certainly maintained my interest in them.

The first thing to realise when starting to grow bulbs in pots is that they enjoy much richer growing conditions than the average alpine. This is particularly true when the bulbs are being grown from seed, an essential activity when branching out into the less well-known or newly introduced species. I use a sterilised soil-based compost made up in the ratio of one part by volume of loam, one part leaf mould and two parts stone chippings (2–4mm). To this mixture a compound fertiliser containing typically $N:P:K$ at $6:8:10$ is added at a rate of 6gm per litre of compost (1oz per gallon).

Bulbs, of course, also grow in moist, humusy soils and in scree conditions. Unexpectedly I have never been forced to make up ericaceous composts for pot cultivation of such bulbs, finding that the standard compost is satisfactory if higher moisture levels are maintained as required. Those bulbs coming from scree-like habitats seem to be more easily grown in a mixture of the standard compost with its own volume of 4–6mm chippings.

Only experience will teach the moisture requirements of each of the many species of bulbous plant. Plenty of moisture during the period of active growth and much less during dormancy is the general rule coupled with the thought that I have rarely, if ever, lost a bulb through under watering during dormancy; it may not flower, however. . . . Until fully mature bulbs are obtained, some of the watering during active growth can usefully be done using a liquid feed containing N : P : K at 5 : 5 : 10 using half the concentration recommended for pot plants.

In growing for showing, annual repotting is beneficial and reduces the need for liquid feeding. The major advantage is the close annual inspection it allows of the bulbs, corms, tubers or rhyzomes and the removal of dead roots, bulb tunics and other matter liable to provide a seat for rots and related disasters. For the amateur I consider the general use of fungicides undesirable as it is likely to conceal the imperfections in the techniques being used. Their use is legitimate to recover from observed attacks, however, and I realise that the professional grower may not be able to afford such niceties.

I do not intend to limit this discussion to the Open Classes of major shows so start by discussing how soon the novice bulb grower can begin to exhibit with some hope of success.

Single bulbs, growing without imperfections and shown in an immaculate 9cm (3½in) pot are very acceptable on the show bench. Bulbs which are not commercially obtainable tend to be higher pointed, other things being equal. *Fritillaria rhodokanakis* will attract more attention than *F. michailovskyi* for instance. A bulb of known provinence, *F. kurdica* BSBE1281, say, with two flowers on the stem and with an additional leaf emerging from the chippings is the next stage up though a bulb of known difficulty in cultivation like the scree dwelling Californian *F. falcata* will compete successfully against much better filled pans.

As we approach multiple stemmed entries the difficulties of showing increase. I hope that most judges would not down-point the flowering pan carrying an aborted young bud, as most seedlings go through this stage and it shows that the entry has probably been grown from seed and therefore involved considerable cultivation. Great care must be taken to remove any damaged flowers or those past their peak even though this may thin the flowers somewhat. This is the place to say that tidy labelling and clean chippings are also essential.

When mature potfuls are being exhibited those grown by division of a single clone would be expected to show uniform growth, particularly uniform height. Delightfully disposed groups of flowers sometimes do arise clonally however and rather boring uniformity sometimes comes from seedlings. Luckily the judges are in the dark about the source of the bulbs!

I have up to this point been discussing plants in clay pots as I have used them for many years. These pots are usually plunged in a tray of sand or chippings with the result that a large proportion of valuable alpine house space is wasted, or at least, is not available to cultivate plants. Technical

22   Bulbs grown in square plastic pots in an alpine house (see page 81)

23   *Narcisuss assonanus* in a 6.5in (16.5cm) clay show pot (see page 80)

24   A Farrer Medal pan of *Dionysia bryoides* (see page 84)

25   A superb pan of *Dionysia lamingtonii* (see page 84)

26   *Phlox bifida* 'Betty Blake' has a very compact habit (see page 90)

27   The fragrant *Phlox caryophylla* from south-central Colorado (see page 94)

28   *Penstemon uintahensis* from the Uinta Mountains (see pages 98 & 206)

manufacturing considerations dictated the shape of these pots, which for many years were the cheapest containers available for growing plants. Plastics manufacture is not limited to space-wasting circular shapes nor, incidentally, to appalling imitation of the colour of clay pots. I have myself recently switched to using square, black plastic pots and increased the capacity of my alpine house by a quarter. Using the same compost as for clay I find that watering is roughly halved and I have found no case where the quality of the bulbs is inferior to that I experienced in clay. I see no reason why a single fritillary bulb should not be shown in a 9cm (3.5in) square plastic pot or, say, three crocuses. In the larger pot sizes it seems that the 11.5cm (4.5in) square pot gives the same results as a 5in (12.7cm) clay and the 13cm (5in) square pot the same results as a 16.5cm (6½in) clay. Larger square plastic pots are not so readily available but I have some 18cm (7in) square which give the same results as a 23cm (9in) clay dwarf pot. That these have been successful on the show bench recently indicates that the judges are not unduly biased!

May I finish with a few further remarks about the larger bulb exhibits. One species may yield seedlings of remarkable uniformity and so a satisfactory exhibit whereas another will yield seedlings of obvious variability. This will sometimes result in an NAS (not according to schedule) card as it has been considered that there is more than one distinct variety in the pan. It seems a shame that we are closing our eyes to the immense variability often found in wild populations. Such exhibits could be confined to the classes for plants raised from seed but our current schedules have severe size limits here.

I have never found it necessary to arrange two layers of bulbs in a pot to achieve a dense planting. Bulk in itself is attractive to judges but height can also be eyecatching. Amongst the good plants however it must be admitted that bulk plus height is the probable winner.

Showing High Alpines

GEOFF ROLLINSON

Anyone interested in growing alpines in pots and eventually presenting them in competition on the AGS/SRGC showbenches must have a variety of attributes: patience, dedication, tenacity, an ability to absorb what is meaningful advice and to reject the opposite. There must be many more, but to list them may deter some future Gold Medallist from taking the plunge into exhibiting.

Personally, my first attempt at the AGS shows was in 1972, it took three years to achieve a Bronze Medal (10 firsts in those days). Two more years to gain a Silver Medal and eventually after much striving and tribulation a Gold Medal in 1979. Subsequently to date 10 Gold Bars have followed, it almost seems without really trying. However, with any absorbing hobby I am certain that the enjoyment overcomes what should be drudgery and even from scrubbing clay pots one can obtain a perverse kind of pleasure.

ACQUISITION OF PLANTS

The obvious source for anyone building a collection of alpines is the specialist nursery, addresses for which can be obtained from AGS, SRGC and ARGS bulletins and some less specialised gardening magazines. Once acquired these can be propagated from saved seed or vegetatively from cuttings. A word of warning, do not spend pounds pursuing and purchasing *Dionysia* until you can grow *Saxifraga* or *Primula*.

The previous named societies each operate annual seed exchanges, in some instances extremely rare and unusual plants can be grown on from these sources.

Professional seed collectors also advertise forthcoming expeditions in pursuit of seed from the high places in various parts of the world. Shares in these can be purchased individually or shared with friends and are often an invaluable source of new and beautiful plants.

However, probably the best source of plants is from fellow exhibitors within the 'showing circle'. I have always found the show fraternity generous to a fault, one has only to admire a plant on the show bench and an offer of a rooted plant, cutting or seed is forthcoming. It follows that to perpetuate this one must similarly reciprocate.

Any grower who has the good fortune to obtain a rare plant by whatever means, i.e. from seed, from swaps or maybe from foreign contacts, has the responsibility to perpetuate the plant, from seed if possible, or, by vegetative propagation and distribute to friends. Similarly, with any good show plant it is in the exhibitor's own interests to propagate and keep a succession of progeny in the inevitable event of losing the original plant.

Advice, when sought, is invariably forthcoming from fellow exhibitors, but, whilst the advice given will be undoubtably sincere, modifications may have to be made to suit one's own composts and general conditions.

In 1976 I inadvertently introduced primula root aphis into my own collection of plants, this manifested itself in September and mainly through my own lack of experience resulted in the decimation of *Androsace* and *Primula*. Since that time any plant, be it purchased, swapped or a gift from a friend, receives a good soaking of half strength systemic insecticide. This also applies to the general collection of plants in pots and is applied monthly during the growing season. (March to September). No recurrence of primula root aphis has been apparent and in addition such treatment seems to ward off other pests with no ill effects to the plants treated. Variance of the brand of insecticide used each month will lessen the development of resistance build up to one particular brand.

CULTIVATION

These notes are written with the intention of assisting the novice exhibitor and those contemplating their debut on the show benches.

Although AGS show schedules differ according to the season and the whims of past and present Show Secretaries, there are ample classes to suit the grower of the widest varieties of alpines, or, someone who specialises in individual genera or family.

I can not offer advice on how to grow conifers, ferns, sempervivums or ericaceous plants for I have never grown them in pots. My experience with *Cyclamen* and bulbs is such that I am still learning and would not presume to have had any worthwhile success.

Initially, try as wide a range of plants as possible, eventually specialising in a narrower range of plants that you personally prefer or find you can grow better in your own conditions.

My own attempts with *Cyclamen* have caused me to solicit advice from others who grow them far better than I. The resultant advice has differed greatly, yet the people who gave it so freely achieve similar results with widely differing composts, treatment and general methods of cultivation. One piece of advice that was consistent from several growers was to allow the corm to get absolutely rootbound within the pot, but I have grown far better *Cyclamen* (*hederifolium*, *coum*, *cilicium*, *purpurascens*) in the open garden where the roots are unbounded than I have in pots. It all goes to show that there are no hard and fast rules to growing any range of plants.

Androsace, *Dionysia*, European and hybrid *Primula* and *Saxifraga* are the main range of plants that I grow, they probably collectively constitute 80% of the plants in pots, the composts I use are as follows:

Androsace. 50% grit (3mm neutral) the other 50% comprising beech leafmould and John Innes No. 1 in equal parts. There is one exception, *Androsace vandellii* is grown in 25% beech leafmould, 75% grit and repotted annually, this compost is so sparse that the plant degenerates unless so treated. Anything richer than 25%/75% results in *A. vandellii* becoming blowsy and out of character and prone to insect and fungal attack.

Dionysia. Although *Dionysia* are lime-loving plants I still use 3mm neutral grit 50% and beech leaf mould/J.I. No. 2 in equal proportions for the other 50%. However, see *The Genus Dionysia* by Chris Grey-Wilson in the section on composts, it can be seen that many successful growers have widely differing formulae for their composts. Suffice to say that the drainage material must be at least 50% for successful cultivation. After discussions with Eric Watson, who over the years has regularly presented superb *Dionysia* on the show benches, I am currently experimenting with J.I. No. 3 in place of J.I. No. 2/leafmould, the results thus far are encouraging, healthy growth remaining in character, next spring will give a better indication. The plants under trial are those which in the past have not flowered well.

Primula (European and hybrids). Equal parts of J.I. No. 2, beech leafmould and 3mm grit. There is one magic ingredient, several fields away from where I live a shorthorn bull and his harem of heifers graze. Occasionally when exercising the dog I equip myself with plastic bag and hand fork and select his stiffly constituent piles for collection. He only takes offence at my intrusions when he has amorous designs toward one of his harem. Upon return the spoils are deposited in a polythene sack and the neck tied. A couple of months later bacteria have broken down the manure into a fine tilth. When repotting I add a little of this bounty to the drainage chippings above the crocks in each pot, subsequently the resultant flowerings seem larger and more colourful.

Saxifraga. Compost as for *Primula* excluding the added bounty.

To generalise on the remainder of plants that I grow. High alpines, those that in native dwell on cliff and in scree have at least 50% grit in the compost, others at least 30%.

It is essential for the well-being of the plants to ensure that an adequate depth of chippings (at least 2cms) or layer of rock slivers are placed between the base of the plants and the top of the growing medium. This provides a break between the dampness of the medium and the plant and assists in the passage of air beneath the plant, reducing the risk of botrytis developing unseen.

'Re-pot as necessary' must be a term familiar to most who have tried to gain knowledge from publications on alpine culture. There are no hard and fast rules, generally fresh compost or top dressing should be introduced at least bi-annually, lack of this can be alleviated by the use of dilute liquid feed. Some growers use it all the time, others not at all – the choice is yours. Personally, I have in the past used dilute feeds on all the plants that I grow in pots and abandoned the practice, for even a dilute feed resulted in gross growth and a general out of character appearance. The only plants now that are fed are *Cyclamen* and any bulbous plants, this assists the bulb to build to flowering size more rapidly. Feeding must *only* take place when the plants are in growth.

I find the best method of inducing quicker growth in young plants is to remove the flowers, unless you want seed, and even then the majority of flowers can be removed. This allows the plant to concentrate of producing new growth, rather than wasting energy on seed production.

GROWING SITUATIONS

For those people who are growing alpines with the intention of eventually exhibiting at the National Shows an alpine house is preferable, but not essential. If you and your plants are under cover it allows necessary work to be carried out in relevant comfort even in inclement weather conditions. Just as much care and attention is necessary in late summer, autumn and winter as in spring when the majority of plants are in active growth. It is essential that plant maintenance is practised throughout the semi-dormant periods. It is at these times that out of season aphid and caterpillar attacks often occur and the threat of botrytis is greater, more about botrytis later.

Many current exhibitors, through choice, grow their show plants in frames or covered raised beds or plunge pots in the open garden and cover them only in the winter months. This method has the advantage of keeping the plants in better character than in an alpine house, owing to the fact that the plants have better access to the available natural light and as often happens with certain plants they do not draw towards the distant glass. For example, it is virtually impossible to grow *Androsace alpina* or *Campanula cenisia* in an alpine house and keep them in character, but much easier to grow them near to the glass in a frame, or totally unprotected when in growth, only offering protection for the buds and subsequent flowers and against the vagaries of winter weather.

I have three alpine houses approximately 3.7 × 1.8m (12 × 6ft). None of these are in an ideal position, one is a lean-to against the garage wall, one only 1m (3ft) away from the gable end of the house and the remaining one runs NE to SW. All have roof lights which are closed only in snow conditions, two have louvre windows and the other has side opening windows. I find louvres preferable for when these are horizontal a far greater volume of air sweeps through the alpine house keeping it cooler and better ventilated than with normal side openers. For choice of structure aluminium is preferable, it is relatively maintenance free and by purchasing lengths of the various sections available one can easily build a special house to suit the amount of space available.

In all three houses the *clay* pots are plunged in 15–20cm (6–8in) of river sand deposited in sturdy raised beds so that the tops of the pots are level with the bottom of the louvre openers, thereby ensuring maximum access to available ventilation.

Plants mentioned previously, and others that are more easily kept in character outside an alpine house, are grown in a raised bed plunged in ordinary garden soil and protected in winter with clear, corrugated acrylic sheeting held just above the plants, ensuring good access to the available light. In all these situations it is imperative to turn each pot, so that each face of the plant benefits from an equal share of sunshine and light. Generally throughout the year each pot is turned through 90° weekly, but when buds and flowers are apparent the turning is done more frequently to ensure even-flowering.

From mid May to mid September the alpine houses are shaded with green Netlon. The plants plunged outside are entirely unshaded but must at all times be well watered to avoid scorching.

PLANT MAINTENANCE

This is a chore that I regard as paramount for the future well-being of the plants. Throughout autumn and winter a close scrutiny of each plant is necessary, this is done weekly throughout that period when the plants are turned. Any dead rosettes and leaves should be removed for these are starting off points for botrytis attacks.

Should an attack occur, I use green sulphur dusted on to the plant after the infected area has been removed. Mostly this is successful, on the odd occasions that infection persists the treatment is repeated. In some instances, for example attacks on Kabshia or Porophyllum *Saxifraga*, can often be eradicated by placing the plants outside totally unprotected and allowing rain, snow, frost etc. to clean up the plant. A word of warning, do not try this latter method with *Dionysia* or *Androsace*.

Winter aphid attacks can have a serious debilitating effect on any plant and unless action is not immediately taken can result in the plant's demise. Effective control can be achieved by placing the plant under an upturned plastic bucket along with a stick of Vapona and leaving for 24 hours. This can be repeated as necessary until the attack cessates.

EXHIBITING

Competition for First Prizes at the National Shows is now so fierce that it pays to ensure everything about an exhibit is as near perfection as possible. Moss and lime deposits since the last re-pot will have defiled the clay pot, copper pan scrubs dipped in water then sharp sand will speedily remove both and leave the pot in pristine condition. Nothing looks worse than a first class plant in a filthy pot, with all other points being equal in competition, the plant in the clean pot should secure first place.

The past decade has seen many exhibitors using great imagination regarding top dressing their exhibits, instead of the usual limestone or neutral chippings, the use of slivers of slate, mica schist, tufa and pieces of limestone have been used to enhance the appearance of the plants and give a more natural effect. Take care not to use limestone to dress lime-hating plants.

When considering plants to take to a show do not be tempted into artificially forcing them into bloom, plants taken indoors and subjected to extra heat and artificial light invariably appear drawn and discoloured and can only detract from an exhibitor's reputation. With experience, by with-holding water and placing out of direct sun, but in good light, flowering can be prolonged. Conversely, with extra water and exposure to all available sunlight, plants can be hurried along to 'make' a show. In some instances with certain plants the latter has to be attempted. Some plants have a short flower life and in just missing one show would not remain in good condition until the following Saturday's show.

When entering a multiple-pan class, attempt to obtain as much variation in plant family and colour unless the Show Schedule is for plants of the same genus or family. Set the plants out at home before travelling to a show to get maximum effect of colour variation by the relative positioning of the plants.

Ensure you arrive at the show with time to spare, staging is an important part of exhibiting. Top dressing may have been disarranged by jolting in the boot of the car and will have to be replaced. Re-examine each plant carefully, you may have missed a couple of aphid (no extra points for live-stock) and more often than not some flowers may have 'gone over' and require removal. Check your exhibit is according to the Show Schedule, seldom does a show go by without some exhibitor inadvertently placing their entry in the wrong class resulting in the entry being labelled by the judges as NAS (not according to schedule).

I sincerely hope these notes will encourage more people to exhibit at the National Shows, the Shows are the shop window of the societies and act as a recruiting ground for new members. Competition encourages friendly rivalry and without doubt makes an exhibitor into a better grower.

Dwarf Phlox and Penstemon

PANAYOTI KELAIDIS

THE OTHER PHLOX

Over seven decades ago Reginald Farrer suggested that 'the day that saw the introduction . . . of *Phlox subulata*, ought indeed to be kept as a horticultural festival'. If anything, *Phlox subulata* and its multifarious offspring figure even more largely in rock gardens nowadays. It is something of a mystery that so few additional species in the genus have gained currency in horticulture since Farrer's day. Many of the finest phloxes for rock gardens still remain to be introduced to cultivation.

Why is this so? There are perhaps a few rare phloxes that might elude casual search, to be sure. Most species in the genus actually constitute dominant elements in the Western American landscape over hundreds if not thousands of square miles. Visitors from Europe are stunned to find phlox carpeting the ground at virtually any stop they make in the Great Basin or northern Great Plains, and there is hardly a meadow or high scree throughout the Rockies without its requisite patch of phlox. Unlike Aretian androsaces, so often restricted to just a few narrow valleys or the tiniest of crevices of the highest Alps, the microphloxes are plants of open soils: rich loam and sticky clay. *Phlox woodhousei* can be found in late April in pink drifts near snowbanks entangled among the giant rosettes of *Agave parryi* near Flagstaff at over 2000m (7500ft) elevation. In May and June the sagebrush steppe throughout the Intermountain region of the West is knit with a more or less continuous carpet of pink and white or sometimes lavender phloxes in a dozen species whose innocent, jasmine-like scent is so strong it can actually penetrate cars whizzing by. There are limestone cliffs in Northern Colorado where *Phlox bryoides* clings vertically like a proper, self respecting alpine. But go a hundred miles north and it is everywhere: in roadside ditches, on gopher mounds, in dense patches of grass, jostling with thistles and dandelions.

Phloxes are so abundant, gardeners can almost be forgiven when they tease layerings into their plastic bags and bring them home. There they usually sit languishing and finally molding in cold frames, or dying even more quickly in a garden proper. It is useful to remember that plants from steppe and dryland enviornments generally are attuned to soils where

88

microbes are kept in check by frequent dry spells and omnipresent sun. Paucity of rain means that there is minimal leaching, and the seemingly barren clays and shales where these plants prefer to grow are often rich in nutrients. In garden soils it is difficult to grow steppe phloxes without proliferating the soil pathogens they are genetically incapable of resisting. In sterile screes the pathogens are starved, but then so are the phloxes. The best way to grow these phloxes in our gardens is to provide a soil matrix that discourages the growth of pathogenic microbes while having abundant nutrients. This means experimenting with slow-release fertilizers in scree, foliar feeding or trying to layer soils in ways that provide drainage and yet access to nutrients. Above all it is imperative to grow the widest spectrum of plants from seed or cutting in order to select plants that respond best to our garden conditions.

The eastern phloxes
The greatest bulk of phloxes currently in cultivation derive from *Phlox subulata*, *P. brittonii* and *P. nivalis*, the three easternmost caespitose phloxes which occur for the most part to the east of the Appalachian crest. *Phlox bifida* from the Midwest, one of the loveliest and most distinct of creeping phloxes has had an influence on a few hybrids. Few of the numerous *Phlox douglasii* cultivars that are grown in gardens resemble the wild Westerner bearing that name: these apparently represent complicated garden hybrids and selections that have earmarks of eastern American ancestry as well. There doesn't seem to be a single widely cultivated creeping phlox of unquestionable Western ancestry. Some day, genetic analysis may let us untangle the wild species involved in these crosses. Few wild phloxes can match the brilliant reds achieved in 'Scarlet Flame', 'Red Admiral' or 'Crackerjack'. Flamboyant multicolored flowers like 'Coral Eye' or Wood-bank Nursery's 'Tamaongalei' are unprecedented in wild phloxes. These and numerous other cultivars are clearly eastern in their ancestry, witness their widely ramifying deep green, leafy stems and ease of culture.

The Cleft Phlox
In recent decades, *Phlox bifida* has attained more and more prominence in North American rock gardens. In nature it is largely restricted to sandy prairies of the upper Midwest which must approximate scree conditions, for few plants naturalize more easily in scree than this distinctive phlox. Typical forms have flowers up to 3cm in width, with the five petals so deeply cleft that they look more like ten petals. The flower colour approximates a whey-like blue that glows whether the day is overcast or sunny. The leaves are six or more centimeters long, curved backwards in distinctive whorls along woody stems that radiate from a taproot without layering. This species produces abundant seed and can become a mild pest on screes where it finds itself utterly at home. I'll never forget one early

May visit to Betty Blake's great garden in Onsted, Michigan at peak bloom time for the cleft phlox. This region boasts plants with particularly dark lavender flowers, and Betty was apologetic that she had not yet had time that spring to weed out the hundreds of cleft phlox seedlings that crowded the margins of her grand screes and crevice gardens. We sought out the very darkest flowered one, and this has subsequently been distributed as *Phlox bifida* 'Betty Blake'. It not only has flowers of a particularly dark violet blue, but a more compact habit than other cleft phloxes. Two albinos derived from *Phlox bifida* are currently available in the North American trade. The one sold simply as 'Alba' or variety *alba* has very large flowers that are particularly spidery. Both designations are improper, and I have often wished it would be distributed as 'Snowflake' since that's what the flowers clearly suggest. The cultivar sold as 'Colvin's White' or 'Whiteout' in America is more shallowly cleft, and the stems root modestly along their bases, suggesting that it must be a hybrid. Both clones propagate readily from cuttings, and are gaining in popularity. Mina Colvin, for whom the last clone was named, introduced a small but distinctive form of *bifida* with tricolored flowers she calls 'Starbrite'. This may constitute a distinct botanical variety since it occurs repeatedly on the eastern fringe of the species' range.

With this sort of variability, is it worth going West to seek out novel phloxes? Since *Phlox subulata* and its eastern American brethren provide such a broad range of flower color and petal shapes what exactly do the far western phloxes have to offer the rock garden?

The western microphlox
Virtually the only extensive horticultural discussions of the rock garden potential of phloxes are to be found in the works of Farrer, Clay and Symons-Jeune, all of whom antedate Edgar T. Wherry's scientific monograph on phloxes. Dr. Wherry named many new species and organized the genus in significantly different ways from his predecessors. Although he was a shining light of the American Rock Garden Society, Dr. Wherry grew mostly woodland phloxes and doubted the horticultural possibilities in the western microphloxes. Recent horticultural literature has very few references to actually growing western phloxes with the notable exception of Claude Barr, who introduced a number of species of Great Plains' phlox to cultivation.

Great Plains' phloxes
Several species of phlox are largely restricted to the Great Plains grasslands. *Phlox andicola* and *P. alyssifolia* share a vigorous rhizomatous habit that presumably allows them to spread quickly in competition with the short grasses that characterize their native range. The former has narrow, needle-like leaves and white flowers with particularly prominent yellow stamens.

It grows 5–7.5cm (2–3in) tall, and can spread through scree at alarming rates. The alyssum-leaved phlox has short blunt leaves 2cm (0.8in) or less long and rarely grows more than 2.5cm (1in) in height. I have only observed it with white flowers, although pink is said to occur sporadically over its range. It is an outstanding ornamental. *Phlox hoodii* occurs in the northern reaches of the Great Plains (as well as over much of the Great Basin and high valleys of the Rockies). It is a variable taxon with frequent pink colonies among the commoner whites and tiny mats of prickly leaves. It is usually the first phlox to bloom, occasionally in late February at its lowest elevations, although most years reaching a peak in March or April. It is often in seed by the time other phloxes that grow with it are in bloom nearby. It is also rhizomatous, forming tiny, loose mats in an astonishing range of soils and altitudes throughout the West. It has a number of subspecies, notably var. *canescens* in the western end of its range that is densely hairy and congested approaching *Phlox bryoides* in compactness and effect. A deep green, dense dwarf form occurs occasionally throughout the range of typical *hoodii* that has been called var. *muscoides*.

This taxon has recently been transposed with *Phlox bryoides* in recent treatments. Both species were first collected and named by Nuttall during his momentous transcontinental trek of 1837. The plant that has traditionally been called *P. bryoides* extends from the Western borders of the Great Plains in Wyoming to the Eastern reaches of the Great Basin. It is a distinctive taxon resembling a selaginella more than any *Bryum*, with silver gray imbricate leaves in the densest of cushions. The flowers are rarely more than a centimeter across, although they smell as sweet as most other Western phloxes. It grows on a variety of substrates from heavy, alkaline clay to crevices of limestone boulders. When growing among grasses or in shadier exposures the stems can grow somewhat straggly with relatively sparse bloom. This can happen when it's grown on too rich a soil or in too much shade in cultivation. It needs as much sunlight and drainage as possible to keep it in character in the garden.

I have not seen *Phlox albomarginata* in nature. Herbarium specimens indicate that this is one of the most intricate and variable of cushion phloxes occurring from the western Great Plains of Montana to the Great Basin of Idaho. It occurs in pink and purple forms as well as the white so characteristic of smaller Western phloxes.

Basin and Range phloxes
The greatest variation in wild phloxes occurs in the innumerable mountains and endless flatlands of the Great Basin. Phloxes like *P. hoodii* and *P. austromontana* cover the landscape uninterruptedly at lower elevations, just as *Phlox multiflora* and *P. caespitosa* fill sagebrush meadows and the understorey of pinewoods at middle elevations. Additionally, there are species with specialized distributions such as *Phlox kelseyi* which resembles a more

silvery, congested *P. alyssifolia* only growing, however, on heavy, alkaline clays that are sopping wet in spring, but dry out in the summer and fall. It will grow along a stream for several hundred feet, be absent for a hundred miles, then reappear in a new locality. It usually comes in pure white, although pinks and lavenders are known occasionally in nature.

Phlox missouliensis is an example of a species with a restricted range in the Northern Rockies, growing on dry prairies among dwarf sagebrush, *Fritillaria pudica*, *Douglasia montana* and the usual riot of paintbrush, penstemons and composites that turn the West into expressionistic canvases of color in early summer. It is also in the alliance of *Phlox kelseyi* only with leaves several times as long as Kelsey's phlox, covered with dense hairs. The flowers are usually in the range of icy blues with occasional lavenders and pure whites. It seems to adapt more readily to cultivation than its steppe origin would suggest.

Phlox pungens is a recently described species in this same group from Central Wyoming that forms congested mats on limestone cliffs. Its prickly leaves are narrower and shorter than Kelsey's phlox that occasionally grows nearby on the valley floor below. Its flowers occur in the same pastel range of colors.

A whole new range of mat phloxes occur in the southerly portions of the Great Basin. Some, like *Phlox jonesii* and *P. gladiformis* from Southern Utah are abundant within a limited geographic region. These form rather larger mats with narrow, prickly foliage and abundant pink or white flowers. *Phlox tumulosa* has occasionally been classed as a subspecies of *Phlox griseola* (a looser, less distinctive taxon): it is the tiniest leaved and most congested plant in the genus. It retains its impossibly smooth mounds, as tight as *Raoulia lutescens* or a dionysia, in cultivation. This holy grail among the phloxes actually constitutes a dominant groundcover over some six or seven ranges of mountains on the borders of Utah and Nevada. It occurs in mind-boggling abundance. Surely when this is firmly introduced to horticulture it will be recognized as the supreme cushion phlox. The flowers are smaller than most phloxes, about the same size as *P. bryoides*, less than a centimeter across. I have only seen them in white, although there must be some variation among the millions of plants in its native range.

Middle and high elevation phloxes of the Rockies

Although many of the phloxes mentioned hitherto will often reappear at higher altitudes, especially as one moves southward in the Rockies, a different assortment of species generally replaces these on northerly exposures and in areas of greater rainfall. *Phlox multiflora* for instance replaces *Phlox hoodii* as the prevalent phlox among sagebrush above five or six thousand feet in the Southern and Middle Rockies. You may still find *P. hoodii* growing among the *multiflora*, but only on hotter, drier exposures, never intergrading or hybridizing in my experience. Superficially, *P.*

multiflora resembles an eastern phlox in its longer, greener, coarser foliage and vigorous growth. In the Front Range foothills near Denver it is usually a deep pink and rather lax in growth, while the variety *depressa* that prevails in higher mountain parks has dense mats of needle-like leaves two or more centimeters long absolutely smothered with sheets of flowers in mid spring. This variety is usually pure white, although paler or darker pinks are not rare. It is among the most fragrant of wild phloxes. In the north end of its range it grades into the controversial *Phlox caespitosa*, which is sometimes merged with the higher alpine *Phlox pulvinata* that's found above treeline throughout the Western United States.

Phlox pulvinata forms tight mounds of blue-green leaves a centimeter or so long. The flowers are frequently lavender-blue, sometimes deepening to violet and ice blue shades of extreme beauty. This is a surprisingly easily grown plant for such a high alpine phlox, reblooming periodically throughout the summer season.

Phlox condensata is the only other alpine phlox in most of the drier West. It has shorter, narrower, grayer leaves that are somewhat overlapping and cruciform along the stem. The flowers tend to be paler pinks and whites rather than blues. It tends likewise to have a more southerly distribution overall in the West, and varies considerably across the Great Basin in the extent of hairiness and congestion of its foliage. Some forms approach *Phlox tumulosa* in compactness, although the flowers are generally larger. These alpine phloxes are intensely fragrant in the wild or in cultivation – reason enough to try to grow them.

In the wetter parts of the Sierra Nevada of California or the Cascades of Oregon and Washington, *Phlox douglasii* and *P. diffusa* finally make an appearance. These form vigorous mats with greener leaves than the more Continental phloxes. They are more commonly bright pink in color as well.

This hardly exhausts the theme of cushion phloxes in the west: there are numerous local species I have never seen, such as *P. variabilis*, *P. aculeata*, *P. hendersonii*. Many distinctive subspecies and variations are still being found, like *Phlox austromontana* var. *lutescens* from the canyonlands with pale yellow flowers. It was only discovered and named in the last ten years. Hybrids between many taxa are not unheard of throughout the West. Ned and Betty Lowry discovered a colony of phloxes that showed definite introgression between *Phlox kelseyi* and *Phlox pulvinata* in Lehmi County, Idaho. Many individuals in that colony had deeper coloured flowers than either of their parents, and Betty made cuttings of one violet-flowered individual which resembles a deep purple aubrieta in colouring. This has been named *Phlox* 'Lehmi Purple', providing an altogether new color among the mat forming phloxes.

Other western phloxes

A welter of taller phloxes, usually bright pink, can often be found growing among the cushion phloxes in the West. In the North these are usually variations of *Phlox speciosa*, a clump forming plant a foot more in height. This is something of a challenge to grow in moist climates or irrigated gardens since it seems to require a summer dry period to persist in cultivation. *Phlox woodhousei* has been considered a subspecies of *P. speciosa*, although it grows far to the south of its relatives, and has many distinctive characteristics. It has narrow leaves which are two to four centimeters long, covered with fine gray hairs. They usually trail flatly on the ground, and the plant can spread far and wide where it is suited by underground rhizomes. The shallowly notched flowers are surprisingly variable in the depth and tint of their pinks. It blooms over a very long season in the spring, and often reblooms just as vigorously in the late summer months. Coming as it does from a region of summer rainfall, this tolerates garden conditions far better than many other Western phloxes. It's startling to see it growing among giant agaves along the Mogollon rim of Arizona, although Parry's agave is in fact not a desert but a montane species thriving in the deep winter snows among the giant Ponderosa pines.

Phlox longifolia occurs universally through the west from sagebrush desert to montane meadows up to 3000m (10,000ft) elevation. It is generally a wispy, uninspiring plant with a few pink stars over a sprawling, leafy clump 15–30cm (6–12in) tall. Nevertheless, along the Western borders of its range, it often grades into the long tubed, compact *P. stansburyi*, one of the loveliest Western phloxes. It is also closely related to *Phlox caryophylla*, a compact, rhizomatous ground cover that stains acres in south-central Colorado pink during its long bloom period. It resembles a dianthus not only in its luminous pink flowers, but in their spicy, clovelike scent.

Out of bloom the Longifolia section closely resembles the Nanae from the deep southwest and northern Mexico. Horticulturally these primitive phloxes represent dramatic departures in the genus: they are timed to bloom with the onset of summer monsoons, but in the garden they will often bloom uninterruptedly from spring to frost. The various species in this complex vary from luminous pinks and white through the entire hot spectrum of colors including pure yellows, oranges and deepest scarlets and vermilions. Paul Maslin, who introduced most of these to cultivation in 1978, postulated that they represent hybridization between several closely related species, and the rare occurrence of the red and orange taxa seems to support his hypothesis. These brilliant flowered Southwesterners are among the most surprising introductions of this half century.

They are plants of lush meadows or sparse pinon-juniper forest of lofty elevations in Chihuahuan highlands. They have nevertheless proven surprisingly hardy throughout much of North America provided they have a warm exposure, rich porous soil with perfect drainage at the crown. In nature they seem to be long-lived, spreading far and wide from deeply seated rhizomes. If they seem transient in gardens, this may be due to lack of sun, drainage or nutrients as much as it is to any supposed lack of hardiness. They have survived $-35°C$ temperatures in Colorado with impunity.

Summary

There are doubtless many fascinating hybrids and variations to be produced even among the well known eastern cushion phloxes. The greater number of species and densest populations in the genus are undeniably found throughout the West, from the hot deserts to the coldest mountain tops. The western phloxes vary astonishingly in foliage, cushion form and in the size, season and color of blossom. Once their cultural needs are mastered, the Western cushion phloxes provide an inexhaustable scope for horticultural study and enjoyment.

THE UNKNOWN PENSTEMONS

Penstemons can be as blue as gentians, red as cardinal flowers, more variable in size and form than primulas and as quickly and easily grown as dianthus. They grow from sea level to mountaintops, from desert to woodland and bog. They even have an international society dedicated to their study and hybridization. And yet few rock gardens have more than a few token representatives of the 250 species in the genus. Why is this so? Many commonly distributed species are rather tall, which has led to the impression that most of the genus is out of scale for rock gardens. And generally penstemons are plants of sunny, dry regions. Rock gardeners fear that they will rot easily, or persist too short a time in the garden. Actually, few penstemons are as sensitive as lewisias in this regard. I have always suspected that rock gardeners are simply not aware of the wealth of dramatic miniature saxatile plants that exist in the genus. When gardeners finally learn to grow these plants, and a good selection of dwarf species are readily available, *Penstemon* will surely join ranks with *Saxifraga* and *Primula* as a giant treasure trove for rock gardens.

Three of the most commonly grown types of penstemons are so attractive and serviceable that gardeners can hardly be blamed for limiting their sights to these. *Penstemon pinifolius* has become everyman's penstemon: resembling a very dwarf conifer out of bloom, the foliage turns a lively plum green in winter. The orange trumpets bloom on and off all summer. A yellow sport appeared simultaneously in 1987 in three British gardens: fallout from Chernobyl?

For most of us, however, rock garden penstemon means Dasanthera, the so-called shrubby penstemons largely restricted to the coastal mountains of the Western United States and Canada, growing inland as far as Utah, Montana and Alberta. This section in the genus only encompasses eight or nine species. The variability within each of these species, and the hybrids between them are such that one could make something of a speciality of this section alone. Many rock gardeners will argue that *Penstemon rupicola* represents the finest alpine in the genus, but recent decades have shown the section still has much to offer. A few recent introductions from this group are proving to be outstanding additions to rock gardens: *Penstemon davidsonii* var. *praeteritus* is restricted to a handful of mountain ranges either side of the Oregon-Nevada state line. It is apparently more closely allied to *P. fruticosus* according to some authorities, although the tiny, wedge-shaped leaves and twiggy shape suggest a hebe on first sight. The lavender or purple trumpets look positively gigantic by comparison. It is proving quite growable in Rocky Mountain gardens.

Penstemon montanus has suffered under the reputation of difficulty for some time. Its furry, white-leaved variety *idahoensis* blooms prolifically in our garden with icy-blue trumpets over a long season. It is a first rate, miniature alpine that would be perfect if its foliage were only evergreen. Several dwarf forms of *Penstemon cardwellii* discovered by the late Floyd McMullen, and named in his honor by friends are proving to be outstanding garden plants. 'Floyd McMullen' has leaves even tinier than 'Holly', the outstanding selection of *Penstemon fruticosus* var. *serratus* from eastern Oregon. 'Floyd's Fatty' has particularly glossy, round leaves that make a decorative mound year around. New hybrids and selections among Dasanthera will always be highlights in a rock garden, but their need for acid soils and cool conditions has misled many growers about the needs of penstemons in general.

Penstemon hirsutus var. *pygmaeus* is altogether more tolerant of sun or shade, thriving in practically any soil types. It can even be mildly invasive by self sowing if conditions suit it perfectly. The deep purple rosettes and long season of white and lavender bloom make it an eminently desirable workaday plant, if not a top flight alpine. It belongs to the section Penstemon, series Graciles, which includes most of the eastern penstemons. These are possibly the most long-lived and easily cultivated penstemons. Most of the rest of this series have rather squinny lavender or blue flowers on tall stems suitable only for borders and wild gardens.

The series Proceri

The Graciles are abruptly replaced at the Rockies by two series that are confined to the West: Proceri are the most moisture tolerant plants in the genus, often growing on the margins of bogs and in wet meadows. Humiles have slightly larger flowers and grow a bit higher and drier in woods and meadows.

The type species, *Penstemon procerus* occurs in wet subalpine meadows throughout much of the American West. It has tiny deep blue flowers in dense clusters resembling a mint more than other penstemons. Typically it grows 15cm or so tall, but the subspecies *tolmiei* often grows only half this tall, spreading to form considerable mounds with time. The subspecies *formosus* is similarly compact, and rather long lived in the garden.

Penstemon confertus resembles a taller, lanker *procerus* with flowers of pale primrose yellow. *Penstemon flavescens* is only half the size of *confertus* with flowers of a deeper yellow color. It is a local species from the Idaho-Montana border that has never successfully been introduced to cultivation to my knowledge.

Most of the rest of this series grow taller, and consequently have more value in the border or wild garden. *Penstemon euglaucus* forming masses of pure blue framed against Mount Hood would tempt most of us into attempting it in the garden.

Series Humiles
Closely allied to the Proceri, the Humiles grow over much the same range, although quite often on drier, more alkaline substrates. *Penstemon humilis*, which gives its name to the series is particularly variable and widespread in the intermountain region. Virtually any variety of this species will have flowers of vivid blue and neat mats of deep green rosettes. Properly sited in a sunny crevice or trough garden, this species is quite long lived with low mounds of brilliant true blue flower clusters. This occurs from the upper limit of sagebrush and pinon woodlands to near treeline on dozens of mountain ranges from Colorado to Nevada, north to Idaho and Montana. *Penstemon aridus* is closely allied, with even tinier leaves and shorter flower stems. It is a superlative plant for miniature gardens with clear blue flowers. *Penstemon virens* might be characterized as *humilis* doubled in size growing a few hundred miles to the East on the Front Ranges of Colorado and Northern New Mexico beneath Ponderosa Pine and on steep slopes at moderate elevations. It forms extensive mats and thrives in partial shade in acid soils, making it particularly adaptable to moist climates. The flowers are usually good, strong lavenders, although albinos and even pinks are not unheard of in its range.

Penstemon albertinus represents another larger phase of *humilis* that varies considerably over its great range throughout the Northern Rockies. The flowers are usually the purest of blues, and the low mounds of lanceolate leaves fully evergreen and attractive. Together with the jagged leafed *Penstemon ovatus* from the Cascades, these represent some of the most adaptable, showy and long lived penstemons for the rock garden. Their blues are so pure and striking, I like to think of these as warm country *Meconopsis*.

Section Glaber (Habroanthus)
This largest section in the genus is famous for the purity of their blues and the spectacular mass displays they provide throughout the Intermountain West. Many of them grow to a meter or more in height, although half of the

thirty to forty species in this section are of rock garden stature. Other species, such as *Penstemon alpinus* often grow 50cm (20in) or more in height, but have dwarf forms occurring at higher altitudes in the Colorado Front Range. This pattern is repeated throughout the entire West where tall Glaber section species grow at lower altitudes and miniature forms dominate the tops of the peaks. Typical *P. speciosus* can grow up to a meter in height, but variety *kennedyi* from the Sierra crest will often stay under seven or eight centimeters.

Penstemon caryi is a local species restricted to middle elevations in the Bighorn Mountains of Wyoming that rarely exceeds 15cm (6in) in height. It has distinctively marked bell-shaped flowers of dazzling blueness that open over a long season in early summer. *Penstemon paysoniorum* from central Wyoming is a steppe desert species invariably less than 10cm (4in) in height. The gem of this section may be *Penstemon compactus* from northern Utah and southern Idaho, a miniature replica of the Wasatch Penstemon, *P. cyananthus*. The dwarf species remains 15–20cm (6–8in) in height with the same piercing sapphire clusters of bloom. *Penstemon fremontii* is largely restricted to the Uinta Basin of Utah and Colorado. It is anomalous in this section because the leaves and stems are covered with a fine layer of hairs. Its stems can rise to 20cm (8in), although they're often quite a bit shorter. It thrives on desolate clay banks and has thyrses of particularly vivid cobalt shades.

In Colorado only two penstemons grow widely above timberline. The commoner and showier of these is *Penstemon hallii*, which forms low mounds of narrow leaves with stems 10–20cm (4–8in) tall. The flowers are a virulent violet purple in mid spring. It grows by the million under bristlecones and on sparse tundra throughout the central mountains of Colorado. *Penstemon uintahensis* is similarly dwarf, growing at high altitudes in Northeastern Utah. Its flowers tend more to the lavender end of the blue spectrum.

Harbouriani section
A strange soboliferous penstemon occurs sporadically at high altitudes in the Colorado Rockies from the Central Front Range to the San Juans. *Penstemon harbourii* superficially resembles *P. montanus* of the Dasanthera in selecting rough, shifting screes on which to grow, and spreading by spaghetti-like underground stems. Its leaves are glossy and succulent rather than viscid and hairy as in the more Northerly Dasanthera. Its flowers are dark lavender or violet purple bells that are quite attractive against the glossy mounds of low leaves. Easily grown from cuttings or seed, it needs well drained scree to adapt to the garden.

Section Caespitosi (Ericopsis)
This distinctive group is largely restricted to the Eastern Great Basin and

Rocky Mountain province. All members of this section are small enough for rock gardens, and many are tiny ground hugging mats with flowers of purest blues and lavenders. These will undoubtedly comprise as important a group of rock garden plants as the Dasanthera once they are tamed in cultivation. Since they produce abundant seed and root virtually any time of the year from cutting, it's doubtful that they will remain a secret for long. *Penstemon caespitosus* has a particularly wide range in nature, and is quite variable. The variety *desertipicti* stretches from southern Nevada and Utah to Northern Arizona. It has gray tear-shaped leaves and gaping turquoise flowers that cover the plant repeatedly during the growing season. The type variety *caespitosus* has narrower blossoms over somewhat greener, more slender leaves. It grows abundantly in Wyoming and northern Colorado. An albino of this species still circulates among enthusiasts of the American Penstemon Society. Variety *perbrevis* occurs in the Tavaputs plateau region of east-central Utah, intermediate both in geography and morphology between the previous two varieties.

Noel Homgren has segregated *caespitosus* variety *suffrutescens* as a new species: *Penstemon tusharensis*. The pouchy, lavender to violet blossoms certainly seem distinct to me as well. It grows at much higher elevations, in cooler regions than most other Caespitosi, promising a greater tolerance of garden conditions as well.

The shape and color of the flower in *tusharensis* has always reminded me more of *Penstemon thompsoniae* than *caespitosus*. Thompson's penstemon has a range of many hundreds of miles from Southern Utah through much of central and southern Nevada and Arizona as well. Many variations occur throughout this colossal range, a particularly striking dwarf form grows on barrens with *Lepidium nanum* near Ely that may be even smaller in leaf than *Penstemon acaulis*. It has proven much easier to grow than its desert origins suggest.

Penstemon teucrioides occurs in most of the high mountain parks of Central and Southern Colorado, usually around 3000m (10,000ft) elevation. The narrow-leaved gray mats are not as decorative as others in this section, although the skinny, turquoise trumpets are produced so thickly that they actually obscure the leaves. It makes a brilliant picture in a trough or in the garden.

Penstemon crandallii is similar to the last, although the leaves lack hair altogether. It is the most variable taxon in this section, in my experience, with tiny teardrop leaves in variety *atratus*, upright stems in misleadingly named variety *procumbens*, and highly variable flowers and habit in the type variety. The color is always a good medium blue, however variable the plant may be. The plant sold for many years now as 'Claude Barr' probably belongs with *crandallii* rather than *caespitosus* since it lacks pubescence—a key character used to distinguish between these two similar species.

Penstemon abietinus would be easily confused with some forms of *P.*

crandallii, except that it grows a hundred and fifty miles further West. It forms a sort of transition to *Penstemon linarioides* and *P. sileri*, two species that grow in the Canyonlands and Navajo Desert regions. They resemble nothing so much as blue flowered and silver foliaged *Penstemon pinifolius*, with flowers produced on stems extending upright, well above the foliage.

A mystery penstemon has recently been introduced to cultivation from this section. *Penstemon ramaleyi* superficially resembles one of the last species except that it is deciduous with leafy upright flowering stems 15–20cm (6–8in) tall. It has flowers of a bright blue color throughout the summer season. This highly distinctive species from Cochetopa Park in southern Colorado was named by David Keck, who neglected however to include it in his monograph on this section of the genus. It was subsequently left out of all floras of Colorado and treatments of Western penstemons, effectively ceasing to exist.

One of the strangest members of this section is *Penstemon discolor* from Southern Arizona which has silvery foliage quite like a form of *P. linarioides*. The flowers, however, are squat, tiny off-white bells strongly stippled with russet dots. The species is narrowly distributed in nature, but like so many rare plants it is almost weedy in cultivation, producing abundant seed.

If I could only grow one penstemon I think I would pick *Penstemon acaulis*. This tiniest of penstemons still occurs in large numbers over a few dozen square miles of northern Utah and southern Wyoming. It produces mats of tiny, deep green needle-like leaves studded for weeks in spring and early summer with stemless turquoise bells. Some botanists now place *Penstemon yampaensis* under this taxon. To my eyes, the Yampa penstemon is distinct, since it can be twice as large, with longer, wider, more silvery leaves in distinct rosettes. It forms mats up to 15cm (6in) across, studded with dozens of bright pink or pale blue trumpets. Only discovered and named in the thirties, it was thought to be very rare. As Brown's Park in Northwest Colorado is studied more thoroughly, the Yampa penstemon appears to grow on practically every hilltop over a range of hundreds of square miles.

Penstemon laricifolius is not only the northernmost of the Caespitosi, it is the only other species in the section to produce a distinct basal rosette. The rosette is somewhat obscured by the grassy leaves. The flowers of the type variety vary from wine purple to a rosy pink. It is a lover of dry limestone slopes in central and northern Wyoming, making a spectacle in moist years. In the southeastern extensions of its range the flower stems shrink to half the size of the type form and the flowers are usually an ivory white. This is variety *exilifolius*, one of the best trough plants in the genus.

Section Caerulei

The Caerulei occur over virtually the entire Western United States. They are easily recognized in bloom or out since they have waxy, almost succulent leaves with smooth margins unlike most other penstemons. Although a few Caerulei, like *Penstemon grandiflorus*, are tall plants a meter or more in height, most members of this section are short enough to include in the rock garden. These are the first penstemons to bloom in the garden year, opening up as early as March most years here in Colorado. They all thrive on heat, drought, limy soils and good drainage. There are records of *Penstemon nitidus* living twenty years in a trough, but in wet climates or acid soils the Caerulei can act like biennials. The piercing blue flower color of most Caerulei becomes muddy pink when soil acidity approaches neutral. They do best with a pH above 7.5.

Penstemon angustifolius is unquestionably the most widespread species in this section. It is found from Southern Canada to Texas, westward to both Southern and Northern Utah. It forms a neat rosette of narrow, lance shaped leaves. Both the type variety and var. *caudatus* can grow 30cm (12in) or more in height, but dwarf forms are common in various parts of its range. On the Laramie Plains, few individuals grow more than 15cm (6in) in height, and I once found a colony with plants under 5 cm (2in) tall! The flowers are often a pure, robin's egg blue, purer than Heavenly Blue convolvulus or *Gentiana farreri!*

Penstemon arenicola grows in central and western Wyoming. It resembles a compact form of *angustifolius* with slightly broader foliage. It has performed beautifully for three years thus far in the garden, although the flower colour is not quite as piercing as the best forms of *P. angustifolius*.

Penstemon nitidus replaces *P. arenicola* in Northcentral Wyoming extending northward as far as Canada. It has even broader basal foliage and broad, distinctive clasping stem leaves. The flower color on alkaline substrates can be as deep a robin's egg blue as the best forms of *P. angustifolius*. This is usually the first penstemon to bloom in Colorado, usually opening its flowers in mid-March.

Penstemon acuminatus carries the theme of succulent blue leaves and turquoise flowers into the Pacific Northwest. This species is largely restricted to sandy soils in the drier interior valleys. It is a challenge to grow well in the garden.

Penstemon flowersii is a recently named species from the central portion of the Uinta Basin of Northwestern Utah. This resembles a plant of the previous species, only its flowers are predictably pink no matter how alkaline the substrate.

The strangest penstemon in this section is probably *Penstemon bracteatus*, which is restricted to steep screes on Wasatch Limestone formation on the Paunsagunt Plateau of Southwestern Utah. The flowering stem rarely exceeds 6cm in height, and the basal rosette is usually only 4–5cm (1.5–2in) across. Most remarkably, it spreads rhizomatously, extending several feet in extent. In nature this forms ancient colonies, belying the genus' reputation for transience.

Most other Caerulei grow 40 or more cm in height, although dwarf forms and mutations are not uncommon. *Penstemon secundiflorus*, for instance, can grow a meter or more in height. However, in South Park it regularly forms colonies 15cm (6in) or so in height that grow no taller even in cultivation. Many other Caerulei from the Great Basin, such as *PP. pachyphyllus, immanifestus, mucronatus* and *carnosus* all occasionally have dwarfer phases of use to rock gardens.

The Cristati (Aurator)

For many years this section of the genus was known as the Aurator, alluding to the furry golden tongues that makes so many species in this group look like tiny animals rather than plants. Again, the best known species in this section is a giant, *P. cobaea*, with flowers 5cm (2in) or more across and stems up to a meter in height. Most of the species in the section grow on dry deserts in the Intermountain region where they can form vast colonies with dazzling flowers in years with heavy rain.

The commonest species of the section is probably *Penstemon eriantherus* which grows from Colorado north to British Columbia in a number of distinctive varieties. Southerly forms are usually a pale lilac, while the northern forms can be a deep, lurid purple colour. The flowers are wide-open bells filled with suggestive streaks and markings, with a giant yellow fuzzy staminode lolling about like a clacker. Over much of Wyoming it rarely exceeds 15cm (6in) in height, but in Montana and Idaho forms two or three times that size are common. The best form of all from the Ferris Mountains of Wyoming rarely exceeds 5cm (2in) in height.

Penstemon cleburnei is often classed as a subspecies of *eriantherus*. Its flowers are shaped somewhat differently, with a sort of crick in their neck, and the flower colour tends to verge on pink.

Possibly the most dramatic species in this section, *Penstemon grahamii* is restricted to oil shale substrates in the Uintah Basin of Colorado and northeastern Utah. In nature it produces low stems 6 or 8cm (2.4–3.1in) tall with two or three lilac-pink bells that resemble a baby bird demanding to be fed. Under garden conditions this species can have up to ten flowers on a stem. It is amazing that a plant from such a sterile, dry environment will do so well on rich scree in a watered garden.

In the garden *Penstemon janishiae* from the Western Great Basin so closely resembles the last that botanists may one day be tempted to lump them. Only *P. janishiae* seems to only grow half as tall as *P. grahamii* under identical conditions. This is a superb miniature for troughs.

Two of the tiniest Cristati are *Penstemon pumilus* from Southern and Central Idaho and *Penstemon nanus* from east central Utah. Both grow on sterile, clay substrates and have giant flowers on stems only 5–7cm (2–2.75in) in height. These tend to be a brilliant blue in colour in both species. The leaves of *P. nanus* are glossly blue-green with reddish highlights, while in *P. pumilus* they are minutely downy. They are dazzling miniatures worth any effort to tame.

Penstemon duchesnensis from the Uinta Basin and *P. dolius* from further West form low mats with vivid blue-purple flowers in late spring. They both stay under 8cm in height.

Most of the other dwarf Cristati are variations on *Penstemon moffattii*: Noel Holmgren recently segregated these as *P. marcusii* from the vicinity of Price, Utah and *P. goodrichii* from the northcentral Uinta basin. The latter two species are remarkable in the genus for having a distinctly rotate, or radially symmetrical, corolla rather than the distinctly zygomorphic flowers otherwise characterizing the genus and the Figwort family in general.

Saccanthera

The greatest untapped potential in *Penstemon* may reside in this remarkably variable section of the genus. Most Saccanthera penstemons look superficially like Dasanthera since they produce low mounds of shrubby, glaucous foliage. The best known species by far is *Penstemon heterophyllus* which is sometimes even sold as a bedding plant along the West Coast of the United States. *Penstemon azureus* likewise produces a low shrub up to 10cm (4in) high, only in this species the foliage is silvery or blue. Both grow widely through the Sierra Nevada. Some, like *laetus* or *leonardii* are starting to enter cultivation. The former has typically bright yellow buds that open to reveal rich purple blue trumpets on and off all summer. *Penstemon leonardii* is an abundant miniature species invariably under 10cm (4in) that would look good in a tiny trough or crevice garden. It is found at middle elevations throughout Central Utah. Noel Holmgren has recently delineated a number of species of Saccanthera in the Great Basin with outstanding garden potential.

Sections Petiolati, Baccharifoli, Gairdneriani

There are a number of species of monotypic penstemons found in the West of outstanding merit. *Penstemon petiolatus* usually grows only on steep limestone cliffs on a few mountain ranges of Southern Utah and Nevada. It has tiny, holly like leaves and deep pink verging on magenta blossoms over a long season in the summer. It is a distinct miniature of outstanding merit for well drained rock gardens.

Penstemon baccharifolius has unfortunately not yet survived a winter in Colorado. The deep green mounds of succulent, holly-like evergreen leaves are attractive in their own right. They produce a constant succession of stems 10–15cm (4–6in) tall with neatly flared crimson trumpets through the entire growing season. Hardy selections of this species from higher elevations would be great additions to the rock garden.

Although *Penstemon gairdneri* is not strictly speaking monotypic, its nearest cousin *P. seorsus* is so similar in overall habit, however, that for all intents it is equivalent in garden value. These desert penstemons produce mounds of wiry, dark gray-green leaves up to 15cm (6in) tall. The flowers are produced on stems of similar height. They are a shocking, baby pink in colour, with such distinctively shaped flat corollas that are unlike any other species in the genus. Unfortunately, these dazzling shrubby penstemons resent irrigation and traditional rock garden culture. In unirrigated gardens in drier regions these may one day provide glamorous focal points.

The greatest variety and number of dwarf, rock garden penstemons occur in the Rocky Mountains and Intermountain region, an area characterized by alkaline soils, intense sunlight and frequent drought. In order for gardeners in maritime regions to master these plants, they must exercise the same ingenuity and principles of selective breeding that's used to tame intractable Mediterraneans, high arctic plants and exotic bulbs from Central Asia. With attention to detail, good drainage, full exposure to sun and air even some of the desert penstemons will adapt to climates and conditions far removed from sagebrush, rattlesnakes and tornadoes.

Bulb Cultivation

PAUL CHRISTIAN

From the outset I have to say that I am using the word bulb in the loosest sense of the word, to encompass true bulbs, corms, tubers, rhizomes and rootstocks in general. I rather like the definition of a bulb as 'Anything that a bulb grower grows'.

Bulbs, like several other modes of growth, are a strategy. Alpines have adapted to survive a cold dry winter, often under snow cover. Deciduous trees have taken another tack, they drop their leaves and overwinter above the ground, as dormant shoots. Annuals over-winter or more usually over-summer as seeds, and there are cacti which sit and brave it out by conserving water and shutting up shop when the weather does not suit their growth. All of these adaptations are a response by a plant to a climatic extreme, a period unfavourable to growth. In some cases it is a cold winter period whilst in the case of many bulbs the unfavourable period for growth is frequently a dry, or hot and dry period, and an underground storage organ has evolved to cope with this. The plant dies back to this when growth conditions do not suit its remaining in active leaf growth. With time this escape has become an essential, the conditions that caused evolution of the storage organ are required to maintain the plant in a healthy state. Much of what we call cultivation techniques are our means of providing a simulation of what happens to a plant within its wild habitat.

Since I first started growing bulbs I have been fascinated by their wild habitats. I can learn from the wild by appreciating what I think is happening there. Trying to decide why the bulbs grow just where they do, or why they don't grow in an even beter spot just nearby when that is obviously better suited to their needs! I want to know if the explanation is to do with goats or bedrock, with seedling mortality that controls their colonisation of new stations, or some inability to fend off a soil fungus that lives in wetter sites. I feel that by looking at their wild habitats I can learn something of what they need, and for many years I have been an advocate of trying to give my bulbs the conditions that they get in the wild, in order to grow them well, or better than I am doing.

My phrasing is important 'The *conditions* that they get in the wild'. One excellent grower whom I used to respect dismissed the idea that wild habitat observations were of any use. Fine but at the most simplistic level how do you know how to grow an alpine if you don't know that it *is* an alpine, and the only way to find that out is to see it in the wild or get the information from someone who has? How do you know that *Calochortus kennedyi* is a desert species whilst *C. uniflorus* likes water, *C. superbus* has cold sensitive roots and dislikes excess water, whilst *C. tolmei* likes cool moist conditions and has a resistance to frost more in keeping with its mountain home.

I have also heard the idea turned around and refuted by those who do not listen. I am not suggesting for one moment that if a plant which proves to be tricky in cultivation, grows in red clay in the wild, then the answer to growing the plant in our gardens lies in importing bucketfuls of red clay to grow it in, that is rubbish. My idea is to see what happens in the wild, in the clay, to find out 'why red clay' and if possible give the plant those conditions. What is drainage like, does the bedrock affect it. What type of soil is present, what sort of ground cover, shade, aspect, altitudes, snow cover, associated flora. What is the total rainfall, is there seasonal variation, perhaps even status of nutrients in the soil. Looking at local crops, agriculture or lack of it can give a guide without the need for precise science. If there is no explanation in any of the above then we might fall back on the old standby, is the soil limey or acid. In most cases this is a total irrelevance, but once in a blue moon it has some bearing, however I have to say that the British alone seem to be preoccupied with soil pH.

Above all I must stress that I am not suggesting that we try to simulate a habitat, I am suggesting that we can learn from it.

PRACTICES

Cultivation consists of bringing together diverse plants from habitats we imagine to be similar and expecting them to grow in a whole range of soils, conditions and terrains that we label simply as 'garden conditions'.

In some cases the plant is tolerant of a wide range of variation within these conditions, or we are providing what it needs without noticing its needs – easy. In others, a wild population from one particular region is particularly well suited to the sort of conditions that we are providing – an easy clone. In some cases a species is particularly demanding of certain conditions or requirements that we can provide with difficulty – tricky. In the worst case the plant is perfectly adapted to a set of conditions that we cannot simulate or are not aware of – ungrowable, squiny-flowered little weed that we didn't want to grow anyway. Sadly there seems as great a co-relation between ungrowability and desirability, as there is between imagined beauty and rarity.

Inevitably cultivation involves compromises and subterfuges which we term cultivational requirements. In the bulb world there are compromises also. There is one thing however that no bulb will compromise on and that is the single most important factor involved in growing bulbs, it is drainage.

Good drainage is important no matter what the species, where it came from or where it is growing. Before you start stretching to those bulbs such as crinum that flower in running water, or juno irises that carpet central Asian slopes with flowers whilst those same slopes flow with water, I have said well-drained, the total amount of water is less important. Those crinum habitats will be dry later and so will those juno slopes. For one thing they are *slopes* and additionally the soil is in intimate contact with bedrock, they are very well drained, the water is moving water, so that the plants are not subject to stagnant conditions.

The porous soil as well as passing water freely will also admit air freely into the network of pores and this soil structure is vitally important in the wild. Soil structure depends on a soil being left alone and we cannot hope to do much about it in a pot, except that we can ensure by careful formulation of composts, that the properties are similar. Equally in the garden we can ensure good soil condition or properties by amelioration of the soil with a variety of ingredients. To achieve good drainage we frequently mix sand, grit or gravel with our composts. As with every ingredient there are good and bad types. Fine seaside-type sand is to be avoided. This is less to do with any salt content as with the small size of the well-rounded grains. This means that the sand is likely to clog together and hold water rather than allow its passage. Coarser sands are better but again too sharp a grain will physically damage an expanding, growing bulb that pushes against it. Rubbish this idea as you wish but a series of tiny scratches and abrasions at best will have no effect and at worst will serve as entrances though which fungal or bacterial diseases can invade. For just this reason I never use the eighth-inch crushed grit that is frequently used to top off alpine plants in nurseries. You might as well put razor blades in the compost. It is worth buying sands specifically marketed for horticulture, as sands in builders' merchants' yards may have been treated with weedkiller to keep them clean. It happened to E.B. Anderson. If you are not sure then take a sample and put some mustard seeds on it, you will know within a few days that all is safe, if they germinate.

My ideal drainage material would be a coarse river or Cornish silver sand that has passed an eighth-inch screen, although the particles will be much smaller than this. It can be bought I assure you and whilst it is not cheap, it is better than replacing a pot of expensive bulbs. It will open up a compost to just the right extent. A further refinement which I am currently experimenting with is the use of water-rounded pumice gravel. It is lighter than many grits or gravels and is porous. That is, the rock itself is full of tiny pores and holds and passes air and water, unlike almost all other grits and gravels.

Feeding for many plants is not needed as long as the plant is in a well-fed situation but there are few bulbs that will not do better for some feeding of the correct balance. We just need to know what and how much and when. I have to say that I have yet to meet a bulb that does not respond to feeding, and most bulbs respond superbly well to regular feeding of the right type. Traditionally we speak of NPK when feeding, that is nitrogen, phosphorus and potassium. If you read bulb literature you will see that most authors recommend either 'low-Nitrogen' or 'high-Potash' feeding. As a simple rule of thumb this is okay but a fuller understanding will reveal its flaws. Far better is to feed the parts of the plants that are growing at any particular time. This I believe is called the Emsweler principle. Thus whilst leaves are developing it is best to direct feeding towards the leaves, when roots are forming feed them, when buds are developing feed the nutrients that they need. So when bulbs are leafing they can take some nitrogen and its application will do no harm. Once the leaves have developed and fully formed, then there is nothing to be gained from feeding nitrogen and indeed it may be damaging in some cases. For instance overfeeding nitrogen to *Fritillaria* after they are leafed up result in deformed bulbs which grow very poorly. I stress overfeeding here, lest it puts you off.

Once a plant is leafed up then feeding should switch more to feeding developing roots and flowers, thus NPK tends towards PK, later still when the plant has flowered, perhaps set seed, then it will also be initiating flower buds for the next season. As early as the second week in July the flower buds of tulips are initiated for the following April. This is even earlier in the case of early spring flowers such as *Scilla* and of course with autumn flowering species, this development is even earlier. In *Allium callimischon* the new flower buds form in April and rise in May to become obvious as the leaves die in June. The buds oversummer above the soil surface ready to open in the autumn, but they were formed in the April! As availability of potassium is known to affect initiation of flower buds April or so seems a sensible time to ensure good levels by feeding, so our NPK has now just become K.

Some of you will have followed this but I would guess that more are wondering just how to put it into practice. Well first of all constant availability means that little and often is the best way to feed plants. Weekly is about ideal. Infrequent feeding is better than none at all but I am giving what I hope is the counsel of perfection. Feeding can start in autumn, as the bulbs make roots, with something such as growmore liquid or granules, on the soil or compost surface. This is high in leaf-feeding nitrogen and once the leaves are fully formed I feel it important to switch to a low nitrogen formula. In the garden this can be simplified to one autumnal application of growmore granules. Natural leaching by rainfall will ensure that the nitrogen level has been reduced by spring. Nitrogen is the most easily leached of the three nutrients under discussion. The next stage is to favour PK. The oft-recommended chrysanthemum, tomato or potato fertiliser can be applied until after flowering. You can also use Phostrogen which has the advantage of containing trace elements. After flowering I switch just to potassium, in the form of one or two feeds of Sulphate of Potash which can be bought in most larger garden outlets.

There are caveats. I would suggest that you forget lawn food, it is aimed just at leaves, and will do more harm than good. This is particularly true if it contains weedkiller. Forget anything that claims miraculous results and comes in small, expensive packets and of course never use anything that does not have a label.

When talking of fertility and feeding I often come across people who do not feel it is needed or beneficial. It is a matter of personal preference but I have no doubts at all about its effectiveness. The more bulbs are fed the better they do, like humans up to a point, except that overfeeding and obesity are not a problem if you can make offsets. In nature nutrients move up through the soil in areas where evaporation exceeds rainfall, as for instance in the Mediterranean type climate in summer. Once rainfall exceeds evaporation, as in autumn rains, then the nutrients move back down into the lower soil level where the plant has its roots. All of the time leaf litter is falling on the soil surface and rotting in, releasing nutrients. Feeding is perfectly natural since it happens in the wild but if natural and unnatural offends you then you should not be gardening at all.

I mentioned above one of the effects of a dry summer, another effect is that bulbs appear to get baked. This has given rise to perhaps the greatest myth in the bulb grower's storybook. On the soil surface the temperatures get high, you only have to sizzle on a Spanish beach, or fry under the Californian midsummer sun to know that. But in the wild bulbs don't do this, they die down to a good depth below the surface and often wrap up in several layers of bulb-tunics and benefit from the insulating properties of these and the soil above. They don't bake, and they don't shrivel as the soil at this depth contains a trace of water. The properties of the heavy or clay soils in which many bulbs occur are such that they keep this life preserving trace of water throughout the dry season. So yes the bulbs are warmer and drier, no they do not bake. I only know of one study that actually quantifies this theory and that is an Israeli study which found that at depth of 15cm (6in) below the soil the temperature did not exceed 64°F during an entire year. This is a far cry from a dry pot of light porous compost on the top shelf of a glasshouse where I have measured temperatures in excess of 130°F in some afternoons last summer. In almost no case is a bake essential, and usually it is detrimental. At one extreme it lightly cooks a bulb or just dehydrates it allowing something in to finish the plant off. If you think that this has never happened to you then I would ask if you have ever had small yellow spots on your fritillarias or light brown areas at the edges of the bulb scales, both are symptoms and consequences of over-drying, as is dry corm rot in *Crocus*, where the bulb looks perfect but is as hard as a hazel nut, the consequences of fungal infection into weakened tissue.

Tulips with thick leathery bulb tunics, and perhaps some *Sternbergia* need a harder, hotter rest than other bulbs but there is certainly no need to put them in the oven after the Sunday joint or roast them on the top shelf of the greenhouse. In the case of bulbs without tunics, most *Fritillaria* and *Erythronium* for instance, they are severely damaged by much more than a light baking. In the wild they rely on the soil properties within their environment to prevent dessication, rather than many bulb tunics.

Bulb tunics are a bit like overcoats, or more precisely Arab robes, they can be used to keep heat out, but a thick layer of overcoats that become sodden clothes if wet at the wrong time, as they might be in a pot of soil suddenly inundated with water. It is worth harking back to water here and remembering that a large volume of soil over a bulb tends to even out sudden changes in temperatures and water levels. The field capacity of a soil, how much water it can hold, what it passes, is important. Soil bulk provides insulation not only from temperatures changes but from sudden water-level changes. The balance between water- and air-spaces in the soil is important, plant roots need air but air occupies the soil spaces which water occupies, more water less air. This is a long way around to saying that bulbs dislike over-watering, it may not kill them unless it is very frequent, but they will not do well. If drainage is correct then so will be soil air. To simulate the 'smoothing' effects of a bulk of soil there is little better than plunging of pots. It helps to avoid overwatering, overheating and freezing. Plunging in sand is fine, but why plunge in a nutrient-sterile medium when you can plunge in compost into which plant roots can grow and feed? Pots can be plunged on a bench, if you wish, in bulb-frames, or in bulb beds (either outside or under glass). I would say that during the construction of any of these it is better to build up a bed on a flat or slightly raised surface and forget the advice that suggests building some kind of soakaway or pit underneath the site, such a construction usually ends up as a sump that attracts water rather than the reverse. The best pots of all for plunging are what I call basket pots. They are often sold for growing marginal pond plants, and are basically a pot made of plastic lattice with holes in the sides and base through which plant roots can grow out into the plunge material. Aluminium labels can be knotted onto pots which prevents their loss or confusion and I have found them excellent. If they have a disadvantage it is that certain colchicums and tulips which wander around by means of stolons can wander out of the pots and into their neighbours, or worse still they can form their new bulbs around the plastic of the lattice, which makes repotting an unusual experience.

Like any plants there are pests of bulbs which need to be acknowledged. The most frequent seems to be nematode (eelworm) infection which is seldom recognised, and more often still denied by 'the not in my garden brigade'. It is no use saying 'I've never seen them', without a microscope you will not see them but their effects vary from obvious to disguised, and much 'fungal' and 'viral' infection can be laid at their door. Leaf nematode seems to be on the increase and for all the world looks like frost damage. I will not dwell on them since there are few cures and most are not available to the amateur grower. Sterilisation of soil will kill nematodes in the soil but will not treat infected plants. A simple method to reduce their impact is one that I owe to Erich Pasche, who advises heavy mulching with either bracken or coniferous leaf litter. This contains tannins which leach into the soil and weaken the nematodes and the presence of the leaf litter also helps to reduce the splashing, by rain, of soil particles. This prevents the spread of some nematodes. Finally elimination of weeds will reduce populations of those nematodes which cannot serve without a host plant. Don't forget the bulb beds when the bulbs are dormant.

Slugs can be dealt with by using pellets, although I find that a top-dressing of very sharp grit is a most effective deterrent. I would say to avoid watering with any liquid slug killers that contain aluminium salts, as these can be toxic to bulbs.

Narcissus fly is also a pest of *Leucojum* and *Galanthus*. The grubs eat out the heart of the bulb and seldom leave enough for the grower. As the females will only lay their eggs in sun, shading the bulbs is an effective control.

For vine weevils HCH is the usual treatment recommended in books and on television. It is a shame that those who advocate its use have never tried it, it is in my opinion a total waste of time and money. The only proper control was Aldrin now rightly banned, but I have seen adults crawling around in HCH powder and abundant and apparently healthy grubs in trays of soil in which granules were clearly visible. HCH is like using air-gun pellets against a rhinoceros. Only true remedies are physical, the foot, the hammer, the tweezers and a jar of hot water at night. Excessive, yes maybe but not when the alternative is losing a row of *Galanthus lutescens* that might be worth £1000.

Aphids are not really a problem that is widespread and usually easily controlled with systemic spraying (in advance) of any plants known to be susceptible. Aphids are vectors of virus so control is probably most important on *Lilium* and *Iris reticulata*, which suffer badly.

Potental fungal diseases of bulbs are many, and growing in sterilised compost will prevent many but I can still detail some. The little hard black resting bodies of sclerotinia that infest some tulips and a very wide range of diverse plants, the fresh-ginger scent and the pink stain around the basal plate that heralds fusarium in Amaryllidaceae, the powdery grey miasma of botrytis, and the black stains of the aptly-named iris-ink spot disease. Fungicides are useful but are better used to prevent than cure. Most fungi will yield but it is important to apply the treatment before infection occurs and to just the plant and not to the soil. You want to kill the bad fungi and try not to harm the bulk of harmless soil fungi which are keeping them in check. This is also worth considering when using weedkillers such as paraquat and simazine which have a weakening effect on soil fungal populations.

Ink spot is something that is untouched by most products available for the gardener. You will see advice to roll infected bulbs in Benlate, but I would advise saving your money. By all means roll bulbs in captab or sulphur flowers but do it before they are infected not after, and make sure that no clumps of reticulata iris stay undivided for more than two seasons, as close packing and poor drainage are two things that seem to encourage infection. Rest assured that the season that you decide it isn't worth it is the one when you could have prevented damage.

Botrytis particularly in *Fritillaria* and *Lilium* can be completely controlled by spraying of systemic fungicides onto the leaves soon after they emerge and repeating this treatment once again after about six weeks. Under glass, do make sure that air circulation is good as this will help to prevent the conditions that aid infection. Spray or water first thing in the morning to allow leaves to dry as quickly as possible. If you cannot water on an airy, sunny day then don't water overhead at all.

I have mentioned wild habitat considerations and to conclude I might mention a recently conceived idea which I am just beginning to experiment with. There are oddities in the bulb world, particularly in California, the serpentine endemics. These are plants which are found, sometimes exclusively, on serpentine rocks. The soils over serpentine are characterised by tremendously high levels of usually lethal heavy metals such as nickel, chromium and others. Bulbs have adapted to these metals and in California can thus grow where there is little other competition. I am not suggesting that there is any other reason than this for their frequent occurrence and success in such places *but* heavy metals have a very powerful fungicidal effect which I and others have documented. We might infer that fungal populations in such areas are inhibited and I might go so far as to suggest that the natural resistance of plants to infection would be of no advantage to serpentine endemics in the wild. Neither would any putative lack of resistance affect their cultivation in sterilised soils in pots, but in non-sterile soils has anyone else noted as I have the frequency of fungal infection that ail many Californian serpentine species. Many *Calochortus* that fall to powdery blue penicillium, American *Fritillaria* that develop yellow stains on their bulbs just before shrivelling or rotting. I can grow *Fritillaria lanceolata* under whatever name is fashionable for it this week, but I struggle with the charming dwarf serpentine form. Even the usually ill-mannered genus *Allium* is not on the whole as robust or invasive. I stress that this is flying a kite, but it could account for why so few Californian bulbs have made garden plants, when we can cheerfully grow so many bulbs from many places which are drier and wetter, hotter or colder and nearer to one or other of the poles.

I cannot in the time or space cover everything, that would need its own conference. I hope that I have covered enough to interest you, or interest you further in cultivating bulbs.

Mountain Flowers of Turkey

MICHAEL J. B. ALMOND

Turkey is bordered by Europe, the Caucasus and Iran, and its flora is influenced by the plants of all these areas; this means that Turkey has a varied and interesting flora. The country can be roughly divided into three general climatic zones, each with its own distinctive vegetation: (i) the Euro-Siberian zone extending along the north of the country, south of the Black Sea, with climate and flora related to those of northern Europe and the Caucasus; (ii) the Mediterranean zone extending along the west and south coasts; (iii) the Irano-Turanian zone (with a flora and climate akin to those of Iran and central Asia) covering nearly all of the interior and extending east and south to the country's borders with Soviet Armenia, Iran, Iraq and Syria. Turkey's varied climate and terrain is also reflected in its large number of endemic species.

Most of Asiatic Turkey consists of a plateau, the mean height of which rises steadily towards the east, bounded on the south and north by steep mountains, and to the east increasingly intersected by mountain ridges of considerable altitude. In the south and south-west limestone predominates; in the east and north the limestone is mainly overlaid with igneous rocks. Most of eastern Turkey, including the plains with their steppe vegetation, lies at a height of well over 1500m (5000ft) above sea level. There are areas near Turkey's southern borders, however, that rise to little above this height but which may still be reasonably termed mountains, as they rise steeply from surrounding areas of much lower average height.

True alpine vegetation in Turkey is confined to the tops of mountains in the south and east (see map), and this survey deals mainly with these alpine areas, the montane areas surrounding and between them, and some of the lower mountain areas in the south (referred to in the previous paragraph). It does not touch on central Anatolia or northern Turkey west of Giresun and it does not cover the lowland flowers of the sea coast or the Mesopotamian plain. It is, of necessity, a personal selection of the flowers that Lynn and I have seen in our various travels in Turkey over the last ten years or so.

West of Antalya, in the extreme southwest of the country, the craggy limestone ridges of the Taurus range turn south and plunge down into the sea with such precipitousness that there are 3000m (10,000ft) peaks within thirty kilometres (18 miles) of the coast. The spring flowers on these mountains, below the melting snow, have a distinctly Mediterranean character: mats of *Anemone blanda* and many distinct *Crocus* species: *C.*

chrysanthus, *C. fleischeri*, *C. danfordii*, *C. baytopiorum* (with its attractive ice-blue petals) and various subspecies of *C. biflorus*. There are also many other small bulbous plants in flower in the same area, such as *Gagea*, *Scilla bifolia* and the spring-flowering *Colchicum triphyllum* and *C. burtii*. Along the rocks and under the scrub can be found *Galanthus elwesii* and *Cyclamen trochopteranthum* in profusion (including the occasional white-flowered form). In the high mountains, *Fritillaria* is represented by the small, yellow *F. carica* ssp. *serpenticola* which we first saw in flower on 6th April 1978, fully two years before the type specimen recorded in the *Flora of Turkey* was collected in the same location by Ole Sønderhousen; we were charmed and intrigued by the small yellow flowers dotted over the open hillside but, this being our first trip to Turkey, we were not particularly surprised that we could not identify them and we did not realise the significance of our discovery. In woods flanking the lower hillsides we sought out and found the magnificent *Sternbergia candida*, with its large pearly-white, scented, daffodil-like flowers.

As the Taurus range continues its march along the south coast of Turkey towards the east, its flora remains essentially similar in character, although changing in detail. *Crocus* still abounds below the melting snow, but different species from further west: *C. graveolens*, *C. sieheanus* and different subspecies of *C. biflorus*. *Eranthis hyemalis* carpets the hillsides and with a sharp eye you can spot the juno irises, *I. galatica* and *I. persica*, so beautifully marked and at the same time so well camouflaged against the bare, brown hillside. Although various species of *Muscari* are common throughout Turkey, we now start to meet other genera we have not found further west, such as *Hyacinthus* and *Eminium*, together with other genera which we found more commonly further east, such as *Hyacinthella*, *Corydalis* and *Globularia*. In the clearings of the pine woods around the Cilician Gates (Gülek Boğazı), among the masses of *Cyclamen cilicium* leaves, we found *Hyacinthella glabrescens* and *Globularia orientalis*, as well as some fine colour forms of *Iris persica*. On the slopes of Ala Dağ, north of the Cilician Gates, we found *Eminium intortum* (a relative of the arum, with a short spathe, dark purple inside and green outside), *Scilla melaina*, *Hyacinthella acutiloba*, *Corydalis solida* and *C. rutifolia* ssp.*erdelii*; this last is found all over eastern Turkey and varies considerably in colour and flower shape, but according to the *Flora* it all belongs to the same subspecies. On the way up Nemrut Dağ, near where the Euphrates forces its way through the eastern Taurus and out to the Mesopotamian plain in a series of spectacular gorges, are to be found *Tulipa aleppensis*, *Crocus leichtlinii*, *Eranthis hyemalis*, *Corydalis rutifolia* ssp. *erdelii*, *Hyacinthus orientalis* ssp. *chionophilus* and *Scilla mesopotamica*.

South-east of the Cilician Gates, where the Mediterranean coast of Turkey turns south to Syria and the Lebanon, the Amanus range branches south from the Taurus massif to form the northernmost part of the mountain chain that runs down the coast of the Levant towards Mount

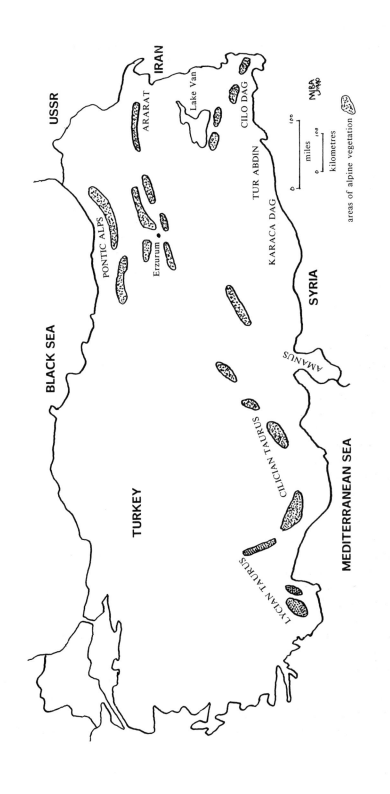

Lebanon. It does not rise much higher than 2000m (6500ft) within Turkey but, as it rises straight up from the sea, it can realistically be termed a mountain chain rather than a range of hills. Among its delicacies are *Cyclamen pseudibericum*, *Scilla ingridae*, *Hyacinthus orientalis* ssp. *orientalis*, *Fritillaria alfredae* ssp. *glaucoviridis*, *Helleborus vesicarius*, a large-flowered *Corydalis solida* (ssp. *tauricola?*) and a white *Primula vulgaris* ssp. *vulgaris*. Its position means that the Amanus has a relatively high rainfall and this, coupled with the presence (which was fairly forcibly drawn to our attention) of a sensitive military radar installation keeping watch over the eastern Mediterranean and Syria, meant that our forays here were somewhat curtailed.

Further east, there is another range that reaches a similar height but which is entirely different in character. From out of the Mesopotamian plain, between the Euphrates and the Tigris, rises Karaca Dağ. It is a rather formless mass of volcanic rubble but harbours some interesting spring flowers nonetheless: *Crocus leichtlinii*, *Colchicum falcifolium*, *Iris reticulata* var. *reticulata*, a fine form of *Corydalis rutifolia* ssp. *erdelii* and a magnificent form of *Caltha polypetala*.

Further east still, with the Tigris bounding it to the north and east, is a range of limestone hills rising abruptly from the Syrian desert to the south, although to a height of only about 1500m (5000ft). This is the area known traditionally as the Tûr Abdin. Here in early spring we found several species we have not seen elsewhere: *Eminium rauwolfii* var. *rauwolfii* (similar to *E. intortum* but with different shaped leaves and a slightly more open spathe), *Hyacinthella siirtensis*, *Muscari discolor*, *Scilla leepii* and various species of *Arum*.

North of the Tûr Abdin and the Tigris, the southern arc of the Taurus continues eastwards as far as the area southwest of Lake Van. On the mountain slopes here can be found *Narcissus tazetta* ssp. *tazetta*, *Onosma alboroseum* ssp. *albo-roseum* and fritillaries greatly contrasting in size: the diminutive *F. minuta* and the majestic *F. imperialis* growing within sight of each other on the rocky slopes, and both within sight of the leaves (only!) of the plant whose flower we had trekked up the mountain especially to see, *Iris gatesii*.

The Cilo and Sat mountains of Hakkâri province in the far southeast of Turkey rise to over 4000m (13,000ft) and contain true alpine habitats and some of the most southerly glaciers in the northern hemisphere. This area forms a salient between Iranian and Iraqi Kurdistan and the Turkish authorities are not happy about foreigners wandering far off the beaten track. Here, as always, our efforts with camera and tripod were noted with bemused incomprehension by groups of the locals, but here, unlike anywhere else, one of them was dressed in khaki fatigues (definitely not Turkish issue) and sported a semi-automatic rifle, with which we had heard him practising earlier.

We have explored this area briefly only in spring, but have not penetrated to the high summer pastures and the summits beyond. Even in May, however, when only the slopes up to 2000m (6500ft) or so are clear of snow, there is a rich variety of interesting mountain flowers. Here too the crags are graced by the statuesque *Fritillaria imperialis* and the slopes below dotted with *F. minuta* and *F. crassifolia*, joined in the wet flushes by *Colchicum szovitsii* and *Merendera trigyna*. On the tops of the cliffs above the crown imperials we found an attractive, pink-flowered woody shrub, *Cerasus brachypetala* var. *bornmuelleri*, and at the base of the same cliff a few *Iris aucheri*, a tall Juno iris with an unspectacular, dirty-yellow flower. In contrast, the Yüksekova (a broad marshy valley lying at about 1700m (5500ft)) was carpeted with marsh orchids (probably *Dactylorhiza iberica*), in various shades of pink, with the occasional white flower. On the drier slopes above were the striking oncocyclus *Iris iberica* ssp. *lycotis* and *Allium akaka*. On a damper slope our attention was arrested by the large, waxy, pillar-box red flowers of the parasitic *Phelypaea coccinea*.

To the north of Cilo Dağ, beside the headwaters of the Great Zab and across the path of the main road north to Van, lies a range of rolling hills rising to well over 3500m. Here in spring can be found such gems as *Iris pseudocaucasica*, *Tulipa biflora*, *T. humilis*, *Bellevalia rixii* and *Puschkinia scilloides*. The stream margins, both here and further north in the mountains guarding the southern shores of Lake Van, are purple with *Primula auriculata* or blue with *Muscari coeleste*. On the slopes above grow *Tulipa armena* var. *lycica*, *Fritillaria crassifolia* ssp. *kurdica*, *F. minima* and *Globularia trichosantha*. Near the main road to Van, north of Hoşap castle, grows the striking and eponymous oncocyclus *Iris paradoxa* f. *choschab*.

The northern shores of Lake Van are dominated by the 4000m (13,000ft) cone of Süphan Dağ and to the north of it there runs west from mount Ararat a ridge of generally unspectacular summits rising on average to somewhat over 3000m (10,000ft), including Çakmak and Palandöken Dağ, and intersected by the upper reaches of the Aras and Murat rivers. Here, in spring, we have found *Iris caucasica*, *Fritillaria armena* and *Tulipa julia*; and beneath the melting snow *Crocus biflorus* ssp. *tauri*, *Ranunculus kochii*, *Anemone albana* ssp. *armena* and sheets of *Scilla sibirica* ssp. *armena* painting the ground bright blue. In summer the Tahir pass (now by-passed by the main road) is a mass of meadow flowers and on the summits can be found *Allium akaka*, *Centaurea cheiranthifolia*, *Gagea*, *Puschkinia scilloides*, *Scilla sibirica*, *Anemone narcissiflora* ssp. *wildenowii*, *Anemone albana* ssp. *armena*, *Erigeron*, *Muscari coeleste*, various campanulas and, on Palandöken at least, *Gentiana verna* ssp. *pontica*, *Androsace villosa*, *A. albana*, *Potentilla ruprechtii*, *Draba polytricha*, *Asperula affinis* and *Primula algida*.

The next line of mountains north is the similar parallel ridge that runs from Spikör Dağ in the west, via Kop Dağ and Kargapazarı Dağ north of Erzurum, to the area north of the Sarıkamış Pass and on to the highlands north of Kars, on the frontier with Soviet Georgia. On the volcanic uplands the flora is similar to the ridge to the south. In addition to those species already mentioned, in spring we have found *Fritillaria caucasica* at the Sarıkamış Pass and *Corydalis rutifolia* ssp. *erdelii*, *Fritillaria pinardii*, *F. latifolia* and *Tulipa sintenisii* at the Kopdağ. In summer the fritillaries are over, but on the summits we have found *Viola crassifolia*, *Androsace armeniaca* and *Ornithogallum oligophyllum*, in addition to many of the species already mentioned. On the slopes of the Kopdağ in spring can be found bushes of bright red *Paeonia mascula* ssp. *arietina*. In summer the paeony is found near the top of the pass, with drifts of yellow *Eremurus spectabilis*. As well as the usual campanulas we have also found there, near a patch of snow that had still not melted by July, *Primula elatior* ssp. *pallasii*, a fine form of *Colchicum szovitsii* (which appears to be the form previously listed as *C. nivale*) and *Crocus biflorus* ssp. *tauri*.

With Spikör Dağ, north of Erzincan, the nature of the range changes. Here the dominant rock is limestone, rising to crags of about 2700m (9000ft). South-west of Erzincan, Munzur Dağ forms a long wall of grey and white marble and is, in fact, a continuation of the northern arm of the Taurus range we last noticed at Ala Dağ, north of the Cilician Gates. East of Spikör Dağ the limestone is overlaid with volcanic rock (mostly basalt) and only outcrops at lower altitudes. The mountainsides to the west of Spikör Dağ are covered with *Daphne oleoides* ssp. *kurdica* (on acid soil) and masses of *Aethionema* (on limestone) and we have also found *Globularia trichosantha*, *Muscari caucasicum* and *Iberis taurica*. At the top of Spikör Dağ, in addition to large globular clumps of *Astragalus*, there is a mass of *Saxifraga kotschyi* and also the pale blue *Onosma nanum*, *Arabis caucasica*, *Scutellaria orientalis*, *Asperula affinis*, *Draba bruniifolia*, *Androsace villosa* (some in very big cushions up to half a metre across), *Salvia pachystachys*, *Erodium absinthoides* ssp. *armenum*, *Arnebia pulchra*, *Asyneuma filipes*, a very attractive small yellow *Alyssum*, various attractive *Oxytropis* and other leguminous species and the usual wealth of attractive campanulas.

The area of rolling upland north of Kars, which falls away to the Çoruh to the north-west and to the lower Kura valley (in Soviet Georgia) to the north-east, becomes damper as one gets nearer to the influence of the Black Sea, but is neither as wet nor as rugged as the Pontic Alps. The flora shows characteristics of the ranges to the south, with more bulbous plants than are found in the Pontic Alps, but at the same time shows some affinities with the climate of the Black Sea coast and the Caucasus to the north. In north-facing valleys in this area we have found *Lilium kesselringianum* and some spectacular campanulas.

The summits in this area continue the type of rolling upland we have already encountered further south and west. Ilgardağ, north of Lake Çıldır and looking across the Kura valley to the Little Caucasus, is heavily grazed in summer as also is Kordevan Dağ and the area around the Yalnızçam Pass.

Kordevan Dağ looks down on the confluence of the Çoruh and its tributary the Savşat Suyu from the east and rises to a little over 3000m (10,000ft). When we explored this area in summer, we managed to get to the following flowers before the cattle and sheep: *Puschkinia scilloides*, *Merendera trigyna*, *Corydalis conorhiza*, *Geranium ibericum*, *Saxifraga sibirica*, *S. exarata*, *Androsace armeniaca* (in a pink form) and the usual wealth of campanulas.

On the sides of the valleys that cut into the ranges east and north of Erzurum can be found the spectacular oncocyclus *Iris iberica* ssp. *elegantissima* and (in a very restricted area) the less spectacular but very beautifully coloured *Iris taochia*, which varies in colour from yellow to purple – with interesting 'peachy' shades in between. Here, as elsewhere throughout eastern Turkey, the drier slopes support a wealth of species of plants such as *Acantholimon* and *Astragalus* (there are 372 species of *Astragalus* recorded in the *Flora*, of which about 214 are endemic to Turkey: the dual constraints of space and ignorance are the reasons for my failure to give them more than a passing mention).

The Pontic Alps themselves form a natural barrier along the eastern part of the southern shore of the Black Sea and run roughly from southwest to northeast. They provide what is probably the largest single area of alpine vegetation in Turkey. Access is not easy, however. Between the Zigana Pass south of Trabzon (at 2000m (6500ft), too low to be of great interest in the summer months) and the Çoruh valley at Artvin, a distance of approximately 225 kilometres (140 miles), there is no all-weather road over these mountains (although the road from Rize to Erzurum, via Ispir, over the Ovıtdağı Pass has been considerably improved in recent years); and between the Ovıtdağı Pass and Artvin, a distance of some 110kms (68 miles) as the crow flies, the main ridge never falls below 3000m (10,000 ft) and is crossed by no roads whatsoever. The range, the highest summit of which is Kaçkar (3932m (12,900 ft), and only about 35km (22 miles) from the sea), forms a barrier over which the winds blowing from the Black Sea must pass, precipitating their moisture mainly on to the northern flanks of the mountains and leaving the southern side in a relative rain shadow (although the high southern slopes receive much more rain than the lower slopes). The southern valleys are well watered by mountain torrents fed by the summit snows but the air is comparatively dry. On these lower slopes we have found *Epipactis veratrifolia*, *Paeonia mascula* ssp. *arietina*, *Campanula betulifolia* (in much better forms than those usually seen in cultivation: large, often very large, white or blush-pink bells cascading down the cliffs), *C. troegerae* (a near relation of *C. betulifolia* in the same range of colours but with very highly reflexed petals, and apparently confined to only one river valley system, where it grows in abundance from 600–1700m (2000–5000ft) above sea level), *Papaver lateritium*, *Centaurea appendicigera*, *Daphne pontica* and *Jurinella moschus* ssp. *pinnatisecta*, with its large purple flowers looking rather like an outsize prostrate thistle.

In the true alpine zone beside the melting snow the vegetation is similar on both sides of the watershed. Alongside the mountain torrents and in damp flushes flourish orchids of several genera: we have seen *Gymnadenia conopsea*, several species of *Dactylorhiza* including *DD. euxina* var. *euxina*, *osmanica* var. *osmanica* and *coeloglossum viride*. There are various varieties of campanula, all probably either *C. aucheri* or *C. tridentata*, *Daphne glomerata*, *Cyclamen parviflorum*, *C. coum* (which we have seen growing up to 2100m (7000ft), well above the tree line), *Asperula pontica*, *Anemone narcissiflora* ssp. *wildenowii*, *Corydalis rutifolia* ssp. *erdelii* (with flowers that look quite different from the forms encountered further south), *C. conorhiza* (in various shades from blue to pink via purple and also, in one place, a beautiful sulphur yellow), *C. alpestris*, *Saxifraga juniperifolia*, *Viola altaica*, *Aster alpinus*, *Pinguicula balcanica* ssp. *pontica*, *Muscari armeniacum*, *Trollius ranunculinus*, *Anemone albana* ssp. *armena* (some hanging their heads like *Pulsatilla vernalis*; others looking up with wide open flowers, and in various shades of maroon or purple, and once white), *Draba polytricha*, *Gentiana pyrenaica* (bluer in colour than those actually growing in the Pyrenees), *G. verna* ssp. *pontica*, *Primula auriculata* (some of them very fine forms with large richly-coloured flowers), *P. elatior* ssp. *meyeri*, *P. longipes*, *Fritillaria latifolia* and sheets of *Rhododendron caucasicum*.

The northern slopes are classed as temperate rain forest. Above the tree line grows *Rhododendron luteum*, and also among the trees or on the edges of clearings, with *Rhododendron ponticum*, *R. × sochadzeae* (a natural hybrid between *R. ponticum* and *R. caucasicum*), *R. ungernii* (a very attractive, large-leaved species with white, green-spotted flowers), *Epigaea gaultherioides*, *Paeonia wittmanniana* var. *nudicarpa*, *Anemone caucasica*, *Cyclamen coum*, orchids such as *Cephalanthera rubra* and *Orchis tridentata*, *Lilium monadelphum* var. *armenum*, *L. ciliatum* and, the baby of the lilies, *L. carniolicum* ssp. *ponticum* var. *artvinense*. In this far northeast corner of Turkey even the beautiful pink primrose, *Primula vulgaris* ssp. *sibthorpii*, which further west is found only at low altitudes, becomes a mountain flower and is found up to 2200m (7200ft) above sea level.

Here this survey stops – for the time being. The northern slopes of the Pontic Alps share their climate with the western slopes of the Caucasus; the flora of the two adjacent areas naturally has much in common as, indeed, has their history and culture. The Pontic Alps, however, have the advantage of being in Turkey, where one can wander very much at will, whereas the Caucasus has so far been beyond the reach of the vagabond tourist. We await future developments across the border with eager anticipation.

DEDICATION

This paper is dedicated to the memory of my parents, Stella and Arthur Almond, who always encouraged me to go and find things out for myself.

REFERENCES

Davis, P.H. *et al.*: *Flora of Turkey and the East Aegean Islands*; Edinburgh, 1965
Mathew, B. & Baytop, T.: *The Bulbous Plants of Turkey*; London, 1984
Rix, M. & Phillips, R.: *The Bulb Book*; London, 1981

FURTHER READING

Albury, S.J.: 'Plant Hunting in Turkey'; *JSRGC* XI(1) no 42 (Apr 1968) pp 7–14
Allison, J. & Ball, P.: 'Crocuses in the Toros'; *QBAGS* 45(2) 1977
Almond, L.&M.: 'Travels in Turkey'; *JSRGC* XVI(3) no 64 (Apr 1979) pp 202–7
   & XVI(4) no 65 (Sept 1979) pp 244–7
Almond, M.&L.: 'North-east Turkey'; *The Rock Garden* XVIII(3) no 72 (Jun 1983)
   pp 274–7 & XVIII(4) no 73 (Jan 1984) pp 382–7
Almond, M.J.B. & L.A.: 'Sites and flowers of south-west Turkey'; *The Rock Garden*
   XIX(3) no 76 (Jun 1985) pp 243–56
Almond, M.J.B. & L.A.: 'The Pontic Alps'; *The Rock Garden* XIX(4) no 77 (Jan
   1986) pp 392–402
Davis, P.H.: 'Why is the Flora of Turkey Interesting and Important?' *The Kew
   Magazine* 2(4) (Nov 1985) pp 357–67
Davis, P.H.: 'Lake Van and Turkish Kurdistan: a Botanical Journey'; *The
   Geographical Journal* 122 (1956) pp 156–166
Walkden, C.M.: 'The Land of the Wandering Hands'; *QBAGS* 54(4) no 226 (Dec
   1986) pp 304–316
Watson, J.M.: 'A New Fritillary'; *QBAGS* 38(4) no 162 (Dec 1970) pp 367–72
Watson, J.M.: 'Memories and Legacies'; *QBAGS* 39(1) no 166 (Dec 1971) pp
   269–303

Auriculastrum Primulas in the Wild and in Cultivation

FRITZ KUMMERT

In this paper I want to give some informations about species and hybrids of the Sektion Auriculastrum, especially an enumeration of the hybrids. Within the lists below, the parents are ordered alphabetical, even if it is known that the second species was the seed-bearing one. Everybody is asked to send further informations to me, especially on the list of artificial and advanced hybrids, but only if both parents, the seed-parent and the pollen-parent, are more or less clear, the plant is still living and a cutting can be given for scientific research!

Primulas of the Section Auriculastrum form in many parts of the European mountains striking, vivid and often scenting elements of the vegetation.

The section Auriculastrum includes 20 species, only native to Europe, and forms together with the sections Cuneifolia and Parryi the subgenus Auriculastrum within the genus *Primula*. The members of this section differ from all other species, with the exception of the species of the subgenus Sphondylia and the species within the sections Cuneifolia and Parryi, because of the involute leaves in the bud-stage.

The species of the section Auriculastrum are dwarf perennials, rarely hanging down out of fissures with long woody shoots. The leaves are mostly coriaceous, never bullate, the margin is entire or variable toothed, sometimes cartalagineous. The bracts are very variable, but never saccate at the base. The mostly cylindric calyx is more or less short and never sharply edged. The surface of the green parts is naked or glandular hairy. Farina occurs especially in the upper parts of the stalk and within the flower region, rarely on the leaves, here mostly on the upper surface. The flowers are pink to violet, often with a white eye, rarely pure white, or yellow, they are always heterostylous.

Since the time of Heinrich Wilhelm Schott (1794–1865), the Austrian gardener and botanist, there exists a subdivision of the section in subsections, kept upright, with slight modifications, up to modern times:

Subsection Euauricula (Auricula)
P. auricula L. Of this variable species I have to mention:

P. auricula ssp. *bauhinii* (Beck) Lüdi is the typical form, with short cilia at the leaf-margins, often with farina, usually scented

P. auricula ssp. *bauhinii* var. *albocincta* Widmer with white margins of the leaves

P. auricula ssp. *bauhinii* var. *monacensis* Widmer from the moors north of Munich with narrow, mealless leaves and light yellow flowers

P. auricula ssp. *bauhinii* var. *serratifolia* (Roch.) Lüdi from the Iron Gates of the Danube with serrate-dentate leaves

P. auricula ssp. *ciliata* (Moretti) Lüdi from the southern Alps is always efarinose and has long cilia on the leaf margins

Where the two subspecies meet, you can find hybrids:

P. auricula var. *obristii* (Stein) Beck, which I produced also artificially

P. palinuri Petagna

Subsection Brevibracteatae

P. carniolica Jacq.

P. latifolia Lapeyr. with

P. latifolia f. *cynoglossifolia* Widmer, a form with untoothed, large leaves

P. marginata Curtis

Subsection Erythrodrosum (Rufiglandulae)

P. daonensis (Leybold) Leybold (*P. oenensis* Thomas)

P. hirsuta All. (*P. viscosa* Vill., *P. rubra* J.F.Gmel.) is very variable, so the stated forms are even more to be questioned as with *P. auricula*!

P. pedemontana Thomas ex Gaudin

P. pedemontana ssp. *apennina* (Widmer) A.Kress (*P. apennina* Widmer)

P. pedemontana ssp. *iberica* Losa & P.Mons

P. villosa Wulfen in Jacq. (incl. *P. cottia* Widmer)

P. villosa ssp. *infecta* A.Kress from Alps of Biella, Prov. Vercelli, Italy

P. villosa ssp. *irmingardis* A.Kress from the Stubalpe, Austria

P. villosa var. *commutata* (Schott) Lüdi from the rocks of the castle of Herberstein and the Geierwand, not far from my home

Subsection Arthritica (Cartilagineo-marginata)

P. clusiana Tausch

P. clusiana f. *admontensis* Gusmus is after my opinion not a hybrid between this species and *P. minima*, but the rare dentated form of *P. clusiana*, which occurs rarely in the populations of this species

P. glaucescens Moretti with

P. glaucescens ssp. *calycina* (Duby) Pax, the more vigorous subspecies, all over the range of the species and

P. glaucescens ssp. *longobarda* (Porta) Widmer, the dwarf subspecies from the eastern part of the range of the species

P. spectabilis Tratt.

P. wulfeniana Schott (incl. *P. baumgarteniana* Degen & Moesz from the Carpathians near Brasov, Rumania)

Subsection Rhopsidium
P. allionii Loisel.
P. integrifolia L.
P. kitaibeliana Schott
P. tyrolensis Schott

Subsection Cyanopsis:
P. deorum Velen.
P. glutinosa Wulfen in Jacq.

Subsection Chamaecallis:
P. minima L.
The heredity of white flower-colour was researched by me in this species. Crosses between pink-coloured and white-coloured plants are pink-coloured, back-crossing with the white-coloured parent gives approximately 50% white-coloured plants. 'White' was transmitted in this case as a simple recessive after Mendelian law.

Naturally-occurring Hybrids

P. allionii × *P. marginata*
P. auricula × *P. carniolica*
P. auricula × *P. clusiana*
P. auricula × *P. daonensis*
P. auricula × *P. hirsuta*
P. auricula × *P. integrifolia*
P. auricula × *P. tyrolensis*
P. clusiana × *P. minima*
P. daonensis × *P. hirsuta*
P. daonensis × *P. latifolia*
P. daonensis × *P. minima*
P. glaucescens × *P. spectabilis*
P. glutinosa × *P. minima*
P. hirsuta × *P. integrifolia*
P. hirsuta × *P. latifolia*
P. hirsuta × *P. marginata*
P. hirsuta × *P. minima*
P. integrifolia × *P. latifolia*
P. latifolia × *P. marginata*
P. latifolia × *P. pedemontana*
P. minima × *P. spectabilis*
P. minima × *P. villosa*
P. minima × *P. wulfeniana*

P. × *miniera* nom.nud.
P. × *venusta* Host
P. × *lempergii* F.Buxb.
P. × *discolor* Leybold
P. × *pubescens* Jacq.
P. × *escheri* Brügger
P. × *obovata* Huter
P. × *intermedia* Portenschlag
P. × *seriana* Widmer
P. × *kolbiana* Widmer
P. × *pumila* Kerner
P. × *caruelii* Porta
P. × *floerkeana* Schrad.
P. × *heerii* Brügger
P. × *berninae* Kerner
not named to date
P. × *forsteri* Stein
P. × *muretiana* Moritzi
P. × *crucis* Bowles ex Farrer
P. × *bowlesii* Farrer
P. × *facchinii* Schott
P. × *truncata* Lehmann
P. × *vochinensis* Gusmus

P. minima × *P. tyrolensis*	*P.* × *juribella* Sündermann
P. pedemontana × *P. villosa*	*P.* × *boni-auxilii* A. Kress
P. tyrolensis × *P. wulfeniana*	*P.* × *venzoides* Venzo

Artificial Hybrids

Beside re-crossing natural hybrids, the following combinations were made in cultivation:

P. allionii × *P. auricula*	*P.* × *loiseleurii* Sündermann
	Hort. Sündermann & others
P. allionii × *P. carniolica*	Hort. Agee
P. allionii × *P. hirsuta*	*P.* 'Ethel Barker' Hort. Barker
P. allionii × *P. minima*	Hort. England, before 1970
P. allionii × *P. pedemontana*	Hort. ?
P. allionii × *P. villosa*	Hort. Kummert, Agee
P. auricula × *P. kitaibeliana*	Hort. Kummert
P. auricula × *P. latifolia*	*P.* × *widmeriana* Sündermann
	Hort. Sündermann & others
P. auricula × *P. marginata*	*P.* × *salomonii* Sündermann
	Hort. Sündermann & others
P. auricula × *P. pedemontana*	*P.* × *sendtneri* Widmer
	Hort. Nymphenburg & others
P. auricula × *P. villosa*	? *P.* × *hybrida* Knaf on different places
P. carniolica × *P. pedemontana*	Hort. Taylor
P. glaucescens × *P. minima*	Hort. Kummert
P. hirsuta × *P. pedemontana*	Hort. Taylor
P. hirsuta × *P. villosa*	Hort. Kummert
P. kitaibeliana × *P. minima*	Hort. Kummert
P. latifolia × *P. villosa*	Hort. ?
P. marginata × *P. pedemontana*	Hort. ?
P. marginata × *P. villosa*	*P.* × *elisabethae* Sündermann
	Hort. Sündermann & others
P. pedemontana × *P. spectabilis*	Hort. Taylor

Certainly several more combinations have been crossed successfully and the plants are in cultivation, but are unknown to me. On the other hand for instance seedlings of *P. integrifolia* were raised in several gardens, so here in my garden or with the Stones, Fort Augustus, of which the parentage is unknown and it is therefore impossible to note their status exactly.

Advanced Hybrids

Only some examples are mentioned, of which the parentage is more or less clear for me:

P. allionii × *P. marginata* hybrids	f.i. *P.* 'Beatrice Wooster'
	Hort. Wooster & others

The parentage of the so called *P. marginata* hybrids, as for instance 'Linda Pope', is quite unclear. To get some informations about this variety, I raised seedlings from self-pollination. The descendants were ugly plants, mostly dirtish purplish in colour, with a yellow eye. This seems to indicate, that perhaps also *P. × pubescens* is involved in the ancestry of this certain variety.

P. allionii × *P. × pubescens*	*P.* 'Margaret' & other vars.
P. auricula × *P. × crucis*	Hort. Kummert
P. × forsteri × *P. × pubescens*	*P.* 'Dianne' Hort. Drake
P. × forsteri × *P. × truncata*	Hort. Kummert
P. marginata × *P. × venusta*	*P.* 'Marven' Hort. ?
P. marginata × *P. × pubescens*	*P. × wockei* Arends Hort. Arends & others

Dubious Hybrids

In several cases hybrids from the wild have been described, but I wasn't able to verify them

P. auricula × *P. spectabilis*	*P. × weldeniana* Dalla Torre & Sarnth.
P. auricula × *P. wulfeniana*	*P. × lebliana* Gusmus
P. glaucescens × *P. hirsuta*	
P. glaucescens × *P. integrifolia*	
P. glutinosa × *P. integrifolia*	*P. × huegeninii* Brügger

Selected Literature

Kress, Alarich (1981). 'Primula sectio Auricula subsectio Erythrodrosum: Neue Unterarten und Hybriden'. *Primulaceen-Studien* (D) 2:1–4.

Kummert, Fritz (1981). 'Hybriden in der Sektion Auriculastrum der Gattung Primula, mit besonderer Berücksichtigung von artifiziellen Bastarden'. *Linzer biol. Beitr.* (A) 13(1):56–58.

Schott, Heinrich Wilhelm (1851). *Die Sippen der österreichischen Primeln.* Verlag Carl Gerold & Sohn, Wien (A), 14 pp.

Schott, Heinrich Wilhelm (1852). *Wilde Blendlinge östereichischer Primeln.* Verlag Carl Gerold & Sohn, Wien (A), 20 pp.

Smith, G.F., Burrow, B. & Lowe, D.B. (1984). *Primulas of Europe and America.* Alpine Garden Society, Woking (GB), 251 pp.

Widmer, Elise (1891). *Die europäischen Arten der Gattung Primula.* Verlag R. Oldenbourg, München (D), 154 pp.

The Micropropagation of Rock Plants

DAVID WALKEY

1.1 INTRODUCTION

Since the mid 1950s when tissue culture micropropagation was first used in France (Morel & Martin, 1952), to eradicate viruses from potatoes and dahlias, it has been increasingly used by horticulturalists as a technique for the rapid vegetative propagation of large numbers of clonal plants. Conventionally such plants would have been propagated by cuttings, grafting, layering etc. Today, micropropagation is still the only procedure by which viruses can be eradicated from infected clonal material, and is also frequently used by the plant breeder and research worker to multiply relatively small numbers of genetically identical plants for their specific purposes (Alderson & Dullforce, 1986).

The 1960s and 1970s saw the establishment of numerous micropropagation laboratories in Europe, America and elsewhere, specialising in the commerical production of micropropagated plants. In addition, some large nurseries and a few public institutions such as botanic gardens and colleges, also established their own micropropagation units. The range of plants propagated by these laboratories has quite naturally been commercially orientated. The cost to the nurseryman of weaned micropropagated plants is generally higher than the cost of producing his own conventionally propagated cuttings (Howard, 1986) and is certainly considerably higher than growing a plant from seed. Usually, therefore, only plants which have a wide public demand and a relatively high retail price will be micropropagated commercially. New introductions or clonal plants that are difficult to propagate vegetatively by conventional methods are especially suitable for micropropagation. Consequently, house plants, ornamental trees and shrubs, fruit trees, larger herbaceous plants, orchids and ferns make up the bulk of the catalogue lists offered by these commercial laboratories and only a few of the listed plants are likely to be of interest to the rock gardener. Nevertheless, a few useful plants, such as *Primula* hybrids, hardy orchids (including *Pleione* species), conifers and dwarf shrubs (such as *Rhododendron* and *Daphne* species) will be found in their lists. These plants will reach the rock gardener through garden centres or from specialist alpine nurserymen who have purchased wholesale quantities from the micropropagator.

In addition, in the United Kingdom at least, a few rock garden enthusiasts have established their own tissue culture laboratories or have access professionally to such facilities. Having no commercial interests, these enthusiasts are able to experiment with a wide range of rock garden species and cultivars (see Section 1.3) and even work on the eradication of viruses from infected clones (see Section 1.4).

1.2 THE PRINCIPLES OF MICROPROPAGATION

The process of tissue culture used in micropropagation can be broadly defined as 'the cultivation *in vitro* of any plant part, whether it be protoplast, single cell, tissue or organ, under aseptic conditions to regenerate a new, complete plant'. The essential requirement of any vegetative propagation procedure, whether it be micro or conventional macropropagation, is that the offspring produced are genetically identical to the clonal mother plant. Research over many years has shown that micropropagation *in vitro* may be achieved by two pathways (Shor, 1986), either by the regeneration of shoots from pre-existing meristems or *de novo* from meristems (adventitious) induced in the tissue culture process (Fig. 1). Experience has shown that for the purposes of clonal multiplication and the regeneration of genetically identical plants, culture from existing apical or axillary shoot meristems is greatly preferable to pathway 2. Plants regenerated from protoplasts (cells with their cell wall removed), single cells or groups of non-meristematic cells, are more likely to be genetically different from their parent. Such variation is referred to as somaclonal and the regenerants as somaclones. Even when plantlets are regenerated from apical or axillary shoots it is advisable to avoid callus growth on the cultures whenever possible and to encourage direct shoot or root formation. The development of undifferentiated callus cells in the plantlet regeneration pathway can often result in plantlets that are genetically variable.

Most, if not all laboratories attempting to micropropagate clonal plants, will therefore start with a meristem-tip from an apical or axillary bud. The tip is taken from a bud on a shoot that has been carefully sterilised by immersion in a dilute solution of hypochlorite, followed by a further immersion in 70% alcohol (see Walkey, 1991). The dissection of the tip is carried out using a binocular microscope in a current of sterile air provided by a laminar air-flow bench. The dissected tip must consist of the meristem dome of cells, plus at least one or two pairs of primordial leaves (see Fig. 2). If the tip is being grown for virus eradication purposes, the smaller the tip taken, the greater are the chances of regenerating a virus-free plant. In practice, however, the tip should measure between 0.5 and 1.0mm

29   *Penstemon hallii* is widespread in the central mountains of Colorado (see page 98)

30   *Crocus baytoporium* seen at Altinyayla in Turkey (see page 114)

31 *Thalictrum orientale* was one of the plants seen by Michael
    Almond in Turkey (see page 113)

32 An unidentified *Campanula* species from Turkey (see page 113)

33   *Tulipa humilis*, one of the many bulbs seen in Turkey (see page 113)

34   *Primula auricula* in the wild near Neuhaus, Lower Austria (see page 122)

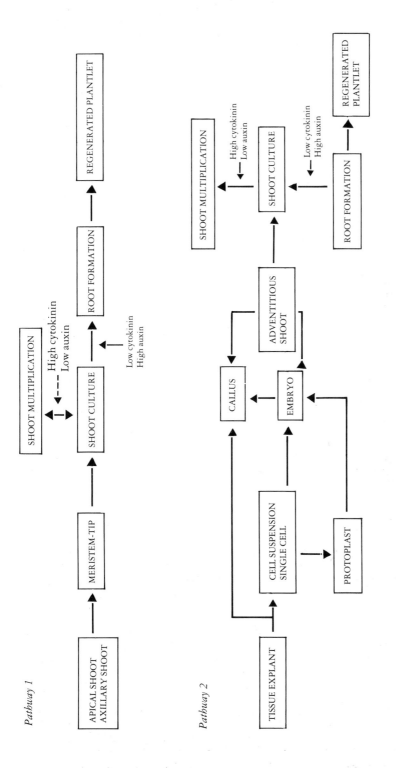

Figure 1 *Possible pathways of regenerating plantlets by micropropagation*

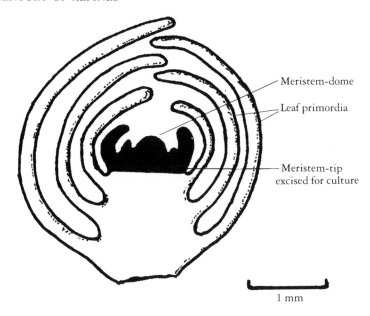

Meristem-dome

Leaf primordia

Meristem-tip
excised for culture

1 mm

Figure 2 *Diagram of a bud showing the meristem-tip region that is usually removed as the explant for tissue culture*

diameter, for it is often very difficult to get a tip smaller than 0.5mm diameter to grow. For the purposes of rapid multiplication of a plant, shoot tips up to 2.5mm or even larger may be used.

The dissected tip is aseptically transferred to a culture tube or other suitable vessel containing a sterile growth-medium and further sub-culture to fresh medium will be necessary every 2 to 3 weeks. Great care must be taken during the excision of the tip, its transfer to the culture tube and during subsequent sub-culturing to ensure that the instruments used are kept sterile. The instruments must be dipped in 70% alcohol and flamed in an alcohol burner before and after every manipulation. Failure to ensure sterility will result in culture medium contamination and loss of the culture. Culture-tubes are normally incubated at around 23 to 25°C and illuminated for 16 hours a day by daylight fluorescent tubes or high pressure sodium or mercury lamps. Finally when the young plantlet has produced a well-developed root system it is ready for transfer to soil. If a plantlet is being regenerated in a very favourable culture medium it may be expected to develop from a tip-explant to a rooted plantlet in 8–12 weeks. weeks.

Most micropropagation laboratories use culture media that are based on Murashige and Skoog's (1962) or Gamborg's (1968) media (see Table 1), which are suitable for many herbaceous and woody species. The basic culture medium requirements for any plant species include mineral salts (major and minor element requirements, see Table 1), a carbohydrate (sugar, generally sucrose), and vitamins, together with growth regulating cytokinins and auxins. The ratio of cytokinin to auxin in the medium is critical, as it governs the type of culture growth. As a general rule, a high cytokinin concentration (10 to 15mg/l kinetin) with a low auxin level (0 to 8mg\l IAA) will result in multiple shoot proliferation, and no or negligible root formation. In contrast, low concentrations or no cytokinin and high levels of auxin (8–16mg\l IAA) will induce rooting. Often if rapid multiplication of a species is required, the tip culture should be started with the former growth regulator regime to produce a mass of shoots, these can

Table 1 Culture media commonly used for meristem-tip culture

Murashige & Skoog (MS)		*Gamborg (B5)*	
Mineral salts (mg/l)			
NH_4NO_3	1650	$(NH_4)_2SO_4$	134
KNO_3	1900	KNO_3	2500
$CaCl_2 2H_2O$	440	$CaCl_2 2H_2O$	0.15
$MgSO_4 7H_2O$	370	$MgSO_4 7H_2O$	250
KH_2PO_4	170	$NaH_2PO_4 H_2O$	150
Na_2EDTA	37	Ferric EDTA	43
$FeSO_4 7H_2O$	28	H_3BO_3	3
H_3BO_3	6.2	$MnSO_4 4H_2O$	10
$MnSO_4 4H_2O$	22.3	$ZnSO_4 7H_2O$	2
$ZnSO_4 4H_2O$	8.6	KI	0.75
KI	0.83	$Na_2MoO_4 2H_2O$	0.25
$Na_2MoO_4 2H_2O$	0.25	$CuSO_4 5H_2O$	0.025
$CuSO_4 5H_2O$	0.025		
$CoCl_2 6H_2O$	0.025		
Organic ingredients (mg/l)			
Sucrose	30g/l	Sucrose	20g/l
Indoleacetic acid	8mg/1*	Indoleacetic acid	8mg/1*
Kinetin	2.56mg/l*	Kinetin	2.56mg/l*
Pyridoxine HCl	0.5mg/l	Pyridoxine HCl	1mg/l
Thiamine HCl	0.1mg/l	Thiamine HCl	10mg/l
Nicotinic acid	0.1mg/l	Nicotinic acid	1mg/l
Myo-inositol	100mg/l	Myo-inositol	100mg/l
Agar (Oxoid No. 3)	9g/l*	Agar (Oxoid No. 3)	6/8g/l*

*The concentration of these ingredients may be changed to obtain the type of growth required or firmness of medium. Alternative cytokinins and auxins may be substituted.

be further proliferated by subculturing on the same medium, and eventually the proliferating shoot masses may be divided with a scalpel into individual shoot cultures and each shoot rooted on the high auxin regime (see Figure 3).

Unfortunately, individual plant species and even cultivars of a species often differ in their specific culture medium requirements, and especially in respect of the cytokinin and auxin levels. It is necessary, therefore, to determine by experiment at the start of the culture of a species not previously studied, the optimum concentrations of growth regulators that are necessary to obtain the required growth stages of that species. This is achieved by carrying out a 'Latin Square' experiment in which meristem-tips are cultured on a range of different cytokinin and auxin concentrations (see Table 2).

Although kinetin and indoleacetic acid (IAA) are often used as the cytokinin and auxin requirements in the culture medium, these are frequently substituted by other cytokinins and auxins (Hu & Wang, 1983). Similarly, other vitamins and various amino acids (such as asparagine, glycine and glutamine) may be added to the culture medium. Some species also grow better on a half-strength mineral salt medium, or a lower strength medium may be required at a specific stage of plantlet regeneration. As with the growth regulator concentrations, however, these differences are empirical for each individual species or cultivar (Alderson & Dullforce, 1986).

For many years woody species were found to be more difficult to micropropagate than herbaceous species (Alderson, 1986), but from the mid 1970s onwards many of these difficulties were overcome and today a wide range of woody species may be easily cultured (Withers & Alderson, 1986). Sometimes reducing the nitrogen and potassium salt content of the medium improves the culture of woody species and regeneration is often more readily obtained from younger, juvenile shoots than mature ones.

Tissue culture media, such as Murashige & Skoog's and Gamborg's B5, may be purchased ready for use from chemical suppliers, either as a complete

Table 2 Examples of varying concentrations of auxin and cytokinin that may be tried to induce different types of culture growth

Kinetin† concentration	Indoleacetic acid† concentration			
	0	4mg/l	8mg/l	16mg/l
0	1*	2	3	4
1mg/l	5	6	7	8
2.5mg/l	9	10	11	12
10mg/l	13	14	15	16

*Number of treatment
†Other auxins and cytokinins may be used instead of kinetin and indoleacetic acid.

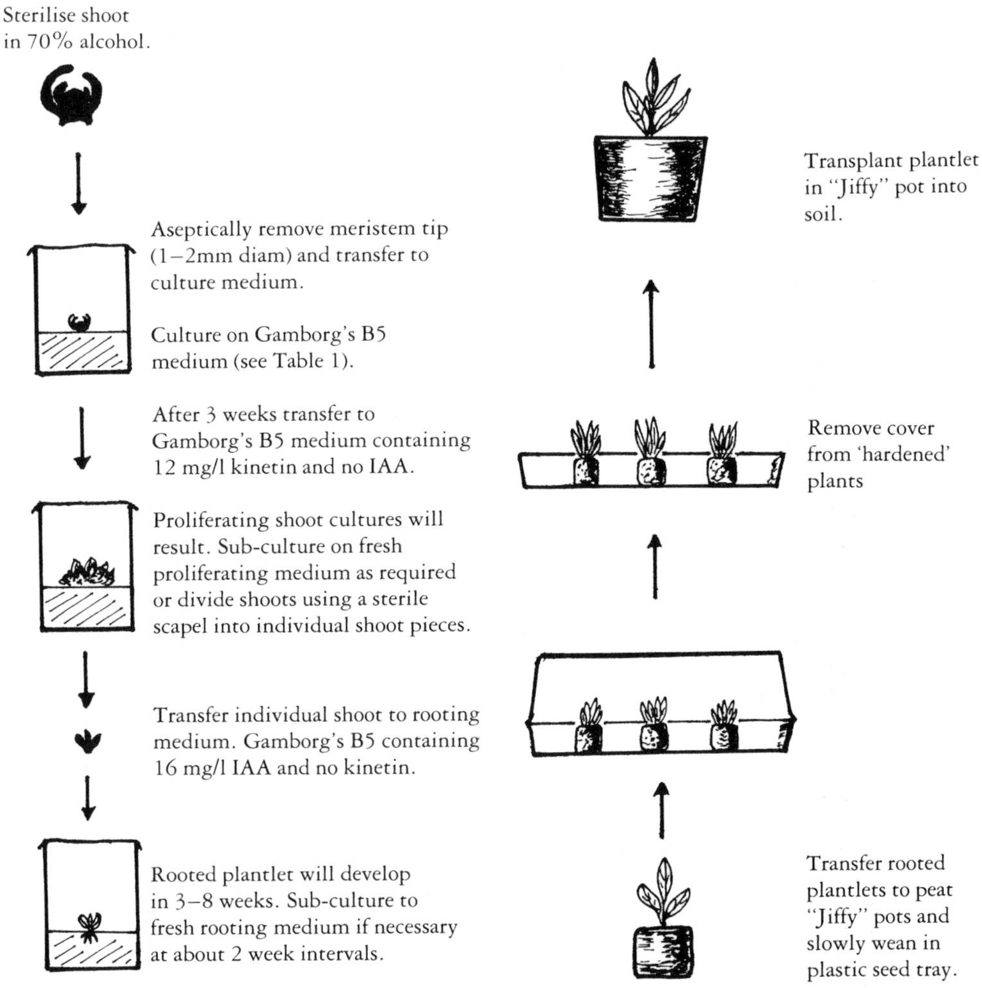

Sterilise shoot
in 70% alcohol.

Aseptically remove meristem tip
(1–2mm diam) and transfer to
culture medium.

Culture on Gamborg's B5
medium (see Table 1).

After 3 weeks transfer to
Gamborg's B5 medium containing
12 mg/l kinetin and no IAA.

Proliferating shoot cultures will
result. Sub-culture on fresh
proliferating medium as required
or divide shoots using a sterile
scapel into individual shoot pieces.

Transfer individual shoot to rooting
medium. Gamborg's B5 containing
16 mg/l IAA and no kinetin.

Rooted plantlet will develop
in 3–8 weeks. Sub-culture to
fresh rooting medium if necessary
at about 2 week intervals.

Transplant plantlet
in "Jiffy" pot into
soil.

Remove cover
from 'hardened'
plants

Transfer rooted
plantlets to peat
"Jiffy" pots and
slowly wean in
plastic seed tray.

Figure 3   *Procedure for the micropropagation of* Primula *hybrids*

medium (containing sugar, vitamins and growth regulators) or as prep-
arations containing only the complex mineral salt elements. For most
purposes the latter is the most suitable, as the various additives may then
be adjusted to give optimal culture growth for the individual species concerned. This is particularly important for rock-garden enthusiasts who
might be attempting to micropropagate a species for the first time.

To prepare the culture medium, the mineral salts together with the
sucrose and vitamins are dissolved in distilled water and the growth
regulators added (see Walkey, 1991), the medium is then adjusted to the
required pH (usually 5.7). Then agar (usually to a final concentration of
0.9%) is added to the medium and thoroughly dissolved, before the
medium is dispensed into individual culture tubes. These are finally
sterilized by autoclaving. As an alternative to using agar to support the tip-
culture, some workers prefer to support the culture on a filter paper bridge
that dips into the culture medium.

When the roots of the culture are well developed, the plantlet may be
transferred to soil. This stage is always a critical procedure in any
micropropagation programme, for the delicate young plantlet must be
transferred from the very high humidity of its protected culture environment, to soil and a variable, often harsh environment. The transfer process
must be very carefully monitored as the high humidity is gradually reduced
to that of a normal glasshouse environment. Plantlets often grow well if
they are initially transplanted into peat Jiffy pots and placed in a plastic
covered seed tray. The humidity can be gradually lowered over a period of
10 to 14 days by first opening the vents in the roof of the chamber and then
gradually lifting one of the sides of the chamber. Finally, the plastic cover
may be removed completely. After the plantlets are weaned the Jiffy pot can
be transplanted into a larger pot containing a suitable soil mixture for the
species concerned (see Figure 3).

Subsequent post-culture treatment should also include the monitoring of
the regenerated plants to ensure they show no obvious genetic changes
resulting from the tissue culture process. This is particularly important for
species that have been micropropagated for the first time and should be
carried out by observing the plants for any changes in agronomic characteristics over several seasons in the garden. Other factors associated with the
post-culture treatments of micropropagated plants are discussed in the
article by Mr Peter Foley (see page 207).

1.3 MULTIPLICATION OF ROCK PLANTS BY
MICROPROPAGATION

The principles and techniques of micropropagation described in Section 1.2
apply equally as well to rock plants, as they do to larger herbaceous and

woody species, upon which the development of most commercial micropropagation has been based. For the commercial reasons discussed in the introduction to this article, most of the micropropagation work with rock garden plants has been carried out by enthusiastic amateurs who sometimes use improvised equipment and facilities very successfully. The utilisation of such equipment by the amateur has been described in a recent publication,

Table 3   Examples of rock-garden species that have been multiplied by micropropagation.

Boraginaceae
  Eritrichium nanum[1]
Campanulaceae
  Campanula allionii[2]
Compositae
  Helichrysum papaphyllum[1]
  Nassauvia lagascae[1]
  Raoulia eximia × *petriensis*[1]
  R. grandiflora[1]
  R. × *loganii*[1]
Gentianaceae
  Gentiana brachyphylla[1]
  G. depressa[1]
  G. farreri[1]
  G. nipponica[1]
  G. occidentalis[1]
  G. parryi[1]
  G. pumila[1]
  G. pyrenaica[1]
  G. oschtenica[1]
  G. stipitata[1]
  G. verna alba[1]
Gesneriaceae
  Briggsia musicola[1]
  Jankeamonda vandedemii[1,3]
  Opithandra primuloides[1]
  Ramonda myconi[1]
Guttiferae
  Hypericum ericoides[1]

Liliaceae
  Trillium nivale[1]
Orchidaceae
  Pleione spp[4]
Polygonaceae
  Eriogonum wrightii[1]
Portulacaceae
  Calandrinia caespitosa[1]
  Lewisia sierrae × *cotyledon*[1]
Primulaceae
  Androsace alpina[1]
  A. brevis[1]
  A. delavayi[1]
  A. muscoidea[1]
  Dionysia archibaldii[1]
  D. curviflora[1]
  D. denticulata[1]
  D. freitagii[1]
  D. involucrata[1]
  D. janthina[1]
  D. lamingtonii[1]
  D. microphylla[1]
  Primula hybrids[2] *(see Table 5)*
Ranunculaceae
  Pulsatilla vulgaris[2]
Scrophulariaceae
  Ourisia microphylla[1]
Verbenaceae
  Verbena microphylla[1]
Violaceae
  Viola cazorlensis[1]
  V. cenisia[1]

Micropropagation carried out by [1]P. Abery, (personal communication), [2]D.G.A. Walkey, (unpublished information), [3]J. Forrest, (personal communication), [4]commercial company

Table 4   Examples of some woody species that have been micropropagated

Ericaceae	*Ranunculaceae*
Kalmia latifolia[1]	*Clematis sp*[2]
Kalmiopsis sp[2]	*Rosaceae*
Rhododendron sp[2,3]	*Spirea sp*[6]
Rhodothamnus sp[2]	*Scrophulariaceae*
Labiatae	*Penstemon sp*[2]
Thymus vulgaris[4]	*Thymelaeaceae*
Leguminosae	*Daphne jasminea*[2]
Cytisus spp[5]	*D. petraea grandiflora*[2]
Myrtaceae	*D. striata*[2]
Leptospermum sp[2]	

Micropropagation carried out by [1]Jaynes (1988), [2]P. Abery, (personal communication), [3]commercial company, [4]Olszowska & Furmanowa (1987), [5]Barbieri & Morini (1987), [6]Norton & Norton (1988).

Pests and diseases of alpine plants (Ellis *et al.*, in press). The examples illustrated in Tables 3 & 4 show just how successful micropropagation can be in the hands of enthusiastic amateurs. The range of rock plants regenerated by tissue culture is considerable and being continually enlarged. In fact, with dedication and time, there should be no reason why the enthusiast, provided he or she is not concerned with commercial aspects of the work, should not extend these lists to cover most plants of rock gardening interest. The cardinal rule that must be remembered, however, is that where multiplication is easy or feasible by seed, micropropagation is unlikely to be better.

For the rock gardening enthusiast who wishes to gain experience and establish procedures for the micropropagation of rock plants, *Primula* hybrids are very good plants to start work with. The procedures that may be used to multiply many well known *Primula* hybrids, including those listed in Table 5, are illustrated in Figure 3. It should be mentioned, however, that difficulties may be encountered with some *P. allionii* cultivars that are very slow growing (Walkey, unpublished information).

1.4 THE PRODUCTION OF HEALTHY PLANTS BY MICROPROPAGATION

1.4.1 Introduction

Probably one of the most important future uses of micropropagation for the rock-gardener is the use of tissue culture to eradicate virus from infected clones of horticulturally desirable cultivars. Once a plant has become infected with a virus, the infection under normal circumstances will be present in that plant for the remainder of its life, for unlike fungal and bacterial diseases, viruses cannot be eliminated by the usual horticultural chemical treatments. In the case of an annual or biennial plant, virus infection may be very damaging in a particular season, but provided suitable precautions are taken (see Walkey, 1991; Ellis *et al.*, in press) there is every possibility that next season's crop grown from new seed will be healthy. If the plant is vegetatively propagated, however, once virus infection has occurred, it will be passed on to the offspring every time the infected plant is propagated. This is, of course, of great importance to the rock gardener, because many of the most popular rock plants have to be vegetatively propagated if their desired features are to be maintained. Many such plants are heterozygous in their genetic makeup and do not, therefore, breed-true if grown from seed.

Sometimes the distribution of virus-infected propagules results in a particular cultivar clone being widely or totally infected and some old cultivars that have been propagated vegetatively for many years may be infected with several viruses (Ellis *et al.*, in press). This is particularly true of many popular *Primula* hybrids which are highly susceptible to common aphid-transmitted viruses such as cucumber mosaic virus. Some *Primula* clones that are totally infected may have a fairly high tolerance to virus infection and may still produce a reasonable crop of flowers, although the flowers will be inferior to those of a completely virus-free clone. Other infected clones may show severely reduced quality, yield and loss of vigour. It is probable that over the years, many desirable garden clones have been lost because of their severe reaction to virus infection, while virus-tolerant clones have survived because gardeners have unwittingly selected them. Virus-tolerant clones are, however, a hazard to the rock gardener, for they present a continuing reservoir of the virus which could be transmitted to healthy plants. It is, therefore, essential that viruses should be eradicated from such popular clones if they are to continue as rock garden plants.

Table 5 *Primula* clones that have been meristem-tip cultured and freed of virus by the author

Primula   cv. 'Beatrice Wooster' (*P. allionii* × *P.* 'Linda Pope')
cv. 'Bewerley White' (*P.* × *pubescens*)
cv. 'Barbara Barker' (*P.* 'Linda Pope' × [*P.* × *pubescens*, 'Zuleika Dobson'])
cv. 'Ethel Barker' (*P. allionii* × *P. hirsuta*)
cv. 'Faldonside' (*P.* × *pubescens*)
cv. 'Prichard's Variety' (*P. marginata*)
cv. 'The General' (*P. pubescens*).

Fortunately, it is possible using the micropropagation tissue culture technique to eradicate virus from *Primula* clones (see Table 5). Starting with a meristem-tip from an infected plant it is possible to regenerate this tip into a virus-free plantlet by the method illustrated in Figure 4. Meristem-tip culture has also been used to eradicate viruses from various bulbs including the genera *Narcissus*, *Iris*, *Lilium* and *Tulipa* (Walkey, 1991). Although most of this work has been carried out with large hybrid cultivars, the methods applied would be equally applicable to rock garden species. Sometimes it is necessary to combine the tissue culture treatment with heat (thermotherapy) or chemical (chemotherapy) treatments to obtain successful virus eradication (Walkey, 1991). A scheme for the production of virus-free plants by these procedures is presented in Figure 5. Plantlet regenerated from meristem-tips by this procedure will usually also be free of any fungal or bacterial pathogens that were infecting the parent plant.

1.4.2 Factors controlling virus eradication during meristem-tip culture

Although the general tissue culture procedure for producing a virus-free plant by regenerating a meristem-tip from an infected parent plant is similar to that used for the micropropagation of healthy plants (Fig. 3), it is only necessary to produce one single healthy plant for the technique to be successful (Fig. 4). It is not necessary, therefore, to include a shoot-proliferation stage in the culture procedure. If a large number of the virus-free plants are subsequently required, it is better to regenerate a single virus-free plantlet and confirm its health status first, and then subject the healthy clone to a rapid micropropagation procedure.

One of the main factors that governs the eradication of virus by meristem-tip culture, is the size of the tip that is removed from the infected

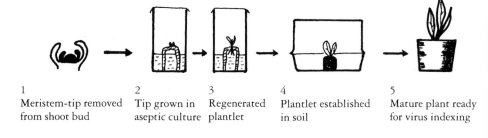

1	2	3	4	5
Meristem-tip removed from shoot bud	Tip grown in aseptic culture	Regenerated plantlet	Plantlet established in soil	Mature plant ready for virus indexing

Figure 4   *The regeneration of a plant by aseptic tissue culture of a meristem-tip explant.*

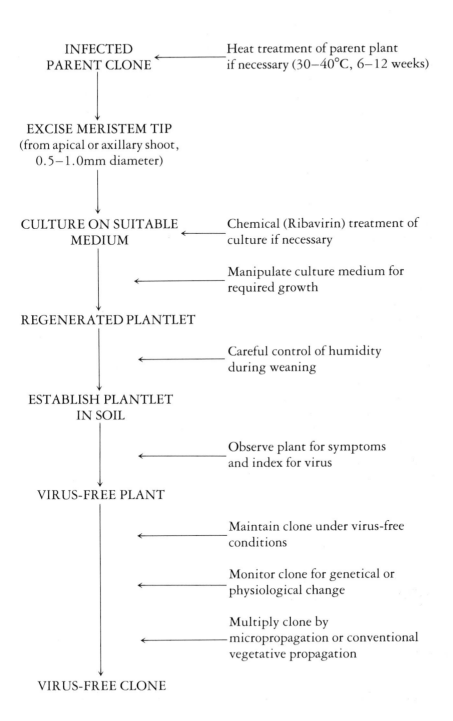

INFECTED   Heat treatment of parent plant
PARENT CLONE   if necessary (30–40°C, 6–12 weeks)

EXCISE MERISTEM TIP
(from apical or axillary shoot,
   0.5–1.0mm diameter)

CULTURE ON SUITABLE   Chemical (Ribavirin) treatment of
MEDIUM   culture if necessary

Manipulate culture medium for
required growth

REGENERATED PLANTLET

Careful control of humidity
during weaning

ESTABLISH PLANTLET
IN SOIL

Observe plant for symptoms
and index for virus

VIRUS-FREE PLANT

Maintain clone under virus-free
conditions

Monitor clone for genetical or
physiological change

Multiply clone by
micropropagation or conventional
vegetative propagation

VIRUS-FREE CLONE

Figure 5   *A scheme for the production of virus-free plants by meristem-tip culture*

parent for culture. This is because different viruses invade a shoot's meristematic dome of cells to varying degrees and the presence of a particular virus in these meristematic cells also depends upon the species of host concerned (Walkey & Webb, 1970). Generally, the smaller the tip taken the greater are the chances that the regenerated plantlet will be virus-free, conversely, however, the greater are the difficulties of getting the tip to grow. In practice tips smaller than about 0.5mm diameter are too difficult to culture, so tips between 0.5 and 1.0mm are usually taken for virus eradication.

In some virus/host infections it is possible to excise a tip small enough to be free of virus, but large enough to be regenerated into a healthy plantlet (see Fig. 6a). In other virus-host infections, viruses can be eradicated from cultured meristem-tips even when the tips that are actually cut still contain virus (see Fig. 6b). In this situation the virus is inactivated '*in vivo*' during the tissue culture process. The reasons why the virus is inactivated are not known, but the inactivation is more likely to occur if the tissues contain a low concentration of virus than a high one at the time the explant is taken. One possible reason for this '*in vivo*' virus inactivation is that auxins and

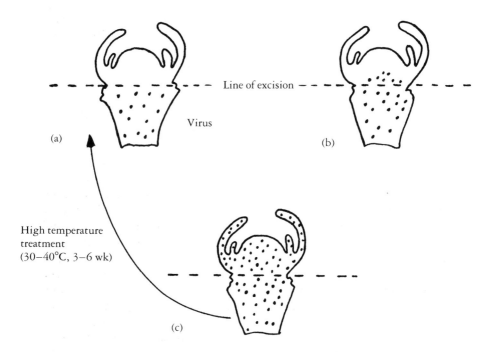

Figure 6   *Diagram showing virus invasion of the meristem-tip in relation to virus eradication by tissue culture and thermotherapy.*

other growth promoting chemicals in the culture nutrient medium, may stimulate a resistance mechanism against the virus within the cells of the cultured shoot.

In many virus/host infections, however, the virus is present in the meristem-tip explant in high concentrations and it is impossible to excise a tip small enough to avoid the virus or to allow '*in vivo*' virus inactivation during tissue culture (see Fig. 6c). In this situation it is still possible to produce virus-free plants from these infected tissues by combining heat treatment (thermotherapy) or chemical treatment (chemotherapy) with the meristem-tip culture.

1.4.3 High temperature and chemical treatments for virus eradication

High temperature treatments have been widely used combined with meristem-tip culture in the production of virus-free plants (Nyland & Goheen, 1969). The treatment involves the infected plant or organ (in the case of a tuber), being grown in hot air in a temperature controlled cabinet at between 30°C and 40°C for a period of 6 to 12 weeks. It is not possible to eradicate virus from a complete plant by heat treatment and it is important to understand the mechanism of the virus' inactivation by the high temperature. The temperature of 30°C to 40°C used for this treatment is well below that for inactivating a virus '*in-vitro*', which is generally between 45°C and 90°C depending on the virus concerned.

In an infected plant, the normal processes of virus synthesis and virus degradation occur simultaneously, but at high temperature (usually above 32°C) virus replication stops, but the breakdown of virus continues within the cells. Consequently, heat treatments of between 30°C and 40°C stop virus replication and eventually the newly formed tissues around the bud-meristem's growing point are free of virus. As the heat-treatment continues whole shoots become free of virus. The length of the heat-treatment period required to free the young shoots of virus differs with different virus/host infections, but usually it is from 3 to 10 weeks. It must be emphasised, however, that the older parts of the plant which do not have cells that are actively dividing, will remain infected and if the plant were to be removed from the high temperature and grown at a lower temperature, the virus would again start to multiply and spread rapidly. It is important, therefore, that meristem-tips are excised from the young heat-treated shoots for tissue culture, immediately the heat-treated plants are removed from the high temperature chambers. Various methods of applying high temperature treatments to virus infected plants have been studied. These are designed to obtain maximum virus inactivation with minimum damage to the tissues of the heat treated parent plants, which normally start to die at around 40°C. These treatments are described in the book *Applied plant virology* (Walkey, 1991).

It was mentioned in the introduction to this article, that viruses cannot be eradicated from infected plants by direct chemical action on the virus as is possible with fungal and bacterial diseases (Tomlinson, 1982). There are, however, some antiviral chemicals which act by blocking virus multiplication in the cells of infected plants, and in many ways the mechanism of virus inactivation by these chemicals is similar to that in the high temperature treatments. The most effective of these chemicals found to date is *ribavirin* (1, 2, 4 – triazole – 3 – carboxamine, which is sold under the trade name Virazole). If this is added to the culture medium at concentrations between 25 to 100mg/l, it will block virus replication in the cells of the cultured meristem-tip. The young cells continue to divide in a virus-free condition, even though the older tissues of the culture remain infected. Eventually, the meristem-tip can be recut from the ribavirin-treated culture in a virus-free condition and subsequently regenerated into a healthy plantlet in a culture medium without ribavirin (Simpkins *et al*, 1981).

Virus inactivation using ribavirin combined with meristem-tip culture is particularly useful for eradicating viruses which are not easily eliminated by high-temperature treatment or when the infected host plant is very susceptible to high temperatures. A scheme for producing virus-free plants by a combination of ribavirin treatment and meristem-tip culture is shown in Figure 7.

1.4.4 Post-cultural treatments

Following virus eradication treatments using tissue culture, the problems and procedures required to wean the regenerated plantlets are similar to those described in section 1.2. In addition, however, it is essential to monitor the growth of the virus-free plants over at least one season to ensure that there is not a resurgence of virus. During this period the plants must be regularly inspected for symptoms and if possible indexed for virus. (For indexing procedures see *Pests and diseases of alpine plants*, Ellis *et al*, in press). It is also essential to maintain the plants during this post-culture period in a virus-free environment within an insect-free glasshouse or gauze covered frame, to ensure that they are not reinfected by insect-transmitted viruses. The virus-free plants should also be monitored to observe their agronomic characteristics, to be certain they are identical to the original parent clone. Experience has shown that besides gross genetical changes, some plants freed of virus may develop small physiological changes due to the virus being removed from their systems. Such changes have included differences in the times of flowering and different cold requirements to break dormancy.

Once it is confirmed that the regenerated plants are virus-free and that they do not have adverse characteristics, they may be multiplied conventionally or by micropropagation to produce useful quantities. It would be sensible at this stage to maintain a small stock of virus-free mother plants under virus-free conditions for future multiplication. This could be done by growing the nuclear stock in an insect-free glasshouse or gauze-frame in sterile soil, or by maintaining a few proliferating virus-free shoots in tissue culture.

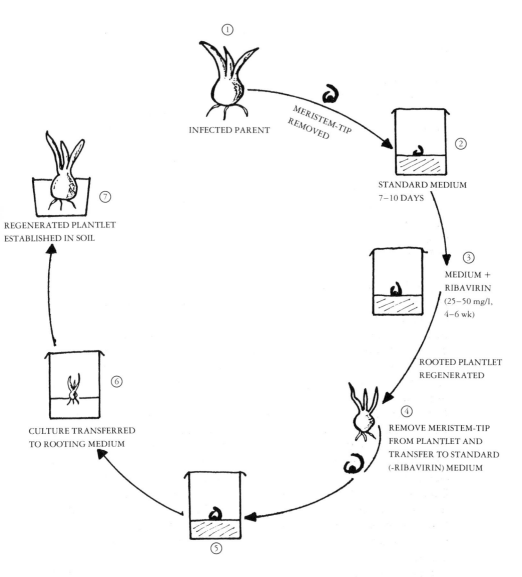

① INFECTED PARENT

MERISTEM-TIP REMOVED

② STANDARD MEDIUM 7–10 DAYS

③ MEDIUM + RIBAVIRIN (25–50 mg/l, 4–6 wk)

ROOTED PLANTLET REGENERATED

④ REMOVE MERISTEM-TIP FROM PLANTLET AND TRANSFER TO STANDARD (-RIBAVIRIN) MEDIUM

⑤

⑥ CULTURE TRANSFERRED TO ROOTING MEDIUM

⑦ REGENERATED PLANTLET ESTABLISHED IN SOIL

Figure 7 *Scheme for the production of virus-free plants using meristem-tip culture combined with chemotherapy*

1.5 FUTURE DEVELOPMENTS

It is probable that the economic restraints on the commercial use of microproduction for the mass production of rock plants that were discussed earlier in this article will continue. Plants with a high retail value will undoubtedly be micropropagated commercially, as well as valuable new introductions. It must be remembered, however, that the demand from rock gardening enthusiasts for rare plants is limited by their numbers and such markets can very quickly be saturated with an immediate fall in the scarcity value of a new introduction.

There is unquestionably a requirement for micropropagation to be more widely used to eradicate viruses from popular rock garden clones. A guarantee of the health status of commercial plants would also be an advantage to the specialist nurseryman, both for sales at home and abroad. The increasing restrictions being placed on the international movement of plant material will undoubtedly mean that all plants for export must carry such health guarantees and micropropagated plantlets, still in their culture tubes and guaranteed disease free, would be an ideal product for international trade. The cost of eradicating viruses from rock garden clones and the relatively small market for them, will probably deter large commercial micropropagation laboratories. It would, however, be very much in the interests of specialist rock plant nurserymen to consider the establishment of a micropropagation unit for this purpose. In addition, this unit could be used to micropropagate healthy plant clones of a diverse range of species and cultivars in sufficient numbers to be economically attractive without flooding the market. The economic viability of running a small operation of this type would very probably be much greater than if a large commercial laboratory was producing rock-plants.

Rock-gardening enthusiasts should also be encouraged by the success that some of their amateur counterparts have had with multiplying rock plants by micropropagation and using it for virus-free plant production. The techniques provide a very stimulating hobby and without the financial considerations faced by a commerical organisation, the amateur may specialise in the culture of highly desirable rock-plants and propagate them in sufficient numbers to satisfy his or her own requirements and perhaps even be able to pay for the hobby by selling surplus plants.

REFERENCES

Anderson, P.G. (1986). 'Micropropagation of woody plants'. *Micropropagation in horticulture* (Ed. Alderson, P.G. & Dullforce, W.M.). Proc. Inst. Hort. Sym., Univ. Nottingham, March 1986.

Alderson, P.G. & Dullforce, W.M. (1986). *Micropropagation in horticulture*. Proc. Inst. Hort. Sym., Univ. Nottingham, March 1986.

35   *Primula pedemontana* (see page 123)

36 *Tropaeolum myriophyllum* is a plant that has adapted to living in screes (see page 148)

37 *Astragalus pennatus* is one of the many astragalus that dominate the cushion steppes of Turkey (see page 149)

38   *Chaetanthera villosa* is a plant of the volcanic Llaima (see page 151)

39   *Senecio* exist in both Turkey and the Andes, this is *S. subdiscoideus* from the latter (see page 147)

40   *Trillum simile* (see page 167)

41   *Trillium erectum* (see page 160)

Barbieri, C. & Morini, S. (1987). *Agario, 43*, 73–74.

Ellis, P.R., Entwistle, A. & Walkey, D.G.A. (in press). *Pests and diseases of alpine plants*. Alpine Garden Society.

Gamborg, O.L., Miller, R.A., & Ojima, K. (1968). *Experimental cell research, 50*, 151–158.

Howard, B.H. (1986). 'Micropropagation in horticultural perspective'. *Micropropagation in horticulture* (Ed. Alderson, P.G. & Dullforce, W.M.) Proc. Inst. Hor. Sym., Univ. Nottingham, March 1986.

Hu, C.Y. & Wang, P. J. (1983). 'Meristem, shoot tip, and bud cultures'. *Handbook of plant cell culture*. Vol. 1' (Ed. Evans, D.A. *et al*). Macmillan, New York, pp. 1–970.

Jaynes, R.A. (1988). *American nurseryman, 167*, 29–32.

Morel, G.M. & Martin, C. (1952) C.R. Hebd. *Seances Acad. Sci. 235*, 1324–5.

Marashige, T. & Skoog, F. (1962). *Physiologia Plantarum, 15*, 473–97.

Norton, M.E. & Norton, C.R. (1988). *Acta Hort., 227*, 450–452.

Nyland, G. and Goheen, A.C. (1969). *Ann. Rev. Phytopath., 7*, 331–54.

Olszowska, O. & Furmanowa, M. (1987) *Polonica, 33*, 137–144.

Short, K.C. (1986). 'Pathways of regeneration in cultures and their control.' *Micropropagation in horticulture* (Ed. Alderson, P.G. & Dullforce, W.M.) Roc. Inst. Hort. Sym, Univ. Nottingham, March 1986.

Simpkins, I., Walkey, D.G.A. & Neely, H.A. (1981). *Ann. Appl. Biol., 99*, 161–9.

Tomlinson, J.A. (1982). 'Chemotherapy of plant viruses and virus diseases' *Pathogen, vectors and plant diseases* (Ed. Harris, K.F. & Maramorosch, K.) Academic Press, London, pp. 23–44.

Walkey, D.G.A. (1991). *Applied plant virology*. Chapman & Hall, London, pp. 1–338.

Walkey, D.G.A. & Webb, M.J.W. (1970). *J. Gen. Virol., 7*, 159–66.

Withers, L.A. and Alderson, P.G. (1986). *Plant tissue culture and its agricultural application*. Butterworths, London, 1–526.

ACKNOWLEDGEMENTS

I wish to thank Mr Peter Abery and Mr John Forrest for giving information about the species they had micropropagated.

Two Hemispheres – Like and Unlike

JOHN WATSON

YESO Y QUESO (SPANISH) – TEBEŞIR VE PEYNIR (TURKISH)*

Certain phenomena invite comparison, perhaps because of startling similarities where none was expected, or the opposite, dramatic differences, but with some common factor. In our field the existence of giant alpines throughout most of the mountains closest to the equator is an example of the former: senecios, lobelias, echiums, silverswords, espeletias and puyas. The latter may perhaps be characterized by rejection of the dominant and brilliant blues of most Eurasian and several Australasian gentians by Andean 'gentians' (strictly speaking *Gentianella* now) in favour of scarlets, crimsons, pinks, yellows and oranges.

These are obvious enough. On the other hand, how many symposiums have been organized, how many series of articles, books even, have been commissioned, all devoted to the subject of alpines of the world? Knowledgeable collectors, travellers or 'endemic' experts are each invited to contribute a section about their particular neck of the woods. However the audience or readership is largely left to form its own opinion, if any, as to the contrasts or similarities between the various assembled floras. Might there not be a variety of potential benefits if someone set out to make conscious comparisons? What follows is one man's attempt to find out, based on considerable personal experience in two widely separated mountainous regions: the Near East, centred on Anatolia (Turkey-in-Asia), and the temperate Andean zone, with Chile as the core.

Subtle comparisons between the floras of these two areas were the last thing on our minds for a long time. After all, we had deliberately chosen to switch to the Andes for the very reason that its alpines differed so radically from those of Turkey (which were perhaps becoming over-familiar at that time to enthusiasts who support seed collectors). Two or three isolated facts did register: to begin with the ludicrous existence of bog-standard dandelions among both choice alpine floras. Then there was the obvious and remarkable ecological convergence between Andean *Barneoudia major* and

*Chalk and cheese, in case you are still wondering.

its fellow in the Ranunculaceae from Eurasia, *Eranthis hyemelis*. As we saw them, both were the first alpines to emerge and flower in the 'stodgy pudding' zone around the melting snow of earliest spring. And they were very close indeed, the only apparent fundamental difference being the dispersal of *B. major* by wind-borne parachute achenes. Its range of colouration, including copper, was welcome but less significant. A bizarre and improbable chance discovery by torchlight of dwarf fritillaries late at night in the Andes after a harrowing drive back down a mountain pass under pressure from snow storms and mountain sickness provides the final example. They grew but a few inches high, with upright open bells of brownish orange to greenish yellow and spotted violet-red on all segments. *Fritillaria minima* from Turkey was the closest reference. In the sober reassessment of daylight, these 'fritillaries' turned out to be alstroemerias, *A. versicolor* (syn. *A. xanthina*)! The scarcity of truly alpine bulbs in South America, in conditions of climate and habitat where they would have existed in variety elsewhere, also registered strongly with us.

These few exceptions aside, we seldom considered the mainly exotic, largely self-contained flora of the Andes in terms of that of Turkey, with its numerous familiar influences and genera. In truth we were more obsessed and fascinated by all manner of other general human and natural contrasts between our chosen venues.

European and Caucasian elements feature strongly in the Pontic alps of Anatolia, becoming ever more concentrated towards the extreme north eastern corner, Lazistan, with Balkan to the west, as well as much Mediterranean adjacent to all coastlines, even small enclaves along the Black Sea. The major contribution though originates from the Irano-Turanian or central steppe flora. There are even occasional distant resonances of the Himalaya. As a result most of Turkey's principle genera at least, if not many species, appear extremely familiar to us, to the extent that many of our common weeds find a natural second home there. Only now and again will our tongues stumble across some local booby trap such as *Tchihatchewia isatidea* or *Rhynchocorys elephas*. By contrast any external influences as may be perceived in the Andean flora scarcely compete with the wealth of its endemic genera. Most evident is a pan-American connection in *Mimulus, Sisyrinchium, Oenothera* and the Cactaceae, though the likes of *Ourisia, Acaena, Pratia* and *Colobanthus* point up a strong Australasian continuity. However, it is home-grown *Nototriche, Loasa, Caiophora, Adesmia, Trechonaetes, Calceolaria, Chaetanthera* & Co. that form the backbone. A smattering of cosmopolitan genera graces both lists. Some, such as most *Ranunculus, Arenaria* and *Erigeron* scarcely differ across the 10,000km (6000 miles) of land and ocean. Yet *Viola, Senecio* and *Caltha* may be so unalike between one flora and the other as to be scarcely recognizable as such close relatives. But statistically, for every alpine genus they have in common, each area has at least two or three not found in the other. Actual shared

147

species are almost non-existent (*Armeria maritima* being the only example to spring immediately to mind).

Both countries have very high levels of endemic plants, that is any not occurring outside their national borders. This may be attributed largely to their mountainous and otherwise quite isolated terrains. Of some 5200 species in Chile, at least 50% are endemics, whilst more than 30% of Turkey's 8600 odd are, thus contributing to another curious coincidence: an almost identical count of just over 2600 for each. If we broaden our concept beyond mere political boundaries to encompass more complete blocks of mountains, say the Caucasus, parts of Iran and Iraq and the Lebanon for the Near East and adjacent Argentina for the temperate Andes, there is some significant increase for the former but the latter reaches a dramatic total of endemism. The reason for this is that in recent geological time the Andean flora has had virtually nowhere to come from or migrate to, except up and down its own chain, and so has developed in relative isolation. Such information may be valuable in helping to assess the potential for continuing plant introductions, and many fine endemic examples from both areas feature strongly in our gardens and literature to act as encouragement: *Primula davisii*, *Lamium armenum*, *Alkanna aucheriana*, *Origanum amanum*, *Salvia caespitosa* from one, *Oxalis adenophylla*, *Calceolaria uniflora*, *Tropaeolum tricolorum*, *Oreopolus glacialis* and *Calandrinia caespitosa* (*rupestris*) from the other.

Another common factor is the remarkable range of geographical and climatic conditions to be experienced in both regions. For Turkey this is largely due to complex relationships with the variety of surrounding land and sea masses and the diverse weather systems they induce. The southern Andes present a simpler picture. Apart to some extent from its mirror image in North America, no other truly major mountain range runs continuously at sheer right angles to the lines of latitude, bisecting one climate zone after another from the wet and chilly subantarctic to the hot dry Atacama. The predominance of sea in the southern hemisphere, and in particular the effect of the cold Humboldt current, are basic modifying influences. As a result, conditions in Turkey are more kaleidoscopic, whilst those of the Andes take on the sequence of a regular spectrum.

Many of these broad climatic conditions and the plants that have evolved to exploit them find rough, but quite noticeable parallels. Desert Meso-potamia and the central salt lakes of the Anatolian plateau find their approximation in the Atacama and the driest parts of Patagonia. These arid to sterile lands, home of tenacious xerophytes, even cacti, and fleeting brilliant floral displays after rare rainfall, attract us mainly for their spectacular, if doubtfully hardy bulbs; *Sternbergia clusiana*, crocuses, col-chicums and biarums from Mesopotamia and various alstroemerias, rho-dophialas, leucocorynes, conantheras and *Zephyra elegans* from Pacific coastal oases. 'Hedgehog' and cushion steppe occurs frequently throughout

inland Turkey, Iran and adjacent countries. It is totally dominated [
innumerable low shrubby *Astragalus* species, but may also including su(
desiderata as globularias, acantholimons, *Daphne oleoides*, *Convolvul*
boissieri ssp. *compactus* and *C. assyriacus*. The Andean equivalents, whilst
from utterly different genera, often present a strikingly similar effect:
Mulinum, *Azorella*, *Chuquiraga*, *Adesmia*, verbenas in the broad sense,
Anarthrophyllum, including *A. desideratum*, *Perezia lanigera (sessiliflora)* and
Gutierrezia baccharoides. Also with matching examples on the two continents, but with floras simply too varied and prolific to list, are alpine steppe
and low to high Mediterranean type vegetation profiles. Wooded or grassy
areas of high rainfall predominate in the northeast of Turkey and occur from
the Andean lake district southwards. Certain landscapes remain wholly
unique to each, the dramatic South American cinder cone volcanoes;
Turkey's numerous and rich limestone alps; the sweeping grassland plains
of Armenia and Kurdistan; and the subantarctic alpine coastal and glacier
zone of Fuegia and Patagonia.

Perhaps exact habitat parallels tell us as much as anything about the
needs of different plants. Adaptations to screes tend to have common factors
such as long running anchor rhizomes or dense powerful tubers, stems that
can stand deep burial or convert to roots, large robust seeds and a structure
able to withstand being disturbed or damaged to some considerable extent
in such an unstable environment. All these features are to be found in the
Turk's *Vavilovia (Pisum) formosa*, *Ricotia davisiana* and various lamiums,
notably *L. armenum*, and their counterparts *Tropaeolum polyphyllum*,
Alstroemeria spathulata, *Oreopolus macranthus* and numerous chaetantheras,
(e.g. *C.renifolia*, *C. villosa*). Other alpines require the sudden heavy flush of
water after dormancy followed shortly by a prolonged spell of summer
ripening associated with persistent snowdrift melt conditions. Specific
examples include high alpine bulbs of Turkey; *Fritillaria minima*, *F.
minuta*, gageas and crocuses, and most of the Acaules section of Andean
calandrinias, especially *C. affinis*, *C. occulta* and the rare and delicate *C.
colchaguensis*, as well as several of the sisyrinchiums and their choice little
allies *Chamelum frigidum* and *C. rubellum*. Chasmophytes, rock-face
dwellers, provide us with many irresistible opportunities, especially for our
alpine houses. The Near East, with its abundance of outcropping limestones, is better stocked in these: *Asyneuma compactum*, *A. linifolium*, *A.
pulvinatum*, *Gypsophila aretioides*, *Primula davisii*, the dionysias and several
alkannas. But the Andes has its response in *Ourisia microphylla*, *O. polyantha*
(could we but find it!), *Junellia (Verbena) uniflora*, several of the tiniest
caiophoras, among them orange *C. rahmeri* and, surprisingly, even a
saxatile calceolaria, *C. lepidota*.

Dramatic dissimilarities between the floras need little underlining. You
have only to look at them. Why and how they come about might be a more
interesting avenue to explore. Certain formative processes have been hinted

at already: the inheritance of surrounding elements by the Turkish flora and the development through isolation of much of its own by the Andes. Pollinators play a major part in the evolution of flower structures and colours. *Alkanna aucheriana*, *Onosma nanum*, *Omphalodes luciliae*, *Gentiana septemfida*, *Veronica orientalis*, *V. thymoides*, *V. telephifolia*, *Asperula orientalis* and sometimes *Salvia caespitosa*: a famous few of Turkey's many important or highly desired blue flowers which shade back into a legion of lavenders, mauves and allied tints. All are aimed at insect pollinators, particularly bees, whose vision is highly tuned to these hues. Occasional lurid, grotesque or distinctive flowers in hot reddish, brown, purple or maroon shades at the opposite end of the spectrum, often extremely smelly as well, *Biarum bovei* and *Aristolochia maurorum*, for example, also seek to induce insects to visit them. They bamboozle carrion flies and wasps or dung midges into thinking they have found a tasty feast rather than actually providing them with one. Otherwise bright red alpines (*Sedum sempervivum*) in Turkey are almost as rare, but not quite, as good blue Andeans (*Gentianella ottonis* and back to *Tecophilea* again). Giant humming birds pollinate the spectacular giant *Puya raimondii* of Peru. More surprisingly, many species of hummers inhabit the Andes between Venezuela and the tip of Tierra del Fuego, from the hot low foothills to the edge of the eternal snows. With their long probing beaks and particular response to reds and oranges and even electric blues and greens, they provide an immediate explanation for many of the more exotic and unlikely Andean alpines (as well as several North Americans): bomareas, the red tubes of bulbous *Phycella ignea*, scarlet *Mutisia subulata*, orange caiophoras, the colour of *Mimulus cupreus*, and perhaps even the bold and exciting red variant of *Calandrinia caespitosa* (*rupestris*). Some helmet-shaped, long-spurred tropaeolums enjoy such a close symbiotic relationship with these tiny birds that nesting is actually synchronous with the peak flowering period, the hummers migrating ever higher as tropaeolums appear progressively from under the snowmelt. Even the distributions of bird and flower are virtually identical. In some moist places it is possible to see ourisias such as *O. alpina*, *O. nana* or *O. suaveolens* with pink 'Eurasian' style flowers for insects, and literally alongside them the scarlet tubes of *O. racemosa*, *O. fuegiana* or *O. coccinea*, advertising for humming birds. One other large and unmistakable genus fashioned by local pollinators in the Andes is *Calceolaria*. These tie in with a particular large species of bees which respond to their different shapes and patterns of pouches and are often rewarded with gum from a special gland in the flower.

I simply cannot resist the temptation to wallow in an idiosyncratic personal comparison between two all-time favourite mountains, Kaz Dağ, ancient Mt Ida, and Volcán Llaima, known simply to its devotees as 'The Llaima'. Here we are down to a subtle comparison between 'feel' and atmosphere, some magical quality about the personality of certain mountains (yes, you *can* wax quite anthropomorphic) that endears them to visitors, at least ourselves, above all others. The fact that they contain many favourite flowers, not least prime objectives successfully in the bag, helps, but does not fully explain their special attraction. Like many of life's greatest joys, this appeal seems deceptively simple, but is really compounded from a great many perfectly interfacing features. Of common factors, both mountains stand isolated, their scale intimate rather than massive or intimidating. They owe a colossal debt to their respective treelines of *Pinus nigra* ssp. *pallasiana* and *Araucaria araucana*, which at once soften them, whilst adding much dimension and character. Indeed, the National Park on the Llaima is named after the Chilean for its monkey-puzzles 'Las Paraguas' (the umbrellas). My definition of heaven could easily be to spend eternity on either in warm sunshine at the height of their flowering season (with the right people, music, etc., naturally). Hell might consist of nothing more than having to choose between them! As far as the first is concerned, those gods perched up there looking down on Troy and occasionally poking their fingers into human affairs knew a thing or two. A sweeping view of dark pine silhouettes against a whiteness of marble and soft mists. If they had a hand in selecting their own rich tapestry of flowers to clothe the flattened summit marbles, one might perhaps only be surprised that they had neglected to include heavenly gentians, but maybe they were only saving these for nearby Olympus. We had been drawn there by mouth-watering herbarium specimens of *Dianthus erinaceus* ssp. *alpinus*, which to our delight turned out to be a summit dominant, even with pure white forms, a fierce little hedgehog among the wiry fescues in springy balding peat meadows. But we hung around to be as enchanted by *D. anatolicus*, *D. arpadianus*, *Centaurea parolinii*, *C. athoa*, *Asperula sintenisii*, *Linum boissieri*, endemic *Jasione idaea*, *Colchicum boissieri*, and *Allium kurtzianum* (our introduction, for so long known erroneously in cultivation as *A. olympicum*), among many fine others. Martyn Cheese swore we were always accompanied there by the shades of those magnificent botanical men in their stove pipe hats, Boissier, Sintenis, Parolin & Co, who were the first to lay claim to this paradise for science. According to my eternity theory, he could well have been right. An equally delectable objective first drew us to the Llaima, the tiny yew-like shrublet, *Viola fluehmannii*, kindly brought to our notice by the late Dr Carleton Worth. Here was a more extensive flora from its colourful basement meadows of white *Chloraea speciosa* orchids, alstroemerias and rhodophialas, up through its nothofagus woods and shrublands and along the fiery embothrium heaths and cinderfields to the final ring of araucarias and fescue meadows, where the viola sheltered, and where skiers or plant-hunters in their different seasons prepared for ultimate revelation and ecstasy above the tree line. For the plant-hunter this came in the irresistible silvery-silky form of *Chaetanthera villosa*, parading her matchless great golden-orange daisies over the brick-red and black cinder screes. Or was it *Viola cotyledon*? Or even *Adesmia longipes*, she of the auburn-haired seed pods? Not to mention *Nassauvia lagascae*, *Chloraea magellanica* or *Pozoa vulcanica*. So easy to neglect to look up, amidst all this wealth at your feet, and surrender yourself for an eternal moment or two to the awe-inspiring dazzling snow-clad cone, gigantic at this proximity and towering into the blueness: in fact almost half the height of the mountain.

The choice of these two widely separated mountain regions has been purely arbitrary, of course. I just happen to have spent a lot of time working in them and nowhere much else. Whether many of the points of comparison are no more than freakish co-incidence, or whether it would be possible to review other areas in the same light, requires further thought by someone with experience complimenting mine. And whether anything practical might be derived from the juxtapositions I have made is equally specu-lative. There is little particularly evocative or descriptive here: for most of the plants listed you must seek that elsewhere. But we plant hunters are always being admonished for our flowery travelogues and exhorted to make more points on how the material we bring back should be grown. So it occurs to me there might always be something to be gained from an awareness that certain plants come from identical habitats or have evolved in a similar way, however far apart they may be geographically. For supposing you can already grow one such, it must surely offer you clues as to how to cope with the others, when and if they come your way.

The American Trilliums

FREDERICK W. CASE, JR.

Trilliums occur in various regions of North America and in eastern Asia, with most taxa known from North America. Our trilliums are woodland plants, primarily, and even the rare ones of very limited geographic range may abound in a favoured habitat.

Wildflower enthusiasts and gardeners hold trilliums in special reverence and they are among the best known and loved of our native wildflowers. Their common names reflect the place these plants held in the lives of early rural Americans: Mayflower, wet-dog trillium, toadshade, bloody-noses, birthwort, wake-robin, woods-lily, little sweet Betsy, stinking Benjamin. In our eastern deciduous woodlands, especially, trilliums dominate the spring floral show.

TAXONOMY AND STRUCTURE

Most botanists place trilliums in the Lily Family (*Liliaceae*), while some argue that the unlike sepals and petals and the net-veined leaves justify establishment of a separate family, the *Trilliaceae*, for these remarkable plants. Into the same family botanists place the American genera *Scoliopus* and *Medeola*, as well as the Eurasian genus *Paris*. Beyond that, botanists do not agree on the number or the distinctness of the species. This is due, in part, to the limited number of structural features present, and in part to the effects of hybridization, although mention of trillium hybrids in the literature is rare.

Trilliums fall structurally into two distinctive subgenera, *Trillium* L. subgenus *Trillium*, the pedunculate trilliums, with the flowers borne upon a stalk or peduncle above the unmottled green leaves, and *Trillium* subgenus *Phyllantherum* Raf., the sessile-flowered trilliums, in which the flower sits directly upon the leaves, has usually erect petals, and leaves mottled with various shades of green and bronze.

To my knowledge, *Phyllantherum* trilliums grow only in North America, and the group is generally considered to be more advanced than subgenus *Trillium* (Freeman, 1975).

While earlier botanists generally only confused the situation, we think that John Freeman, in *Brittonia*, Vol. 27, No. 1, January–March, 1975, pp. 1–62, 'Revision of *Trillium* subgenus *Phyllantherum*', did a superior job of distinguishing the structure and distribution of the sessile trilliums. He admits that what he treats therein as 'species' may indeed be at some other taxonomic level. His 'species', however, seem to accurately reflect what my wife and I have seen in wild American populations.

Nobody seems to agree on the taxonomy of the pedunculate trilliums, and a definitive taxonomic treatment of subgenus *Trillium* to my knowledge does not exist. Species like *T. grandiflorum* (Michaux) Salisb. are clearly distinct, but species related to *T. flexipes* Raf. or *T. erectum* L. cannot always be clearly assigned to one species or the other. At times, the reason for this is clearly due to hybridization between species, but at other times, local populations do not seem to fit any established species and the reasons are not readily apparent. Usually, however, such perplexing populations occur at or near the geographical contact zone between *T. flexipes* and one or more related species. Thus most of these difficult to place populations probably represent complex hybrid swarms.

THE TRILLIUM PLANT

Structurally, all trilliums grow from an underground more or less horizontal rhizome. In some species, the rhizome is clearly elongated and fleshy-brittle. *Trillium lancifolium*, for instance, is nearly impossible to extract from its gummy substrate without breaking the brittle rhizome. In some species, the rhizome is compact, almost bulb-like.

True leaves are not produced, rather, the 'stem' is a highly modified flowering peduncle produced from buds along the subterranean rhizome. What appear as leaves are actually modified floral bracts, now adapted to substitute for the leaves in photosynthesis.

In sessile trilliums, the bracts (henceforth referred to as leaves) are mottled in interesting, sometimes dramatic patterns of bronze or dark maroon with overlays of frosty blue-green tones. These patterns generally become faded and more and more obscure as the leaves age. What function the colour patterns serve is unknown.

In the pedunculate trilliums, the leaf colours are rich, apple or forest greens, without mottling. Leaves of *T. grandiflorum*, *T. undulatum*, and the various subspecies of *T. pusillum* and *T. catesbyi* contain an overlay of dark maroon pigment, especially early in the season.

Trillium fruit is a fleshy, sometimes juicy berry. In many of the pedicillate trilliums, the berry flesh is pink, red, or occasionally dark maroon-red, and smells delicately fruity. In sessile trilliums, the berry is smaller, drier, but still fleshy, and not particularly fragrant. Inside the berry are many hard-coated seeds the size of a fat sesame seed, each possessing a light-coloured, oily, tail-like projection, the elaiosome. The seeds are myrmecochorous, that is, the elaiosome contains oils exceedingly attractive to ants which in collecting seeds for the oil disperse them. The insects often cannot wait until the fruits fall to get at the seeds, but instead, eat holes into the ripening fruits and remove all the seeds before the berry falls.

Ants apparently eat only the fleshy seed coat tail (eliaosome) discarding the rest of the seed in piles in their tunnels, where it later germinates. In our garden, ants seem indiscriminate, and clusters of seedlings consisting of individuals of several species appear regularly.

According to Norm Deno (personal communication) who as many rock gardeners know is currently researching seed germination, trillium seed must never completely dry out or it loses its viability. We have had some long-stored and fairly dry seed germinate, but the rate was very low.

SEED GERMINATION

To grow trilliums from seed requires some patience, for the seeds appear to possess a double dormancy. In reality, the seeds must undergo a proper temperature regimen over a period of two seasons. Following a period of cool, then cold, then warming temperatures (corresponding to soil temperatures in autumn, winter, and early spring) germination occurs, but only the root portion of the shoot develops and penetrates deeper into the earth. The rest of the embryo plant remains inside the seed coat, digesting stored food and differentiating. Before a leaf appears above ground, another temperature regimen of warm, cooling, and cold must take place. Upon a warming following the second cold period, in the spring of the second season, a single, tiny, narrow leaflet appears above the ground. Each year thereafter, if the plant is fortunate, the leaflet enlarges, reflecting increased food storage. After two or three years above ground, sometimes earlier, the three leaflets characteristic of the trillium plant are produced. It takes several more years for the plant to build a mature rhizome and stores food before first flowering. Thus, from five to seven years elapse from seed germination to first bloom in the wild. Fertilizers speed maturation. One can also hurry the process by carefully subjecting the seedlings to condensed and extra growth and dormancy periods, but it is a lot of bother, and most gardeners will not want to do it.

STEM DORMANCY

There is a popular belief among American conservationists and nature enthusiasts, that picking a trillium kills it. This is simply not true. The confused belief is based partly on fact and partly upon observational error. It is true that if a trillium stem is picked (or damaged or grazed), no new stem or leaves will appear again that season.

Once a given rhizome bud sends up a shoot, any growth from other buds on that rhizome becomes inhibited and made dormant through the action of hormones produced by the growing stem. The action is effective until that stem dies back *and* another period of low temperatures passes. A healthy, mature plant will produce a normal leaf the following season, if picked. It may even flower. Of course, no plant depending upon photosynthesis can survive removal of its leaves season after season.

American deer love to eat trillium leaves in early spring. In the wild and in our garden, plants have suffered. On one 300 acre estate in North Carolina, thousands of trilliums disappeared naturally in the years immediately following an increase in the deer herd in the region.

PROPAGATION METHODS

Because maturation from seed takes so many years, there has been much interest in applying tissue culture techniques to reproduce favoured trillium clones. Such attempts have generally proved unsatisfactory utilizing mature plants because the rhizome becomes invaded by soil fungi (perhaps symbiotic or beneficial in the wild) which multiplies and destroys tissue cultures in vitro. When this problem is overcome, propagation of special clones and rare species will be extensive.

The home gardener, today, can multiply plants fairly well by carefully disbudding the large terminal bud on a rhizome. The best time for this seems to be just after flowering is completed. Disbud the plant and replant the rhizome. Lacking the terminal bud and its inhibiting hormones, long dormant buds along the rhizome will develop into offset 'bulblets'. Another method suggested by some is to girdle the rhizome completely a distance behind the large bud. The effect is the same, but more often invites the possibility of the rhizome rotting. I would experiment for some time on my less valuable plants to perfect my method before trying it on my only fine double.

AMERICAN TRILLIUM SPECIES

In North America, trilliums grow in two rather distantly separated areas, the Coastal, Sierra Nevada, and Cascade Mountain regions of our West Coast, from near San Luis Obispo, California, northward into Canada and Vancouver Island, and extending inland to Idaho, Montana, and Colorado. The larger area is most of the forested portions of eastern North America east of the Great Plains and south of a line from southern Manitoba to Newfoundland.

In my talk and this paper, we shall follow the taxonomic usage of

Freeman (1975) for the sessile trilliums. For the pedunculate species, we follow various authors and our own field experience, but I do not in any sense intend this paper to be taken as a taxonomic work: rather, we are attempting to lay out to rock gardeners and plant enthusiasts, the types of plants which occur in nature, no matter their exact taxonomic status.

In the tables, I present a listing of the American trillium species by broad region. Several far-ranging species occur in areas larger than 'my' regions. Generally, I detail them only once on the table, in the 'region' where they are most abundant. In other areas where they occur, I merely list them.

Because North America has so many trilliums, and because of the space constraints in this paper, I do not discuss the companion plants, merely append a list of useful native species to grow with our trilliums.

Western American species (Table 1.)
Most western trilliums are sessile-flowered, and most of these were formerly known collectively under the name *Trillium sessile* var. *californicum* Torrey, especially by horticulturalists. This name has no botanical legality, and *T. sessile* L. *does not* occur in the western United States. Freeman's treatment of the sessile-flowered species of the West seems accurate.

In an abstract of a lecture presentation such as this, it is impossible to present much detail when so many species are involved. Therefore, I present, in tabular form, a few significant details of each species.

Eastern American Species (Table 2.)
With more species distributed over a larger area, designating regions of occurrence of selected species becomes more difficult. The regions given are my own usage, based at least in some degree upon natural regional groupings according to climate or soil needs, and in part so that members of this conference not closely familiar with the regions of the United States can know the approximate range of each species. Several far-ranging species occur in several of my 'regions'. Again, I list them only once with details, in other areas merely give the names.

COLOUR VARIATION

Most trilliums, while variable, have a characteristic colouring. Base colours in the pedunculate trilliums tend toward whites, often aging to deep rose before the petals fall. *T. rivale* frequently produces madder-purple or deep rose red flecks over its base white colour. Occasional individuals have flecking over most of the petal making the plant striking indeed!

T. undulatum bears an inverted 'V' of red on each white petal, but colour-free individuals and paler colourings occur.

Sessile trilliums generally appear in dark maroon reds, brownish-purples

Table 1 Western Species

Name	Distribution	Features	Habitat	Michigan winter-hardiness
Pedunculate species:				
T. ovatum Pursh.	Santa Cruz, Cal. N onto Vancouver Id., inland to western Montana, Colorado	Slender and less robust version of *T. grandiflorum*, generally, but not always with narrower petals. Petals less ruffled.	Deep woods, both conifer and deciduous. Much humus.	Not reliable
var. *hibbarsonii* (of Hort.)	Vancouver Id. B.C.	a dwarf form of exposed headlands. 7.5–18cm (3–7in) tall.	Woods, headlands along ocean.	unknown
T. rivale Wats. One of the very finest for horticulture.	Siskiyou Mts of N. Calif. and S. Oregon	small, to 10cm (4in) tall, leaves petiolate, sometimes with white tessellations on veins. Petals broad, short, flower almost round, pure white or flecked and streaked basally with madder or maroon purple. Very beautiful!	Open, rocky woods, grassy sunny glades & around shrubs and stumps.	needs winter protection
Sessile species:				
T. angustipetalum (Torey) Freeman	Southern Coastal Ranges & Central and Southern Sierra Nevada Mts California	Very large leaves, umbrella-like. Tall 30–50cm (12–20in) petals clear maroon-red, to 10cm (4 in), very narrow.	moist ravines in chaparral, oak woods.	moderate with protection
T. albidum Freeman. Very good	San Francisco Bay area north into Oregon & Washington State? (see next species)	Medium height, large leaves, obscurely mottled. Petals white, cuneate or diamond-shaped, acute tipped, ovary always white, petals occasionally with rose-bases or veins.	streambanks, rich flat-woods in mts.	hardy

Species	Distribution	Description	Habitat	Hardiness
T. parviflorum Soukup.	Northern Oregon, Washington State (the northern race of *T. albidum* in Freeman)	moderate size, shorter, narrow white petals (than *albidum*)	Coniferous & mixed forests.	unknown
T. chloropetalum (Torrey) Howell var. *chloropetalum*	Mts surrounding & S. of San Francisco Bay	Moderate size & leaf spread, to 50cm (20in) tall. Petals liver brown, yellow-green to deep purple.	Wooded ravines, moist slopes	moderate, best to protect
var. *giganteum* (Hook. & Arn.) Munz.	San Francisco Bay region and slightly north.	Well-marked leaves, tall, robust, to 60cm (24in). Petals maroon-purple greenish-white, pink, rose. If white, ovary with rose colouring.	Oak woods, brushy stream banks, river bluffs and flats.	moderate
T. kurabayashii Freeman	Northern California, S. Oregon, Sierra Nevada Mts (north)	Robust, moderate to tall, mottled leaves. Petals large, diamond-shaped to cuneate, 6–10cm (2.4–4in) long, 2–3cm (0.8–1.2in) wide. Deep red-maroon or dark purple-maroon.	Wooded hillsides, upper floodplain woods, stream ravine woods	unknown, probably moderate
T. petiolatum Pursh. Most untrillium-like in appearance	Eastern Oregon, Washington & Idaho	essentially scapeless, leaves long-petiolate just above ground, narrow-petalled flowers brown-red to green-yellow, at soil surface.	Open woods, often coniferous, meadow borders, around shrubs on palouse prairie.	not reliable

Table 2 Eastern Species

Name	Distribution	Features	Habitat	Michigan winter-hardiness
CANADA, GREAT LAKES STATES AND NEW ENGLAND REGION.				
Pedunculate species:				
T. cernuum L.	Manitoba to Newland, south to Virginia in Mts S. to northern Illinois, Indiana and Ohio.	Flowers declined below leaves. Plant tall, with narrow leaf-spread. Leaves rhombic. Petals white, thin-textured, recurved. Stamen and filament equal, pale to medium lavender purple. Fruit large, rosey red. Petals deep pink or reddish in forma *Tangerae* Wherry.	Moist woods, streambanks, Thuja swamps.	Very, but resents cultivation
T. erectum L. (southern erect form [forma *sulcatum*] often treated as a species)	Newfoundland to Michigan, south eastward to and along Appalachian Mts at higher elevations to Alabama and Georgia. America's most widespread species.	Variable by district; leaves rhombic, plant to 55cm (22in) tall, clump-forming. Flowers erected or declined, esp. northward. Petals dark maroon red, fading purple, yellow, white or greenish. Ovary round, dark purple-black. Flower faintly fetid, of a wet-dog. Early	Neutral to acid soils, upland forests, mixed with conifers, or Thuja swamp borders, not in heavy alluvium.	very easy
T. flexipes Raf. (formerly also called T. gleasonii or T. declinatum)	S. Minnesota across s. Great Lakes region to New York and southward. Barely enters s. Ontario. South in central lowlands to N. Alabama,	Quite variable. Leaves rhombic, robust and tall, to 60cm (24in), leaves widespreading. Flowers erect, or variously declined. Petals flat or recurved, thick-textured, ivory white, rarely coloured.	Neutral to alkaline soil, often on limestone. Lower fertile slopes to floodplains.	very hardy

Species	Distribution	Description	Habitat	Ease
...very abundant in parts of our region and in parts of its Tennessee & Kentucky range, also Alabama		...manifests very short. Fragrant of old roses.		
T. grandiflorum (Michx) Salisb.	Minnesota and Great Lakes region, across Ontario to Quebec, south to N. Illinois, Indiana, Ohio and Pennsylvania. S. along mts to N. Carolina	Large, white, thin-textured but firm petals, widest beyond middle, veined, aging to rose pink. Strongly angled ovary. Double forms, hose-in hose, and other abberrations occur. The green striped and green and white forms with leaf or flower distortions are diseased. The pathogen, a mycoplasma organism, can be vectored to other species. Such plants should not be grown. Can spread.	Deciduous and Pine and Hemlock forests, sandy or rich. Sub-acid to neutral	easy
T. nivale Riddel — Now threatened or endangered in parts of range. Common in some regions. Extremely desirable rock garden plant, easy from seed, and fast maturing.	In a narrow band along S. margin of Pleistocene Glaciation from Maryland to Pennsylvania, Ohio, Indiana, Illinois and Minnesota. Outlying stations in Kentucky, Michigan, Wisconsin, & Nebraska.	Extremely early flowering, often blooming in late snow-falls. Dwarf-5–10cm (2–4in) tall. Leaves short-petiolate, blue-green. Stem 6-angled in cross section. Flower large for plant, petals white, thin, narrow-acute or in Indiana, broadly ovate, Ovary 3-sided.	2-types, limestone crevices and talus, atop boulders and rock detritus, or, highest sandy, gravely flood-plain deposits.	easy
T. undulatum Willd.	Ontario to Quebec, S. to E. Michigan, Pennsylvania and New England, south at high	Late emerging. Leaves petiolate, acute, petals white, each with a dark red 'V' mark. Fruit erect, scarlet.	Very acid rich deep humus, cool soils, in deep shade. Pine,	hardy but difficult

Name	Distribution	Features	Habitat	Michigan winter-hardiness
	elevations in mts to N. Carolina.		Hemlock groves, under *Rhododendron* & *Kalmia*, or low swampy oak-maple woods N.	

Sessile species:

T. recurvatum
T. sessile
T. viride

AMERICAN MIDLANDS; CENTRAL LOWLANDS, MISSISSIPPI VALLEY AND OZARK PLATEAU

Pedunculate species:

T. flexipes
T. pusillum var. *ozarkanum*

Sessile species:

Name	Distribution	Features	Habitat	Michigan winter-hardiness
T. recurvatum Beck.	Illinois to SW Michigan & barely into Ohio, south through Missouri, Arkansas, and N. Louisiana. East into Kentucky, Tennessee, N. Mississippi & N. Alabama.	Lanky plant, leaves petiolate, mottled. Sepals strongly recurved against scape. Petals ovate, clawed below, maroon red, or clear yellow in f. *shayi*.	Rich lowland woods, heavy, fertile soil, riverbanks, flood-plains.	very hardy
T. sessile L.	Very local in Maryland, Virginia, New York, and Pennsylvania. Much more common in Ohio S	Low stature, to 10cm (4in). Leaves sessile, mottled but fading rapidly. Petals brownish red without basal claw, erect. Blooms early. Albinos	On limestone, any forested cover. Or on rich alluvial neutral	easy, very hardy

Species	Distribution	Description	Habitat	Hardiness
	Missouri, but almost absent from Illinois. S. locally to Tennessee & Alabama.			moderately hardy
T. *stamineum* Harbison	Central Tennessee, south to inner Coastal Plain of western Alabama and eastern Mississippi. Locally abundant	Distinct; 20–35cm tall. Leaves sessile, mottled ovate. Petals linear, 2–3cm long, *carried horizontally*, dark purple-maroon, rarely yellow. Stamens large, erect, conspicuous, 2/3 length of petals.	Rich fertile upland woods of oak or tulip, or heavy clay floodplains	
T. *viride* Beck	Northeastern Missouri and adjacent Illinois in Missouri River Valley.	25–40cm (10–16in) tall, lanky. Leaves sessile, narrow ovate, poorly marked, upper surface with stomates throughout (microscopic). Petals thin-linear-lanceolate, clear green, green with maroon base, or rarely all maroon, faintly clawed basally.	Rocky woods, hillsides.	hardy but requires rich soil to keep.
T. *viridescens* Nutt. (Many authors merge this with the above species)	Western Missouri & Arkansas, eastern Oklahomas to Texas.	Similar to above, larger to 45cm (18in) tall. Leaves ovate elliptic, without stomata on upper surface, mottled. Petals green to purple, usually green with purple basal claw, 4–7cm (1.6–2.8in) long, 0.5–1cm (0.2–0.4in) wide.	Alluvial slopes, rich upland woods, floodplains	hardy

WESTERN GULF COASTAL PLAIN, MISSISSIPPI EMBAYMENT

Pedunculate species:

T. *pusillum* var. texanum
(T. *texanum*)

163

Name	Distribution	Features	Habitat	Michigan winter-hardiness
Sessile species:				
T. foetidissimum Freeman	Upper coastal plain of E. Louisiana and W. Mississippi	Short, 9–25cm (3.5–10in) tall, leaves strongly marked, showy. Habit similar to T. sessile. Flowers maroon, petals narrow. Early.	Floodplains, ravine slopes, alluvium.	moderate
T. gracile Freeman	Eastern Texas, western Louisiana	Not distinctive, similar to T. viridescens, and intergrades with it. Flowers purple, petals narrow. Not horticulturally distinct.	Floodplains, heavy soils, often flooded while in flower.	barely so with protection.
T. ludovicianum Harbison	Upper coastal Plain of Louisiana, 1–2 Mississippi stations	Strongly mottled leaves, 15–28cm (6–11in) tall. Petals narrow, curved greenish maroon, purple, rarely yellowish.	Slopes, floodplain ravines, often in deep woods under Beeches.	requires protection
T. cuneatum				
T. decipiens				
T. underwoodii				

EASTERN GULF AND CAROLINA COASTAL PLAINS

Pedunculate species:

Sessile species:

T. decipiens Freeman	S. Alabama, western Florida, W. Georgia on upper Coastal Plain, local.	Tall, stems 2–3 times longer than leaves, leaves lanceolate, brightly mottled, with light central stripe and with dark and bronze tones.	Rich woods in oaks, or low ground along streams.	hardy but in north emerges too early and freezes

Species	Distribution	Description	Habitat	Hardiness
		...long, oblanceolate. Maroon with brown undertones, sometimes aging to orangeish.		
T. maculatum Raf. A fine plant where hardy, best red colour in a sessile Trillium	Inner Coastal Plain from Alabama to S. Carolina and on adjacent Piedmont	Robust, with broad leaf-spread, often with bright leaf colourings, 20–40cm (8–16in) tall. Petals oblanceolate to linear, *spatulate*, spreading, clear deep red maroon rarely lemon yellow.	River bluffs, slopes, and flood plains, rich woods.	needs some protection
T. reliquum Freeman U.S. Endangered, very rare, local. Desirable for rock garden *if* from propagated stock	Two disjunct areas: Southwestern Georgia and along Savannah River near Augusta, Georgia. Rare & local. 1–2 other Alabama sites.	*Semidecumbent*, with weakly reclined stem. Leaves broad, highly marked, with a light central stripe. Flower petals linear lanceolate, brownish red.	River bluffs, ravine slopes near streams. Calcareous soils with Dicentera sp.	fully hardy
T. underwoodii Small	Northwest Florida, Southeast Alabama & Southwestern Georgia north into Piedmont along large rivers	Short, leaf tips often touch ground at flowering. Leaves strongly mottled. Petals narrowly oblanceolate, dark maroon-purple, brownish, or rarely, clear yellow.	rich oak woods, bluffs, slopes, neutral to acidic soil.	poor, needs protection.

UPPER PIEDMONT AND REGION AT SOUTH END OF APPALACHIANS IN ALABAMA, GEORGIA, AND TENNESSEE

Pedunculate species:

Species	Distribution	Description	Habitat	Hardiness
T. catesbyi				
T. erectum (including T. sulcatum)				
T. flexipes				
T. persistens U.S. Endangered, almost extinct. Not a worthy	4–5 square mile region in forests at head of Tallulah Gorge, Ga. and adjacent	10–15cm (4–6in) tall, leaves narrow-lanceolate, petals white, narrow. Similar to *T. catesbyi*, not	*Rhododendron* thickets, open woods under	hardy

Name	Distribution	Features	Habitat	Michigan winter-hardiness
horticultural subject!	S. Carolina	reflexed or declined. Fading rose, but with a white inverted v-shaped patch at base.	*Kalmia*.	
T. pusillum var. *rugellii*				
Sessile species:				
T. decumbens Harbison. A super plant!, most striking of sessile trilliums for the rock garden	Northeastern Alabama, Northwestern Georgia, at south end of the Appalachian Mts abundant in restricted range.	Decumbent, leaves upon ground, showy, darkly mottled. Petals linear-lanceolate, slightly twisted, flame-like, 5–7cm (2–3in) long, deep burgundy maroon, rarely soft yellow. Forms dense colonies. Leaves persist only a few weeks.	Rocky woods, shaley bluffs, flats along small streams.	hardy & easy
T. lancifolium Raf. A most distinctive species	Widely & sporadically occurring, N. Florida, S. & central Georgia, NE Alabama, SE Tennessee, locally into S. Carolina. Commonest along SE edge of Cumberland Plateau in Alabama & Georgia.	All segments narrow, slender. Delicate or robust, 15–30cm tall. Leaves sessile, drooping, mottled. Petals narrow-spatulate or linear 2.5–3.8cm (1–1.5in) long, clawed at base, greenish purple to brown purple, somewhat twisted. Sepals not recurved.	Alluvial woods, slopes, flood-plains, clays.	hardy & easy

CUMBERLAND PLATEAU, AND WEST FLANK OF THE SOUTHERN APPALACHIANS AND BLUE RIDGE MTS OF TENNESSEE AND NORTH CAROLINA.

Pedunculate species:

T. catesbaei

Species	Distribution	Description	Habitat	Hardiness
T. rugellii Rendle	Eastern Tennessee, western North and South Carolina, N. Georgia and Alabama	Leaves rhombic, large. Flowers declined under leaves *on a short pedicle*. Petals white, ovate. Heavy-textured, recurved slightly, except in the Alabama form where petals recurve so strongly the flower suggests Dodecatheon. Stamens dark purple. Flowers fragrant. Colored forms are hybrids.	Rich woods, coves, stream-banks or lower slopes and floodplains.	hardy
T. simile (Gleason) Patrick One of the finest species	Under *Rhododendron* and in coves and sheltered slopes, Smoky Mt. Nat'l Park and S into Georgia, eastward into N. Carolina	Flowers semierect, *large*, stem 20–40cm (8–16in) tall. Leaves rhombic, thick, 10–15cm (4–6in) long, 2–4cm (0.75–1.6in) wide. Not reflexed or wide-spreading ovary round, dark purple	Rich coves and banks in shade of *Rhododendron*, *Kalmia*. Rocky outcrops along streams	hardy
T. sulcatum Patrick (*T. erectum* var. *sulcatum*)	Cumberland Plateau & lower mountain slopes, N. Carolina and east Tennessee	Similar to *T. erectum*, larger, leaves very broad, rhombic, umbrella-like, margins overlapping. Peduncle stiffly erect, flower facing outward at right angles to peduncle. Petals nearly as wide as long, heavy textured, dark smoky-maroon-black to maroon red. Sepals & petals sulcate tipped. Odour faintly fetid.	Rich woods, stream bluffs, often over limestone.	hardy
T. vaseyi Harbison Superb flower, but obscured under leaves	lower elevations, Mts of east Tennessee, western N. and S. Carolina, N. Georgia and NE Alabama	Tall, to 60cm (24in), very large rhombic leaves. Flower declined below leaves. Petals oval to almost sub-orbicular, dark maroon-red in	Deep, sheltered coves or ravines on steep slopes at lower elevations	hardy but resents wind

Name	Distribution	Features	Habitat	Michigan winter-hardiness
		most forms, veined. Whites occur. Largest flowered pedunculate. Faintly fragrant.	in mountains.	
Sessile species:				
T. cuneatum Raf. Best forms make excellent garden plants	Wide-ranging from S. Kentucky & Tennessee and N. Carolina southwestward through S. Carolina Piedmont to Alabama & Mississippi. Best in E. Tennessee	Plant robust, 17–40cm (6.7–16in) tall. Leaves sessile, ovate-elliptic, mottled. Flower sessile, variable. Petals oblanceolate to obovate, cuneate, tips acute-rounded, thick texture. Deep brownish maroon, red, rarely clear green or yellow. Sweetly fragrant.	Woods, bluffs, rocky woods, floodplains, Ordovician limestone soils.	hardy
T. luteum (Muhl.) Harbison.	S. Kentucky, E. Tennessee, western N. Carolina, N. Georgia	Similar to above. Robust, leaves strongly mottled, Petals elliptic-Lanceolate, 4–7cm (1.6–2.75in) long, lemon yellow or greenish yellow, lemon-oil fragrance.	Rich woods, coves, open hillsides on basic soils.	hardy

EAST FLANK OF BLUE RIDGE AND SMOKY MTS & UPPER PIEDMONT, SOUTH AND EAST OF APPALACHIANS

Name	Distribution	Features	Habitat	Michigan winter-hardiness
Pedunculate species:				
T. catesbaei Ell. (*T. catesbyi*, *T. stylosum*)	Piedmont and Mts Virginia, N. & S. Carolina, East Tennessee, Georgia, & Alabama.	Slender, somewhat delicate, 15–40cm (6–16in) tall. Leaves ovate, faintly petiolate, deeply veined, often somewhat raised, exposing the declined flower. Flowers opening white to deep pink, strongly reflexed, petals thin-	Thin open upland acid woods, often under *Kalmia*, or Rich shaded stream flats in	hardy

Name / Distribution	Description	Habitat	Notes
T. pusillum Michaux var. *virginianum* Fernald. var. *ozarkanum* Palmer & Steyerm.	wide, often folded along midvein (keeled) in upland forms. S. Carolina cove form opens pink with larger, flatter petals.	*Leucothoe*, especially in S. Carolina Mts.	hardy, rapid seeder
Islandic occurrence, colonies often remote from one another. In Virginia, N. & S. Carolina, Alabama, Tennessee, Kentucky, Missouri, Arkansas, and Texas.	Plants small, 5–20cm (2–8in) tall, leaves elliptic, tips rounded, dark green with maroon overtones. Flowers white, large for plant, 1.5–2.5cm (0.6–1in) long, 10mm (0.4in) wide, petal margins undulate crisped. Long-pedunculate except in var. *virginianum* which is sessile or subsessile. Blooms early.	Typical var. low swampy ground, flood plain swamps in mildly acidic sometimes peaty soil.	
var. *texanum* Buckl. (other vars. have been proposed) U.S. Threatened Plant *T. rugellii* *T. vaseyi*	Vars. *ozarkanum*, an upland form, and *texanum* often treated as distinct but close species.	var. *ozarkanum*, upland Beech-Oak woods, on cherty shales.	
Sessile species:			
T. discolor Wray ex. Hooker Rare, local, legally protected in some areas. Excellent garden plant, slow to multiply.	Sessile, short, 10–25cm (4–10in) tall. Leaves sessile, 7–12cm (2.75–4.75in) long, elliptic to sub circular, well mottled in greens. Petals erect, spatulate, clawed at base, slightly twisted, apex with a nipple-like tip. Soft sulfur yellow. Late flowering in north in cultivation.	Rich open woods, slopes, ravines, bluffs and on small stream flats.	hardy

Upper Savannah River Drainage in N. Georgia, western N. Carolina & Georgia, only.

or in tones of brownish-green. Many have forms purplish at the base of the petal, grading to green above. In most species green or occasionally clear yellow plants appear. These appear to be 'albinos', that is, there has been a deletion or suppression of the red-purple colour gene (which probably produces an anthocyanin pigment) leaving only the presence of chloroplasts and xanthoplasts, green or yellow, to colour the petals.

Colouring in the *T. erectum* group is complex, but holds much interest and promise for the gardener and hybridizer. *T. erectum*, var. *sulcatum*, and *T. vaseyi* produce dark maroon red flowers. But especially in the first two species, many colour forms, even entire local races occur. The usual yellow-green 'albinos' occur, but so do pink tones, pale lavenders, brown-reds or bicolours. At least two factors, I believe, operate here.

The colours humans see, I believe, consists of several different colour overlays in the petal cells. These various colours are controlled by various genes for presence and other expression or suppression genes, located on various chromosomes. Gene deletion mutations, presence or absence of expression or suppression genes alters the visible petal colour to lighter pinks, rose, red or white tones.

But more is involved. Many plants guide insect pollinators along a specific path to stamens and stigma guidelines of colour in the heart of the bloom. This colour 'bull's eye' can be visible to humans, but often it is not. Insects, however see reflected ultraviolet light we cannot see. Many (to us) unicoloured flowers, when photographed under UV light and proper filters, reveal the 'bull's eye'.

Erectum complex trilliums apparently have the 'bull's eye' but invisible to humans. But when members of this species complex hybridize, strange things happen. Removal of certain colours, by deletion, suppression, random gene distribution, or masking, renders the bull's eye visible. Thus many hybrids possess pale colours distally and a dark flower centre, similar to the painted trillium and very striking. More interesting, a reversed form occurs with the distal petal region dark and the centre white, also very striking. Imagine what hybridization using selected forms for erect flowers, large, well-shaped petals and striking colour patterns can produce!

In our garden there has been an explosion of interesting coloured hybrids and mutants. Some patterns not seen in the wild have appeared.

CULTIVATION

Trilliums grow in woodlands. In my opinion, they look best when grown under woodland conditions, *or the illusion* of woodland conditions. Grow them with other forest species, particularly those with which they grow naturally. For species such as *T. nivale*, a calciphile, you may need to add limestone chips to your soil if it is acid.

Fortunately, as adults, most species will tolerate any generally rich neutral soil, even if the species normally does not grow in it. So, purchased rhizomes, if healthy, will usually grow. Seedlings however, may not appear or survive in the wrong soils. For many, this is not a problem.

Painted trillium (*T. undulatum*) is particularly difficult to cultivate. To grow it, you must excavate an area about a yard square to a depth of 7–8 inches, and remove any neutral or alkaline soil. On the floor of the excavation, place a layer several inches thick of silica sand (sandblaster's sand is ideal). Place the rhizomes on the sand. Cover with a mixture of silica sand, leafmold, and sphagnum peat, pulverized. Mulch the surface with pine needles, heavily. In our warm climates, *T. undulatum* requires heavy summer shade.

Western species prove difficult in eastern middle American climates, but ought to do much better in Great Britain, as that climate is similar to parts of our West Coast. The problem with western and some Gulf Coast species is that they are controlled more by day length than by temperature. During late winter warm spells, they attempt growth, only to be cut down by later freezing conditions.

Trilliums are beautiful and distinctive woodland plants. Clump them, grow them in masses of several species. Use the different species' characteristics to create textures of height, colour and shape. Grow them with native companions. Use the natural rock-dwelling and dwarf species in the rock garden, the larger ones along woodland paths, under shrubs, or in the wildflower garden. They will always create interest and beauty.

Grow your plants from offsets, seedlings, or other propagules. Within a few years tissue culture techniques will provide an abundance even of the rarest species and forms. Most species abound within their natural ranges, so obtaining material (by qualified nurserymen) for propagation and sale need not be vandalism. Hybridize your own new beauties. Enjoy them — you will not be sorry.

OUTSTANDING COMPANION PLANTS FOR TRILLIUMS

Aesculus discolor
A. pavia
Arisaema dracontium
A. stewardsonii
A. triphyllum
Cornus canadensis
Clintonia borealis
C. umbellulata

Cypripedium acaule
C. calceolus var. *pubescens*
C. kentuckiense
Dalibarda repens
Darlingtonia californica
Dentaria sp.
Dicentra canadensis
D. cucullaria

D. eximia
Diphylleia cymosa
Dodecatheon meadia
D. hendersonii
Erythronium, all species.
Ferns, most forest species
Galax aphylla
Haleesia sp.
Hepatica acutiloba
H. americana
Hexastylis shuttleworthii
Hexastylis speciosa
Houstonia sp.
Hydrangea quercifolia
Jeffersonia diphylla
Lysichiton americanum

Mertensia virginica
Mianthemum canadensis
Mitella diphylla
Pachysandra procumbens
Phlox bifida
Phlox divaricata
P. pilosa vars.
Pyrola sp.
Sanguinaria canadensis
Shortia galacifolia
Silene virginica
Staphylea trifolia
Stylophorum diphyllum
Tiarella cordifolia
T. wherryi

REFERENCES

Barksdale, Lane. 1938. 'The Pedicellate Species of *Trillium* found in the Southern Appalachians.' *Journ. Elisha Mitchell Sci. Soc.* 54: 271–296.
Case, F.W., Jr. 1981. 'Eastern American Trilliums, part 1.' *Bull. American Rock Gdn. Soc.* 39: no. 2, pp. 53–67.
    1981 'Eastern American Trilliums, part 2.' *Bull. American Rock Gdn. Soc.* 39: no. 3. pp. 108–122.
    1982. 'The Snow Trillium, *Trillium nivale*, in Michigan.' *Mich. Bot.* 21: 39–44.
Case, F.W., Jr. & Burrows, G.L., IV. 1962. 'The Genus *Trillium* in Michigan. Some Problems of Distribution and Taxonomy.' *Pap. Mich. Acad.* 47: 189–200.
Freeman, John D. 1975. 'Revision of *Trillium* subgenus *Phyllantherum* (*Liliaceae*).' *Brittonia* 27: no. 1, pp. 1–62.
Gates, R.R. 1917. 'A Systematic Study of the North American Genus *Trillium*, its Variability and Its Relation to *Paris* and *Medeola*.' *Annals Mo. Bot. Gdn.* 4: 43–92.
Hooper, G.R., Case, F.W., Jr., & Myers, R. 1971. 'Mycoplasma-like Bodies Associated With a Flower Greening Disorder of a Wildflower, *Trillium grandiflorum*.' *Plant Disease Reporter*, 55: 1108–1110.
Radford, A.E., Ahles, H.E., & Bell, C.R. 1964. *Manual of the Vascular Flora of the Carolinas.* U. of N.C., Chapel Hill. Pp. 289–293.
Steyermark, J.A. 1963. *Flora of Missouri.* Iowa State Univ. Press, Ames. pp. 444–448.

Techniques of Growing Alpines in Sweden

HENRIK ZETTERLUND

INTRODUCTION

A brief history

The cultivation of alpines has a long history in Sweden. It started in Uppsala Botanic Garden, founded in 1655. We know that rock-garden plants, such as *Rubus arcticus* and *Helianthemum oelandicum*, were grown here at an early date. Linnaeus became in charge in 1741. In the Botanic Garden as well as at his private residence, Hammarby, he created special constructions devoted to the cultivation of rock-garden plants. An area at Hammarby was called 'Hortus Sibiricus' and contained plants received from empress Katarina II of Russia. Traces of this remain and some plants, like *Corydalis nobilis* and *Sempervivum soboliferum*, still exist in cultivation from the original collections.

For over 200 years the growing of alpine plants was restricted to botanic gardens. By the late 19th century the Bergius Botanic Garden in Stockholm, as we now know it, was set up in Stockholm. Here an enormous rock-garden was built – 'Wittrock's rock-pile'. It still exists but it is poorly maintained due to financial problems. The Göteborg Botanic Garden (GBT) was not opened to the public until the early 1920s and here alpines have played an important role from the start.

Among private people rock-gardening is a rather recently acquired addiction. A limited *avant garde* started in the beginning of this century. In the late 30s they united and formed the society called Amateur-Gardeners which has now grown to over 2000 members.

Climate

In a country touched by the mild Gulf Stream in the south, cut by the Polar Circle in the north, approximately 2000km (1250 miles) long and 400km (250 miles) wide, the climate can not be expected to be uniform. As I am mainly dealing with Göteborg I must restrict myself to that area.

Briefly, the west-coast, where Göteborg is situated, has a very uncertain climate. The summers are quite cool with a mean temperature for July of

+17°C. Winters are most unreliable! A series of cold winters (−20°C to −26°C) with or without a plant-protecting snow-cover is mostly followed by two or three mild, wet winters with only short periods of snow. Consequently, rock-gardening in the open is at times a depressing struggle.

In the rest of the country the climate for alpines is much better, with a prolonged period of snow in winter.

THE SITUATION OF TODAY

Though we have a long history of growing alpine plants, we can not claim to have made any special contributions to the art. Frankly, most ideas have been stolen from abroad. These have been adapted and changed to suit Swedish conditions.

Generally spoken, Swedish growers grow their plants in the open. The rock-garden, the peat-garden and gradients in between these are the commonest constructions. Walls, sand-beds, raised beds, frames and troughs are used to some extent. Alpine-houses are still rare, though an increasing interest is noticed. In our garden they have been in use since the 1950s.

In time the growers have learnt to master the art of outdoor-cultivation. Some amateurs, particularly those from winter snow-cover areas ('the alpine banana-belt'), are very successful, growing magnificent specimens in the open of plants like *Pleione limprichtii* and *Corydalis cashmeriana*.

THE CULTIVATION OF ALPINES AT GBT

There is a continuous flow of new plants reaching us from other botanic gardens and amateurs throughout the world. The instruments at our disposal for growing these are as follows.

Different kinds of alpine-houses, some used for displaying collections to the public, others for growing the more difficult plants and for propagation. Some of these are kept just frost-free during the winter, others are left to freeze. The bulbs are grown in a special garden in which some beds are covered with glass.

The rock-garden is relatively large and includes different kinds of environments such as peat-walls, sand-beds, bogs and wood-lands.

GROWING UNDER GLASS

Ever since the 1981 AGS conference, which was when our techniques for alpine-house cultivation were lined out, the basics for pot-cultivation have remained unchanged. They have not been adjusted until recently to meet with new times.

Potting-composts

Most plants are very tolerant to a degree of variation of the compost. To make it easier for ourselves we have reduced our assortment to the following standard composts.

	Neutral	Acid
Coarse peat	20l	30l
Clean, coarse sand	20l	20l
Granite chips, 2–5mm	20l	20l
Sterile loam	20l	10l
Composted, fine bark	–	10l
Bone meal	0.15l	0.15l
Dolomite lime	0.08l	0.03l
pH	6.5	5.5
cond. mS/cm	1.3	1.0

These alternatives will do for most purposes. For special plants the composts can be easily adjusted by increasing or reducing the different ingredients. Formerly our *Dionysia*-compost was one part standard, neutral to one part granite chips.

For sowing the composts are the same but devoid of bone meal.

Planting

Young, newly regenerated plants are mostly very vital. After some time in the propagation-line one has to decide which plants will receive the honour of being alpine-house subjects. The selected few are transferred from plastic- to clay-pots in order to meet with the harder times linked with maturity and, later, with senility. The composts mentioned form the base. Normally a lot of granite-chippings is added ($1/3$–$2/3$ of total volume) to help with the drainage and aeration of the substrate.

The items are planted in a way that allows a dressing of granite-chippings on top of the soil. This layer varies according to the neck-length of the plant. The really tricky cushion-plants are normally planted very high so that the compost and the mulch has to bulge from the pot-rim to the cushion-base. This may look weird but improves air circulation in and around the cushion in an invigorating way.

Watering

After planting the pots are plunged in sand and watered with the systemic fungicides Benomyl and Propamocarb that deal with different groups of fungi respectively. Now water is supplied via the sand which is kept moist. As the plants establish and the season is getting warmer the plunge-bed fails to compensate for the water loss. From late May the pots are watered weekly with a weak solution of standard fertilizer to the amount of 1.5 per mille for cushions and other slow growers whereas coarser plants receive a 3 per mille dose. During heat-waves the pots are soaked at least twice a week. The described routine continues through the season until late August when the fertilizer is excluded. From late September we only keep the plunge moist, in winter the sand is kept fairly moist since winter-drought is lethal.

NEW TRIALS

Composts

To grow 'tricky' plants for a few years presents few problems, just 'pump 'em up'. The problems will come, say, after three or four years, at which point you can tell a superb cultivator from a decent one.

The method mentioned earlier works nicely as it allows the plants to be nursed by different people which is necessary in a botanic garden. However, sometimes growth is too prolific. Cushions become lax in growth and more vulnerable to attacks from insects, mite and fungi. They also loose much of their natural look. Because of this we have been looking for alternative techniques.

Inspired by the unorthodox composts used in the Grand Ridge Nursery (WA, USA) and Michael Kammerlander (Würzburg) and their remarkable results, I was convinced that something could be done in Göteborg. When Icelandic Vikur-pumice became available we made some trials that lead to the composition of two basic composts.

	Alkaline 'Dionysia'	Acid 'Raoulia'
Vikur-Pumice	20l	30l
Coarse sand	20l	15l
Bone meal	0.1l	0.1l
Ashes, pref. from deciduous trees	0.05l	0.025l
Peat	–	15l
pH	7.2	5.9
cond. mS/cm	0.7	0.5

Contrary to some other volcanic materials and the artificial Leca, Vikur-pumice absorbs water (roughly equivalent to its own dry-weight). Its main constituents are SiO_2 and Al_2O_3.

These composts have well-composed nutrient-levels. The nutrients are of a slow release fashion and after two years of trial we have not yet added any liquid fertilizer. Growth is very slow but the plants are nicely coloured. The alkaline mix suits *Dionysia* species well and success has finally been achieved with *Viola cotyledon* and *Notothlaspi rosulatum*. The acid one pleases the cushion *Raoulia* species and *Mertensia tibetica*.

42   *Trillium cernuum* (see page 160)

43   *Trillum decumbens* (see page 166)

44   *Trillium albidum* (see page 158)

45   *Astragalus coccineus* growing in tufa at Gothenberg (see page 178)

46   *Mertensia tibetica* growing in an acid mix at Gothenberg (see page 176)

47   *Ranunculus seguieri* in the Dolomites (see page 184)

These mixes dry out fairly quickly. This means that one has to water often but the risk for over-watering is more or less eliminated. So the standard phrase 'if in doubt – don't water' nowadays reads 'if in doubt – water'. To date I can say that the plants look better and are more resistant to botrytis and other pests. But we have only used the composts for two growing-seasons.

The wind-tunnel
Shading is always a problem in the alpine-house. Most alpines require as much light as possible but this can't be provided without scorching the plants, particularly April to early June, before the new foliage has built up the cuticula. After trial we have ended up using a very thin fibre-screen, made from polypropene, found under different trademarks such as Lutrasil, Agryl and Agronet. This gives a pleasant reduction of sun-rays during the hottest days. A problem is that temperature builds up in, and sometimes kill, the plant-tissues. Inhibited air-movement and increased humidity reduces the cooling effect from evaporation.

For many years we have used fans to improve ventilation around the plants, but only in dull weather and at night. To use them in a sunny day seemed contradictory to the purpose. After having the Himalayan poro-phyllum *Saxifraga* scorched and ruined every spring we decided to be drastic.

Wires were put up 1 m above the plunge and a screen-tunnel applied over this. Efficient fans were installed inside. These are now blowing all year round and the shading-curtain is on in sunny days from April to August. The increased cooling effect was very surprising.

THE DISPLAY-HOUSES

Of the green-houses open to the public, one may be of interest here. It has been landscaped to represent different environments and the plants are growing without pot restriction.

'The limestone house'
The house is unshaded and bright, here a wide range of medium to dwarf species dwell in different landscapes. The main area is an indoor rock garden constructed out of limestone. In this the plants are mainly of Mediterranean affinity like *Pancratium illyricum*, *Incarvillea emodii*, *Primula edelbergii*, *Helleborus lividus* and *Paeonia cambessedesii*.

For many years, fruitless efforts were made to find a compost that would suit indoor cultivation of dwarf and cushion plants. Encouraged by the success we had experienced with tufa we gave up soil-mixes and decided to grow all small plants in a tufa-wall, a wise decision it has proved.

The tufa suits most plants: easier *Dionysia* species like *D. tapetodes*, *D. curviflora*, *D. janthina* and all the larger species and hybrids are surprisingly long-lived. Other plants that do well are *Viola delphinantha*, *V. cazorlensis*, *Primula allionii*, *P. forrestii*, *Sarcocapnos crassifolius* and *Diosphaera asperuloides*.

After drilling as small a hole as possible we clean the soil from roots in running water. We do not want any humus or clay particles to hold water near the plant's most sensitive point. After insertion the remaining cavity is filled with sifted dry sand, a plug of tufa closes the opening and the plant is carefully watered. We only plant in early spring, February to March, and attend new plants carefully with water and shade for about a month. Some species, like *Astragalus coccineus*, can be sown directly in the wall. Others like *Saxifraga luteo-viridis*, *Ramonda* species and *Myosotis arnoldii* are spontaneously seeding around.

Water and nutrients are supplied from overhead which takes a lot of time and encourages moss-growth. As we are planning to expand the tufa we must first learn how others have mastered these problems.

ALPINE PLANTS OUTDOORS – THE ROCK GARDEN

This is situated in a gully a fair distance from the entrance and beautifully framed by huge gneiss cliffs. The total area is about two acres and divided into geographical sections, Scandinavia, Europe, Asia, North America and the Southern Hemisphere are represented. Each section, in turn, contains different biotopes and exposures so that the widest range of plants as possible shall be pleased.

Construction
During the last decade a major reconstruction has been undertaken and we are at the moment dealing with the completion. These years have been most educative. We have been able to try different ways and ideas with subsequent success and failures.

The local rock is very good for construction work and large boulders can be brought in from nearby areas. In the early years they were positioned by manpower and later by tractorpower. Today we use an excavator and mobile crane to save manpower for the final adjustments.

One important thing we have learnt is to make the contours out of sharp, draining sand. The rocks are then put in and, at last, a 40cm thick layer of compost.

The composts
The ingredients are basically the same as for the potting-compost. We use three standard mixtures. These have been changed over the years and at present the recipes are as follows:

	Neutral	Acid	Scree
Sterilized loamy compost-soil	4 parts	2 parts	4 parts
Peat	2 parts	2 parts	2 parts
Coarse sand	1 part	1 part	1 part
Granite chips (5–8mm)	1 part	1 part	1 part
Granite macadam (0–60mm)	–	–	8 parts
Bone meal, litre to cubic-meter of mixed compost	5	5	3

These proportions make up composts with ample nutrition-levels, pH and a sharp draining porous structure. Further variation can be easily obtained by adding the ingredients that one believes might be of benefit for individual plants.

Drainage and exposure

Plants are quite adaptable to soil and it is my opinion that most alpines will grow in any compost as long as drainage is excellent. In our wet and cold winter, frost blocks the drainage so the surface water must be diverted by an ever sloping soil-surface. Never a flat area in the rock garden!

Exposure is of equal importance when it comes to the choicer plants. We strive to attain gentle north-slopes for the true alpines and arctic plants that are most susceptible to heat. In a north slope more of the solar energy is reflected so the soil stays cooler without too much loss in light-intensity. The south-facing areas are made steep in order to suit rock-garden plants of Mediterranean origin. These gain from the energy absorbed by the rock and by the drier atmosphere. Nooks and crannies that provide special micro-climate are used for selected items that are carefully hidden from admiration from all but the chosen few.

Growing in and on sand

This is a method that recently has received much attention as a short-cut to success for many, otherwise, intractable jewels.

In the early 1950s this method was introduced in Uppsala Botanic Garden. A 20cm (8in) thick layer of coarse sand is spread over the clayey soil and alpines are planted in the sand. The result is an extremely good drainage around the plants' necks and the roots are given the chance to seek for water and nutrients at the depth and environment individually preferred.

Recently we have constructed two sand-beds devoted to American and Asian steppe flora respectively. These do not rest on a fertile subsoil but are just piles of sand restricted by rocks. To make up for the lack of nutrients bone meal in quantity has been mixed in the bottom layer.

Peat in the rock garden

The Swedish climate favours the vegetation of peat-moors, so *Spaghnum*-peat is readily available and comparatively cheap. The peat-blocks harvested are of a different size and quality than can be seen, for instance, in Britain. The normal size is 25 × 50 × 50cm (10 × 18 × 18in) and the quality is a coarse, porous young peat. Such peat is perfect for the building of peat-walls and related constructions. During the last decade peat has become a favourite building-material amongst Swedish growers.

In our garden, peat is used in the woodland areas, in ordinary peat-walls and incorporated in the rock garden constructions. As we all know, the blocks are perfect for ericaceous plants as well as for related plants such as Diapensiaceae. *Diapensia lapponica* which in nature is found in wind-swept sites with its roots in silty mineral-soils can only be grown by us in peat-blocks exposed to sun. Its relative, *Pyxidanthera barbulata* enjoys exactly the same site. A third representative of the family, *Shortia uniflora*, flourishes in the same substrate under shadier conditions.

In other gardens sun-exposed peat-walls are used for all kinds of slow-growing alpines like *Androsace alpina*, *Gentiana pumila*, Auriculastrum *Primula* and the choicer New Zealanders, to mention a few examples. So the material has a much wider potential than one normally imagines.

The arctic plants

The most intractable plants, those that require maximum light combined with a cool micro-climate (the Arctic, the Antarctic plants and the high alpines) always present a problem. With some of these we have been successful by building north-sloping but unshaded peat-walls. Such a light but cool area forms the only possible solution for growing *Cassiope hypnoides*.

At Uppsala Botanic Garden, where they are growing the most comprehensive collection of Scandinavian alpines, they point out another key to success with these plants. Here they water daily and heavily in spring and early summer during sunny periods, a drenching that is withheld by midsummer.

Postscript

I have here (within the 3000 words at my disposal) tried to focus on a few things that I think are important for successful cultivation of alpines in a Scandinavian climate. I hope that some will be relevant to others and inspire to new trials and errors. The number of paths leading to success is unlimited.

A Closer Look at Some of Northern Italy's Best Alpines

JIM JERMYN

On arrival at one of the busy airports in northern Italy's main city of Milan we must decide in which direction to head to make our base. We are on the doorstep of Europe's grandest natural display of alpine scenery and its special array of flowers.

The scene is set, our route is clear, we are bound for the Dolomites; as the great man said, 'if we have been allured to the Dolomites we will return again and again' (Farrer), and there I shall take you now, but briefly I mean to stop on route for I guess I am not a little romantic at heart and I could never pass my former base on the side of Lake Garda. My choice for our temporary base would be the bustling village of Torri del Benaco on the eastern side of the Lake. Here we have easy access to the full range of peaks that make up the exciting Monte Baldo, running north to south on the eastern side of the Lake. While my period of employment in Italy afforded me the luxury of exploring these mountains at any time during the main season for flowers, we will have to choose the optimum period for our return visit. This must be the last two weeks of June and the first in July. I fear though, we may be a little late for the vast patches of *Primula spectabilis* and related members of the Auricula section. Yet during the latter weeks we are sure of some exciting endemics on Monte Baldo.

I prefer to avoid the lift from Malcesine and make the exciting ascent by motor to the village of Prada where we can take the lift to the Rifugio Mondini. Our path leads to Monte Maggiore. My memories bring me to those grassy hills rich with so pleasing an association of *Geranium argenteum*, *Daphne cneorum* in richest form and *Myosotis alpestris* popping up amongst tufts of *Rhodothamnus chamaecistus*. The alpine summits reveal plentiful supply of the local endemic *Callianthemum kernerianum*.

The views across the Lake lead towards that well-known 'stamping ground' of Farrer by Cimas Tombea and Tremalzo luring us later by ferry from Torri del Benaco to Maderno and then continuing by car northwards to Tremosine where we turn northwest into the steeper valleys leading to Mt. Tremalzo. We must pause by the steep pine covered slopes. The rich fragrance in the air alerts us to fine forms of the precious *Cyclamen purpurascens*. Our track continues, steep and winding, a little precarious in places and from 1500m (5000ft) we do well to stop and walk. The fragrance has changed to the familiar perfume of Daphne. An upward glance at the fierce limestone walls reveals ancient mats of gnarled evergreen stems clothed with rose coloured bloom, certainly one of Italy's choicest treasures, *Daphne petraea* in all its glory with some notable variation in form. Careful search in the precipitous cliffs reveals well-formed buds of *Physoplexis comosa* which flowers at higher altitude towards the end of July, while even later these same limestones are the home of the vibrant carmine pink, shaggy flowers belonging to *Silene elisabetha*. Still flowering in June is the local form of the universally popular auricula, *Primula auricula albocincta*, here it is to be found on shaded rock faces as enormous clumps of richly farinose foliage and typically golden yellow flowers.

I realise now that my brief pause around Lake Garda has occupied several days and I couldn't move north without another look in to that high alpine pass, the Passo di Croci Domini. Since four wheel drive is quite normal these days in a standard car I will take you round Lago di Idro to the south west side and the village of Anfo. We shall rise up steeply again utilising these wonderful military tracks to find ourselves in the same habitat for the *Daphne petraea*, this time not quite so abundant but equally spectacular. The once again steep and winding road takes us by damp meadows filled with the splendid *Primula spectabilis* in finest forms along with a sea of *Ranunculus alpestris*. As our high altitude journey continues we lose the grey limestone and move into a red porphyry formation offering a change in *Primula* species to PP. *glaucescens* and *daonensis* easily identified and abundant as ever. Further search on the steeper grassy slopes will reward us with superb forms of *Anemone narcissiflora* amongst which are the slender stems of the local *Fritillaria tubiformis*.

Here too is the *locus classicus* for that exciting endemic, *Campanula raineri* choosing an unusual outpost of marble for its home and partnering the equally respected *Saxifraga vandellii*. A visit to this location in July may well be too early for the *Campanula* flowers. Well, here ends the initial pause by the restful Lakes to catch an all too brief glimpse of some of the best alpines in this very special land full of fun and surprises. Our departure from Lake Garda is only complete when we have indulged in the local specialities including the *Prosciutto con Melone*, pizzas so fine that have later caused me to retract when my children drag me into those well known British pizzarias, and of course the ice cream which defy any rational comment since I am supposed to be writing about Italy's alpines and not its cuisine.

Heading north now I will take you through the rich and productive orchards of the Adige plains, past Trento towards Bolzano where we join the old road north and head off east towards the Val Gardena. We can do no better than make our base in Selva-Wolkenstein, yes we have arrived or returned to the heart of the Dolomites. We shall require two weeks to search for the best alpine plants, to soak up the finest mountain scenery and live as the Italians do – in these parts, very well indeed.

By preference I would choose a second base in either Predazzo or San Martino di Castrozza to enable me to thoroughly botanise the Monzoni Valley and the immediate surroundings of the Passo di Rolle. But from our base in Selva we can do no better than use the various lifts that hoist us right up to the alpines and afford us more time to enjoy the plants and the high altitude views. From the village of Ortisei we will take the lift to the Seceda 2518m (8261ft) a spectacular, angular peak which at this time is the home of fine cushions of *Androsace helvetica* quite perfect at their zenith of flowering and particularly pleasing in the knowledge that such a performance is a hopeless challenge in our alpine house. The south-facing meadows are typically rich with an abundance of *Pulsatilla alpina apiifolia* (syn. *P.a. sulphurea*) and fine forms of *Gentiana acaulis*. For those who are not faint of heart a way appears in the form of a steep drop through screes to the north, here you will find some of the finest running clumps of *Anemone baldensis*. Looking across the Val Gardena towards the spectacular Schlern or Sciliar 2448m (8031ft) our eyes scan the vast alpine meadow called the Alpe di Suisi surely Europe's finest example of a natural alpine meadow. We can reach these meadows by lift again from Ortisei and a day in this vicinity is never to be forgotten. We do well to respect the farmers' wishes and utilise the well-marked paths wherever possible, yet I must admit that on a hot day one is strongly tempted to lunge into the meadows with full liberation to enjoy every flower which varies to such a degree, most notably as we change contour and enjoy a different association of composite and orchid. You would not thank me for an endless list of the flowers to be found in these meadows but one is seldom guilty of exaggeration here when we venture into comments such as acres of the fragrant orchid, *Gymnadenia conopsea* amongst masses of golden composites with notable heads of *Arnica montana* so pleasing with the bearded *Campanula barbata*. Rich summer perfumes seem to emanate most strongly from the wide mats of pink *Trifolium alpinum* while each vanilla orchid, *Nigritella nigra* reveals a subtle change in hue. Sunken valleys trap all the moisture and dazzle with millions of globe flower, *Trollius europaeus* a sheen of lemon yellow, while a picnic lunch amongst some of the finest forms of *Daphne cneorum* just about seals the virtues of this wonderland of Italy's finest meadow alpines.

Selva lies at the foot of one of the greatest Dolomite landmarks, the Sassolungo or Langkofel 3181m (10,436ft) which provides some of the finest changes of colour from pinks to purple as the sun sets on this spectacular mountain. We will approach its calcareous screes from the eastern side by driving up to the Passo Sella. The meadows here are notably rich with some of the finest *Pulsatilla alpina apiifolia*, clean drifts of *Ranunculus pyrenaeus* flowering along with *Soldanella alpina* in the snow-melt. *Primula halleri* grows abundantly here with fine forms of *Gentiana verna* where each one seems to surpass the next. The scramble up the limestone screes brings us through wide mats of *Dryas octopetala* and *Silene*

d another subject that generally misbehaves in cultivation, *Thlaspi*
um. Care is needed to both avoid trampling upon and indeed
in the first place, the seeding, single rosettes of *Androsace*
i, sticky and spectacular in bud, sadly not quite coming up to
—ｐᴇᴄᴛᴀᴛɪon when fully open. Some huge boulders fallen from higher parts
provide a home for cushions of *Androsace helvetica*, happy on dolomite here,
and a few tiny congested tufts of the rare *Gentiana terglouensis*.

Clearly the richness of the alpine flowers and their diversity in the
Dolomites can be attributed to the complex geology of these mountains.
This is well typified by the close proximity of the Col Rodella 2484m
(8150ft) which is composed in part of a softish sedimentary rock, free of
available lime, yet just a short walk from the Dolomite screes under the
Sasso Lungo. Here the flora changes with the short turf filled with spreading
mats of *Primula minima*; *Soldanella pusilla* replaces the related *S. minima* and
higher up on the steep screes formed from this soft brown rock I am always
baffled by the quality of the *Ranunculus seguieri*. Most frequently at home in
the limestone screes but on the Rodella we find perhaps the finest of all the
European alpine buttercups, with its huge pure white stemless upturned
cups growing cheek by jowl with other calcifuges, *Gentiana brachyphylla* fat
and prosperous and loose mats of *Douglasia vitaliana*. Sitting amongst all
these treasures on a clear day affords us the best views of Italy's highest peak,
the Marmolada 3342m (10,964ft), and we are beckoned across to the
Pordoi Pass so that we can make the easy ascent to the famous Vial del Pan
or Bindel Weg well worth botanising, and home to fine stands of the satiny
heads of *Pulsatilla vernalis*, quite the most desirable of its genus. Yet I plan
to take you across to the Passo di S. Pellegrino, for the best is yet to come.

By motor we travel south from Canazei through the Val di Fassa to the
busy township of Moena where we turn east to the Pso. S. Pellegrino. A
comfortable ascent is made, first up an uneven track to the very well
appointed Rifugio Paradiso and then on through open meadows to the little
shelter perched at the top of the Passo di Selle 2528m (8294ft). As you
stand upon this very pass Farrer rightly stated you may scan the very
'miracles of the mountain world'. Before you falls away the Monzoni Thal
full of treasures surely brought about by the extraordinary marriage of white
Dolomite rock to the north and the hard brownish volcanic and igneous
formation to the south. The end of June or beginning of July seems to suit
the present seasons admirably at this altitude and we are almost guaranteed
to enjoy Italy's best alpines. The king of the Alps, *Entrichium nanum*
abounds here seeding around in the acidic formations amongst the finest
Ranunculus glacialis I have seen with the best forms bright red in colour
dazzling beside the purest blue of the *Entrichium*. Odd patches of snow
persist in sheltered hollows where the short turf is carpeted with the sticky
Primula glutinosa, violet blue in acres of purity. A change in contour shows a
shimmer of bright pinks in every shade from rose to carmine as *Primula*

minima gets in on the act desperate to mate with its violet compatriot. The result is that for once I'm speechless and return to Farrer who exhausted three or four pages of diversion trying to describe the beauty of all these hybrids.

The steep igneous screes support fine stands of *Ranunculus glacialis* in various hues with vast patches of that exquisite *Geum reptans*, such a valuable jewel with its clean yellow flowers followed by those bronzing, fluffy heads of seed. The cliffs above reveal a new *Androsace* for me, the white Dolomite form of *A. alpina*, clean and pure, surprisingly sharing a crevice with *Primula minima* more usually spreading its mats in the turf. I suspect that the peaks would surprise us with further treasures, possibly a disjunct outpost for *Androsace wulfeniana*, but wives become anxious when one disappears too far afield so I will await these treasures another day.

But what of the Dolomite side of the valley where the flora shows a typical range of flowers, including the local and sadly disappointing form of *Ranunculus parnassifolius* amongst splendid exhibits of *Dryas*, *Silene acaulis*, *Anemone baldensis* and the promise yet to come of wide silver mats of *Potentilla nitida*. The closing days of July or early August will see these shining mats aglow in shades of pink, still remaining one of Italy's finest alpines. Such is my taste for damsons that I am forced to call into that lonely hut perched on a rock called the Rifugio Taramelli where a cool beer or frothing Cappucino will accompany the newly cooked damson tart which is so deliciously prepared here, but now we must return to base via the Rifugio Paradiso where the same fruit provides us with a welcome damson schnapps to warm the inner parts as we reflect on our day's hunting.

Our return to the Dolomites and the alpine treasures that we seek is satisfied only after motoring on to Predazzo and eastwards to the Passo di Rolle 1980m (6496ft). The journey takes us winding up through ancient spruce forests and then finally out into the open where somehow we are held in expectation as first just the tip of that cruel pinnacle called the Cimon della Pala 3184m (10,446ft) is visible to us. That great Yorkshireman was right when he said that this is the mountain of mountains, 'there is nothing like it for the cruel and naked insolence of its splendour' (Farrer).

We will follow the track to the Baita Segantini and from here the whole panorama opens up before you, surely the finest in all the Alps as the Pale range towers above you. First the stable scree reveals ancient, gnarled shrublets of purest pink as *Rhodothamnus chamaecistus* abounds, yet as we clatter down to inspect those huge glacial boulders we pass rich masses of golden *Papaver kerneri* and the ever present *Thlaspi rotundifolium*. Early June is the best time for the sunny sides of these boulders for then we may catch a brief glimpse of the rare endemic to these parts; the close relation of the precious jewel *Primula allionii*, the crevices here are filled with the sticky rosettes of *P. tyrolensis* and further specimens may be found on the sheer Dolomite cliffs under the Pale Group. Its flowers vary from pale to deep pink with or without an eye. Another of Italy's real treasures is to be found on the reverse side of these boulders. I well recall visiting this valley with some friends in early August and borrowing their shoulders upon which to perch to photograph the purple bells of *Campanula morettiana* tucked into tiny cracks in the rock. Evidence would suggest that these rocks have been the hunting ground of an over-zealous plant collector armed with a hammer and chisel. While it is sad to report such pillaging in these mountains it must be said that generally my experience shows great abundance of the treasures and those that are on the scarce side often owe their survival to their inaccessible homes.

When Farrer trod these hills he held to a staunch dogma regarding the sites for *Entrichium* which he felt were solely to be found on acidic formations. Today nearly a century on we venture further afield and can save our legs with the many magnificent lifts which have been constructed in the Dolomites. An impressive example of such a lift will take us from San Martino di Castrozza to the Passo di Rosetta 2572m (8438ft), a hoist of over 1100m (3600ft) from the village where we gaze in amazement at vast hanging pads of *Potentilla nitida* and leafy tufts of *Physoplexis comosa*. A gentle climb from the lift station takes us into a white world of stark limestone, hardly plausible that plant life would have adapted to such an environment but where little else survives we find dotted in open and sheltered crevices the tightest cushions of perhaps still the most popular 'No. 1' – Italy's finest alpine in true Dolomite surrounds, the king of the Alps, *Entrichium nanum*. Here I must leave you to ponder while I return to base, then homeward bound. A brief stop in my favourite village of Castelrotto or Kastelruth at the foot of the Schlern where I will find a peaceful cafe beside which one can sit under the canopy of a huge, old walnut tree and consume for the last time the local Cappucino and Sacher Torte while rejoicing at the treasures we found again, and reflect on the pleasure these mountains provide with their friendly populace ready to welcome us back again and again.

Where Mekong, Yangtze and Salween Divide

RON McBEATH

China is a massive country, in area almost as big as Europe and slightly larger than the USA. Extensive tracts of the centre, south and east are warm, heavily populated and intensively cultivated and contain few if any plants of interest to the alpine plant enthusiast. The north and west has severe winters and therefore the plants are very hardy but much of this area is very dry and the resulting flora is not particularly rich. In contrast, the south west provinces of Yunnan and Sichuan (Szechuan) are one of the great plant paradises of the world, as far as rock and alpine gardeners are concerned, although lying at the same latitude as Egypt or the Gulf of Mexico.

There are several factors which have combined to create this abundance of good, adaptable garden plants. The area is mountainous with much land above 3000m (10,000ft), a bench mark for hardy plants at this latitude, with mountain summits reaching up to over 5500m (18,000ft). The mountains are relatively young and precipitous with much broken rock and erosion still in progress, which provides open and changing habitats. The geology is varied with a good proportion of the rock limestone. During the last ice ages, which almost wiped out the floras of much of the northern hemisphere, south-west China was far enough south to escape severe glaciation and the plants were probably able to survive by migrating south along the north-south mountain chains, or descend to lower altitudes until warmer times prevailed, rather than become eliminated as happened in so many places.

Isolation in a changing environment may lead to the evolution of new species and this may be one reason for such a diversity and richness of species, as this region is deeply divided and dissected by the great rivers Mekong, Yangtze and Salween which flow south from the mountains in the north west, through deep river gorges, to create difficult physical barriers for the migration of plants on an east-west axis, thereby encouraging speciation to fill the niches in the rapidly changing environment.

For those and possibly many other reasons yet unknown, we find a remarkable range of beautiful primulas, rhododendrons, gentians, lilies etc, many of which readily adapt to grow in our gardens.

Wild plants have always been of considerable importance to the Chinese for medicine as well as for food and the local people in the countryside have an extensive knowledge of the plants around them. The richness of the flora gradually became apparent in the West through the introductions by merchants from the nurseries near the sea ports, then through the massive collections in the second half of the 19th century by the religious missionaries, who must have spent much more time collecting plants than converts. Perhaps the greatest was Jean Marie Delavay, many alpine plants are named in his honour, *Meconopsis delavayi*, *Fritillaria delavayi*, *Incarvillea delavayi* etc, he is reputed to have collected over 200,000 specimens (George Forrest collected over 31,000), many from remote areas in northwest Yunnan. Unfortunately most of the collections by the missionaries were of dried plants and few alpine plants were introduced alive.

Although a good number of people were engaged in collecting seeds and dried specimens in Yunnan and Sichuan in the first half of this century, four stand out due to the extent of their collections. The Austrian Joseph Rock collected on behalf of a number of American institutions, his principal interest was trees and shrubs and we are indebted to him, as many of the rhododendrons we now grow are direct descendants from his introductions. Ernest Wilson at first collected for the nursery firm Veitch of Exeter, then for the Arnold Arboretum in the USA, he collected in Yunnan and Sichuan but like Rock his main interest was in trees and shrubs. Without doubt the greatest traveller and collector in eastern Asia was Francis Kingdon Ward, he made approximately 24 expeditions between 1909 and 1957 and visited Yunnan and Sichuan on at least four occasions near the start of his career, although he collected and successfully introduced into cultivation many plants which we now take for granted, it is difficult to know how many direct descendants of his early Chinese introductions are still with us.

Our greatest debt must be to George Forrest who made seven expeditions between 1904 and his death in the field in 1932. At first he collected for A.K. Bulley of Ness and latterly a syndicate of private subscribers, although employed by the Royal Botanic Garden, Edinburgh. Most of his expeditions lasted between one and two years and this gave him ample time to travel widely, select and mark the best forms when in flower, then return at the appropriate season to collect copious quantities of seed from the most desirable plants found in the wild. His collections exceeded 31,000. Although his collecting area had been worked by the industrious Delavay, Forrest found and introduced many plants new to science, which were of great garden value and are still amongst our most popular garden plants; *Primula beesiana*, *P. bulleyana*, *P. forrestii*, *Rhododendron forrestii*, *R. russatum* and *Pleione forrestii* to name just a few. It also highlights the adaptability of such plants as many have continuously remained in cultivation for over 60 years.

During the 1940s China closed up as a collecting area for western plant hunters and it was not until 1981 that the first major expedition again gained access. Travel and conditions have changed and it is now no longer possible for one man to go alone on an expedition into the wilds for a year or two at a time. A number of individuals have made valuable collections during short field trips, but the norm now is for expeditions to consist of about six people and visit one area for about two months intensive collecting. This does not allow selection of the best forms but does enable collection of seed from a wide range of the plants in a population, when there are many collectors spread out across a mountain side. In 1981 the Sino British Expedition to Cangshan (SBEC) gained access to the Cangshan range above Dali and amongst their best introductions were *Gentiana ternifolia*, *G. melandrifolia*, *Paris* sp., *Anemone trullifolia* and the true plant of *Pleione forrestii*. In 1987 the Sino British Expedition to Lijiang (SBLE) visited Yulong Shan and although in the spring flowering season, they were able to introduce *Primula forrestii*, *Androsace rigida*, *A. spinulifera*, white forms of *Roscoea humeana* and a number of *Iris* and *Arisaema*. In 1990 the Chungtien Lijiang Dali (CLD) expedition gained access to the Chungtien (Zhongdian) Plateau, Yulong Shan and Cangshan ranges in the autumn and were able to return with seeds of *Meconopsis delavayi*, *Incarvillea lutea*, *Gentiana sino-ornata* and many *Primula*, *Iris*, *Lilium* and *Nomocharis*. With luck there may be a gradual opening up of more remote areas in the years to come and a steady stream of new introductions to grace our gardens.

As well as the opportunity to collect and introduce plants into gardens expeditions into the field allow one to examine the natural habitat and conditions in which the plants grow and to search out for variation in species which are represented by only one or a few forms in gardens.

THE CHUNGTIEN PLATEAU

This plateau, which was visited on several occasions by George Forrest, lies to the north of the Yangtze river and is a southern extension of the Tibetan plateau. It consists of rolling, rounded hills and wide, flat valley floors at an altitude between 3000 and 4000m (10,000–13,000ft). The hills which have not been cleared of trees are covered with conifers, birch, rowan and many species of *Rhododendron*.

In forest clearings and in light shade, one of the most spectacular plants in flower in September is *Gentiana trichotoma*, a perennial with a loose basal rosette of leaves up to 20cm (8in) long and with an upright flower spike 30–60cm (12–24in) tall, the flowers are a brilliant electric blue and occur in several whorls of two to five upright flowers on the stem, as well as in a terminal head. The soil it was growing in was a reasonably drained, brown earth, but I have no doubt it requires plenty of moisture in the growing season, as do all the plants from this region.

Most of us expect to find *Androsace* growing in scree, rock outcrop or amongst exposed, high alpine turf in the wild, so I was rather surprised to find square metres of *Androsace rigida* growing amongst moss, in the total shade of tall *Rhododendron*, *Acer* and firs. (Although others were in more open habitats). This species flowers in early summer when it produces terminal heads of rose pink flowers on stems up to 3cm (1.2in) tall. If you acquire one, do not coddle it in the alpine house, plant it outside, although it may respond better if provided with shelter by a sheet of glass in winter, as it would normally be covered with a deep layer of snow. In those forests *Lilium* or *Nomocharis* are frequent along with orchids, *Smilacina* and *Polygonatum* and it was nice to see *Sorbus reducta* running about and forming clumps up to 60cm (24in) tall, with many clusters of its pinkish white fruits.

The open, flat valley floors were often very wet and boggy. Several primulas in the candelabra and sikkimensis sections were common and strong clumps of *Iris* were everywhere, most probably *I. chrysographes* or something similar. The great joy here was to find *Gentiana sino-ornata* in abundance. Whenever one walked into a wet boggy meadow it was there, often in surprisingly wet conditions, where you would get your feet wet when you stopped to take a photograph, often it was with dwarf sedges and rushes amongst peaty pools, as well as in short turf. It is surprising that it ever survives in eastern Scotland with 600mm (24in) of rain a year. The standard form of *Gentiana sino-ornata* varies little in cultivation whereas in the wild plants of many shades of blue could be found in any bog, the most frequent colour seemed a little paler than the form in gardens and white and pale yellow forms could also be found.

On drier grassy slopes and in open *Rhododendron* shrubberies *Gentiana veitchiorum* was equally common, the flowers were a violet blue with little variation other than the occasional white, a similar colour to plants in cultivation. The two gentians came together where bog and dry grassland met but no hybrids were apparent.

Other outstanding plants in the autumn are several species of *Euphorbia* which set the hillsides ablaze with their fiery autumn tints and *Saussurea stella* which grew with the *Gentiana sino-ornata* as a bog plant. In cultivation, the scree, raised bed, or in a pot in the alpine house, is the norm, yet in the wild it seldom ventured far from wet meadow and bog. When in growth its leaves are green and merge into the grassy background, but when it is time to flower the leaves turn light reddish pink and prostrate themselves like a starfish. The purple flowers are held in a tight stem less head in the centre of this colourful starfish. Then the plant dies after flowering and setting seed.

THE YULONG SHAN

The Yulong Shan is in sharp contrast to the Chungtien Plateau in that it consists of a massive limestone ridge reaching 5596m (18,360ft), there are extensive permanent snow and ice fields near the summit, precipitous cliffs, screes of loose white limestone, grassy meadows and great forests of conifers, shrubs and *Rhododendron*. The Yangtze river cuts a deep gorge on the west and east side of the mountain and only the east side has ever been botanised due to the precipitous nature of the western flank. Spring is the main flowering season when *Stellera chamaejasme*, *Daphne aurantiaca*, *Meconopsis delavayi*, *Fritillaria delavayi*, *Lilium lophophorum* and many species of *Rhododendron*, *Primula*, *Corydalis* and *Cypripedium* distract the plantsman. In the autumn *Gentiana sino-ornata* can again be found in the damp meadows, whereas in stable limestone screes, often partly shaded by *Pinus yunnanensis*, can be found *Gentiana georgi*, a species which forms a low clump up to 30cm (12in) across, with foliage quite similar to the European *G. acaulis*. The flowers are slightly larger than *G. acaulis*, quite tubby, with wide spreading lobes, the colour is a pleasant rich purple with white lines near the base of the tube.

Other gems flowering in the autumn are several species of *Cyananthus*, dwarf *Delphinium beesianum* and the attractive *Spenceria ramalana*, a member of the rose family, with clusters of golden flowers which resemble a dwarf *Hypericum*, on stalks up to 30cm (12in) tall.

LI TI PING

Li ti Ping lies on the watershed between the Mekong and the Yangtze. An area of rolling hills covered with conifers, rhododendrons and grassland exceeding 3500m (11,500ft) high. In the spring one can find moorlands covered with *Rhododendron saluenense* ssp. *chameunum* growing like heather in Scotland. The flowers are mostly purple red with the odd pink variant and growing 30cm (12in) tall.

Amongst the rhododendrons in surprisingly moist, grassy clearings the solitary maroon purple flowers of *Lilium soulei* can be found on 20cm (8in) tall stems, while nearby *Primula sino-purpurea*, *Meconopsis integrifolia*, *Cassiope pectinata* and both *Omphalogramma vincaeflora* and *O. soulei* grow. On drier grassy meadows the yellow flowered variant of *Stellera chamaejasme* is often dominant, making a breath taking display when in flower in June.

CANGSHAN

In western Yunnan the Cangshan range is the most accessible large mountain as it is only one day's drive from Kunming. This mountain is a long ridge reaching a height of over 4000m (13,000ft) and is clothed to the top with conifers and many species of *Rhododendron* including such diverse species as *RR. sino-grande*, *edgeworthii* and *fastigiatum*. In spring *Primula sonchifolia*, *Nomocharis pardanthina* (*mairei*) with heavily spotted and frilled flowers and the cream *Diapensia bulleyana* are eye-catching.

In the autumn the gentians are again the speciality, with *Gentiana ternifolia* replacing *G. sino-ornata* as the 'bog gentian'. The leaves of *G. ternifolia* are in whorls of three rather than in pairs and the individual flowers often have six or seven petals rather than the usual five. There is a little variation in the shade of blue with a light sky blue the norm. A few with white flowers were seen. This species is now well established in cultivation from the 1981 SBEC collections.

In much drier, semi-shaded banks amongst rhododendrons, *Gentiana melandrifolia* is abundant, producing tumbling sprays of sky blue flowers on short stalks. We have not found this the easiest species to please in the garden, but after seeing it in the wild it is well worth every effort to try to please it.

After so many botanists have combed those hills over the last century, it could be expected that desirable new plants would be few and far between, yet no more than 5m (16ft) from the main path up the mountain, we were fortunate to locate *Cassiope myosuroides* amongst moss on a rocky outcrop. As far as I know this is the first record for a *Cassiope* on the Cangshan and its nearest known locality is far to the west near the border with Burma. This *Cassiope* is a prostrate species resembling *C. lycopodioides* in habit, with grey green leaves and stems and solitary white flowers. I hope it will establish in cultivation.

Many amateurs now have the opportunity to visit south-western China by participating in specialist botanical holidays and will be able to see and photograph many superb plants in their natural habitats, even though they may not be able to collect them. Remember the motto 'Seek and you shall find'.

48   *Trifolium alpinum* in meadows below the Schlern in the
Dolomites (see page 183)

49   *Cypripedium tibeticum* growing in Yulong Shan in China (see page 191)

50   *Cypripedium margaritaceum* growing in the same area (see page 191)

51   *Meconopsis delavayi* grown from seed collected in China (see page
       191)

52   *Saussarea laniceps* growing in Yulong Shan in China (see page 191)

53   *Gilia caespitosa* from Wayne County, Utah (see page 202)

Corydalis

MAGNUS LIDÉN

*C*orydalis comprises close to 400 species with the vast majority in Asia; in North America we find less than fifteen, in Africa one only, and in Europe twelve (or ten, depending on how we choose to deal with the *cava*-complex). In the kingdom of Nepal, which is about the size of England, there are at least 43 species, and in China perhaps around 220. The highest diversity is found in the classical plant hunting districts in SE Tibet, Yunnan, and Sichuan.

The American species belong in the sections Archaecapnos (e.g. *C. scouleri*, a rhizomatous perennial with a very attractive foliage when growing in dense stands) and Sophorocapnos (yellow-flowered annuals, biennials or rosulate perennials, of which *C. aurea* is frequently found in seed catalogues), with some species growing in quite arid country and even reaching Mexico. In Africa *Corydalis mildbraedii* is found at high altitudes on the East African volcanoes. Whether it is specifically distinct from *C. cornuta* from the Himalayas is not yet clear, but anyway the disjunction is remarkable, and long distance dispersal is an inescapable conclusion. Most of the Himalayan and Chinese species grow high up in the mountains, in alpine meadows, screes, forests, or in rock crevices. Some, like *CC. hendersonii* and *mucronifera*, which are widespread in Tibet, reach 6000m (20,000ft) and beyond, and compete with few other genera for the altitudinal record for vascular plants. Several species benefit from moderate disturbance of their environment, though few are true weeds.

The genus is confined to the northern hemisphere. The southernmost local endemic species (the above-mentioned *C. mildbraedii* excepted) is found on Mount Victoria in Central Burma, yet undescribed, and so far only known from the type collection by Kingdon Ward. A couple of more or less weedy species traverse the Tropic of Cancer to about 20°N in Thailand and North Vietnam. The opposite record is held by the Alaskan-Siberian *C. arctica* (sect. Dactylotuber) which grows as far north as 73°N. With a little assistance from the Gulf stream, *C. intermedia* manage to survive at a latitude of 70°N in Norway.

In the last years there has been a marked increase in interest in *Corydalis* as garden plants, but the fact is that some of the species have been cultivated for several hundred years. *Corydalis solida* and *cava* were grown in ancient times in monasteries, as ornamentals and for their medical properties, hence the Swedish name *nunne-ört* (nun's herb). In a few places north of its natural distribution range, *Corydalis cava* still survives, where only broken walls remain of the monastery. *Corydalis nobilis* is another early introduced species which is rather common in Swedish parks and gardens. Probably all that are now in cultivation originate from the seeds that Linnaeus got from one of his disciples, Laxman, under the name of '*Fumaria spectabilis*'. It is still cultivated in his garden Hammarby near Uppsala.

Like all papaveraceous plants, they contain a lot of alkaloids, and have been used for various diseases. In the eighteenth century *C. cava* was frequently confused with, or substituted for, the highly valued *Aristolochia rotunda*. The common *C. intermedia* was sold in pharmacies during the eighteenth century as a remedy for menstruation problems. In China, the boiled and dried tubers of 'yanhusuo' are very important in traditional medicine to facilitate smooth running of blood in the veins, and several other species are used in Kashmir. *Corydalis* has also been used as food; the Aïnos are said to eat tubers, and some Himalayan tribes appreciate the spindle-shaped storage-roots of *C. juncea* and other species of the section Fasciculatae.

In recent years several species have found their way into our gardens, the majority of which are tuberous vernal ephemerals, mostly from the sections Corydalis and Leonticoides. The section Corydalis is the largest, and new species are constantly being added. In fact, no less than five species of this section are known only from recent collections of live material. When the badly-known complexes in Manchuria and Korea have been worked out, I believe that the section will number close to 50 species. Presently about 28 of them are in cultivation in Göteborg. They are among the hardier and easier *Corydalis*, and they also display a wide variety of colours, forms and sizes. As examples we can select a commonly grown azure-blue *Corydalis* from Hokkaido, hitherto confused with *C. ambigua* from Kamchatka but actually very close to, if indeed separable from, *C. fumariifolia*; further, the yellow-flowered *C. bracteata*, a hardy and vigorous species; *C. schanginii* ssp. *ainii* has tri-coloured white and yellow flowers tipped with dark purple; *C. nudicaulis* is likewise tri-coloured, but brown instead of yellow. Closely related to the two last mentioned species, and rather similar in habit to *C. nudicaulis*, is *C. ruksansii*, yet only known from the type collection by Janis Ruksans. It is distinguished by its much fewer and larger seeds, and the lack of brown colour. A recent addition to our collection, also from Janis Ruksans, is *C. turczaninovii* (syn: *C. remota*) from East Siberia. One of its forms has pale flowers with blue margins set in long graceful racemes with red pedicels.

The majority of the European and Anatolian species belong in this section, several of them quite recently described. The Swedish *C. gotlandica*, endemic to Gotland in the Baltic area, is an allo-polyploid derivative of a hybrid between two common and widespread species, *CC. solida* and *intermedia*. It is probably a rather recent neo-endemic, nicely set in its *locus classicus* (Västergarn, one of its two localities) in a surrounding of old ruins and fertile pasture land. Its weedy tendencies promise success in cultivation, and in the Botanic garden of Visby (Gotland) it has established a vigorous population, seeding itself around.

During recent collection trips, Henrik Zetterlund, curator of the alpine houses in Göteborg Botanical Garden, found *C. zetterlundii*, a close relative of *C. integra*, in South Jugoslavia, and *C. henrikii*, which is taxonomically more isolated, near Gaziantep in Anatolia. The last species is quite handsome with dense racemes of pale flowers with long thin spurs. No doubt, some of the recently discovered species have escaped notice until now because they are already past flowering when botanists leave their dens for the season, and there are perhaps still isolated mountain peaks in this area that have not been explored by botanists in early spring.

The species in this section are usually easy to multiply, as the number of tubers will approximately double each year. The majority of them are self-sterile, and have to be crosspollinated to give seeds. Hybrids are usually easy to produce, though in most cases their fertility is low. If bumble-bees have access to the plants, they will frequently pollinate the flowers, and various hybrids will appear in the plunge-bed after a few years.

The next largest among the tuberous sections is Leonticoides. The name alludes to a certain similarity in foliage with this genus. These are more demanding, and often disappointing in cultivation, as they tend to be etiolated and sprawl over the pot-edge in a diffuse way. As the racemes are generally laxer than in the section Corydalis, their often remarkable flowers often lose themselves among entangled stems and foliage. Keep them cool and give them a maximum of light for best results. Fortunately, there are some species which are less prone to etiolation, and stay firm and erect, e.g. *CC. popovii* and *darwasica*, both also ranking high in beauty. Fifteen of the twenty species I recognize are presently in cultivation in our greenhouse. Still missing is for example the low-statured *C. cyrtocentra* with large, almost sessile flowers, known only from two collections from Chitral on the border between Afghanistan and Pakistan. *Corydalis verticillaris* from Iran has very long, gracefully curved spurs, and the best forms of this species from the Elburz mountains just north of Teheran could, judging from herbarium specimens, match any of the cultivated species.

Hybrids are easily formed, also between species with different chromosome numbers. As in the previous section, most species are self-sterile, with one notable exception, *C. uniflora* from Crete. Comparing this species with the closely related *C. rutifolia* from Cyprus reveals substantial morphological differences in addition to the different reproductive systems, *C. rutifolia* being quite attractive.

Corydalis seeds are equipped with whitish fleshy appendages, elaiosomes (with one or two exceptions: *C. semenovii* from Kuen Lun). In addition, the majority of them has explosively dehiscent capsules, and scatter their seeds in all directions. Thus, if you are too late with your harvest, there will be nothing left to collect. The tuberous species (except most of the species of the section Dactylotuber) have a different strategy, and gently release their seeds, thereby providing a higher concentration of nutrition and more efficient myrmecochory. In *C. intermedia* in Sweden, a seed heap, once discovered, can be emptied within an hour by the inhabitants of a neighbouring ant-nest. The larger species of ants are less methodical, but may instead carry the occasional diaspor quite long distances. Fifteen metres (50ft) is the record so far. However, in the greenhouse this is not important. A more serious problem for us, has been that a family of field-mice has acquired a taste for the tubers of *Corydalis*, to the extent, in fact, that we now use *Corydalis* tubers as baits in our traps.

The first sight of the seedling in spring may be quite surprising: unlike most other dicotyledons, the tuberous species of *Corydalis* germinate with one cotyledon only. Also, this is the only leaf appearing the first season. Normally it takes three to four years to build up a tuber large enough to support a flowering raceme.

The non-tuberous species also includes several pretty examples. The azure-blue *C. cashmeriana* (sect. Fasciculatae), widespread in cultivation, has several cousins in south-eastern Tibet and western China, none of which is in cultivation. Two species from Sichuan belonging in the section Elatae, have recently been introduced *CC. elata* and *flexuosa*, both with the same azure-blue flowers. Why is this colour so common in the land of the blue poppy, and virtually absent here in Europe? Is it because the sight of a blue sky is so rare during the monsoon-months, that the pollinators are attracted by any object reminding them of sunny days?

CC. elata and *flexuosa* are characterized by horizontal rhizomes densely clothed with thick fleshy whitish scales and thickened petiole-bases. They are, apparently, very easy to multiply vegetatively, and perhaps will be available to a wider audience in a couple of years.

Several of the Chinese species are very beautiful, and perhaps the odd one will find its way along the old silk-route to Europe and past. Perhaps we will some day get a chance to admire the grace of *C. acuminata* with its pink corolla with an extraordinary long and thin spur, or the related *C. quantmeyeriana* with crenate leaflets and large yellow flowers. The remarkable scandent *Corydalis saltatoria* from Burma has pedicels, peduncles, and bracts so thin and delicate as had the plant vanished, like a vegetable Cheshire cat, leaving only the flowers dancing in the air as sparks of gold. Whether or not such sights will ever be possible to see in gardens or greenhouses, lies in the laps of the Gods. Some of the high altitude species have proved rather tricky in cultivation, and the ones just mentioned have never been tried. There are challenges enough for a lifetime, provided you have got the money and time to travel.

Survivors – Some Specialised Endemics of the American West

JIM ARCHIBALD

If we were to slice a neat section out of the western half of the United States of America, we could isolate an area of extraordinary diversity in topography and climate. For these and other reasons this is also an area of exceptional variety in its vegetation with a very high number of species which are extremely limited in their distribution. We can delineate this area roughly by running East from the Pacific a little North of the southern borders of Oregon and Idaho through Wyoming to the Laramie Range, going straight South through the cities of Cheyenne, Denver and Pueblo into northern New Mexico before following a parallel line back due West, through northern Arizona and southern Nevada until we reach the Pacific again in California. Within this area we have the Coast Ranges and Sierra Nevada, the whole of the Great Basin and much of the Colorado Plateau, the whole of the southern Rocky Mountain system. It would take many lifetimes to acquire an intimate knowledge of the plants of this vast area. In a few words it is impossible to do more than give an inadequate impression of a small fraction of the species which have succeeded in surviving in restricted specialised niches within about half a million square miles of land surface, much of which is hostile to plant growth.

The early (Cretaceous) vegetation of this area has very little relevance to the plants which are there today. *Ginkgo* and *Araucaria* no longer grow in North America. The descendants of the *Sequoia* which once grew in central Utah now survive only in a few sites in California. During the Tertiary Period, about 60 million years ago, the foundation for the present flora was laid. During this period, two geofloras jostled for supremacy. The Arcto-Tertiary flora from the North and the Madro-Tertiary flora from the South both dominated according to the prevailing climate. While their descendants are still in place today both were in part confounded over much of the area by another factor. Quite recently, in geological terms, towards the end of the Tertiary Period, extending into the present Quaternary Period, the Sierra Nevada underwent its greatest uplift, more efficiently cutting off the rain-bearing clouds from the Pacific. The Great Basin itself was raised extensively. As well as having to contend with an increasingly drier and colder climate, the vegetation was to be subjected to the fluctuating climatic conditions of the Pleistocene glaciation, which receded substantially only around 10,000 years ago. While the ice sheet extended much further south to the east of the Rockies, in the west it did not reach much below what is now the border with Canada, leaving our area free from an overall ice-covering but subject to the vicissitudes of extreme climatic change in comparatively recent times. Although this has led to the extinction of many species or their extermination over most of their earlier range, it has opened up many opportunities for plants to diversify and evolve new species, adapted to newly available habitats in a changed climate.

SERPENTINE ENDEMISM IN CALIFORNIA AND SOUTHERN OREGON

The reason for the uplifting and mountain-building in this area lies in the juxtaposition of the tectonic plates of the earth's surface. The North American Plate is over-riding an adjacent oceanic plate, roughly along a line following the Californian coast. Apart from the sudden releases of pressure, which manifest themselves in the earthquakes for which this region is noted, this has also resulted in the intrusion of the mantle of the oceanic crust along the margins of the two plates. These ultramafic rocks, which occur over about 1000 square miles of California, are popularly known as serpentine and constitute one of the most specialised habitats of the entire area. Serpentine is extremely inhospitable to vegetation and weathers to very infertile soils, deficient in nitrogen and phosphorus, with a low level of calcium and often a high level of heavy metals, coupled with a very high concentration of magnesium, leading to magnesium toxicity. A large number of species familiar in cultivation occur on serpentine in California. Particularly notable is the genus *Lewisia*, exclusively of the North American West and centred on California but with affinities to the predominantly southern genera *Calandrinia* and *Portulaca*. *Lewisia triphylla*, *L. oppositifolia* and *L. cotyledon* all grow on serpentine. Even the widespread *L. rediviva*, which grows elsewhere on granitic soils, is largely confined to serpentine in California. The petaloid monocotyledons are particularly rich in serpentine endemics. In the South *Calochortus clavatus* and *C. obispoensis* grow in limited, stony, serpentine habitats. The extraordinary *C. tiburonensis*, with no close affinities to any other in the genus, survives on the Tiburon Peninsula overlooking San Francisco Bay. Little *C. coeruleus* var. *fimbriatus* grows in dry coniferous woodland of the northern Coast Ranges with the local *Allium hoffmanii* in more exposed serpentine scree nearby. Loose serpentine talus is also the habitat for *Fritillaria falcata* and *F. glauca* with *F. viridia* narrowly confined to the serpentine 'barrens' near New Idria in San Benito County. Most of the Californian species of *Erythronium* grow on serpentine with several narrow endemics, like *E.*

tuolumnense and *E. helenae.* As most of the serpentine occurs at lower elevations, there are fewer serpentine-endemics among the alpine plants but Mt Eddy on the border between Trinity and Siskiyou Counties possesses a rich flora with many local species. Much more field work would need to be done to establish which of these are exclusive to serpentine but it would seem to be the case with *Lewisia leeana, Eriogonum alpinum, Lupinus lapidicola* and *Campanula scabrella,* all exquisite alpine species. The greatest concentration of riches, however, occurs in that part of the Coast Ranges which run along the northern edge of Del Norte and Siskiyou Counties, California, into adjacent Curry, Josephine and Jackson Counties, Oregon. These appear to be referred to in gardening literature as the Siskiyou Mts, which in fact lie to the East of the area, but could be loosely referred to as the Klamath Ranges if a label is needed. Here, on the serpentine, grow such species as *Lilium bolanderi, L. kelloggii* and *L. vollmeri, Erythronium citrinum* and *E. howellii, Viola cuneata* and *V. lobata* subsp. *psychodes, Dicentra formosa* subsp. *oregona, Silene hookeri* and, one of the loveliest and most restricted of all serpentine endemics, *Epilobium rigidum.* There are also a number of local species here to which the occurrence of serpentine is probably irrelevant. Such are *Calochortus howellii, Trillium rivale* and *Phlox adsurgens,* a species very closely related to *P. stolonifera* which grows on the eastern side of the continent. The existence of such plants indicates that this area is an important refuge where many species, formerly of a much wider distribution, have survived. This possibility is reinforced by the existence of *Kalmiopsis leachiana,* just to the North in Oregon. This little shrub is most closely allied to *Rhodothamnus chamaecistus* of the south-eastern European Alps and to *R. sessilifolius* of north-eastern Turkey. While it is a matter of choice whether the two genera are united botanically, they have certainly been united horticulturally in the hybrid × *Kalmiothamnus ornithomma. K. leachiana* would appear to be a relic from the Arcto-Tertiary geoflora.

PALEO-ENDEMICS IN THE AMERICAN WEST

The concept of paleo-endemics as isolated species, usually saxatile, woody perennials, at an evolutionary standstill and neo-endemics as plants with close relatives nearby and occurring in groups in which active speciation is evident is a generalisation more easily applied to the plants of the Mediterranean region and south-west Asia. There, where circumstances have allowed some of the flora to survive undisturbed for a very long period, we can point to such genera as *Ramonda, Jankaea* or *Wulfenia* as classic paleo-endemics. Fewer species in the American West meet these criteria. *Kalmiopsis* would certainly qualify as would such a species as *Maurandya petrophila,* a survivor from the South stranded on the limestone of the Grapevine Mts beside Death Valley. The extraordinary, pulvinate member of the Rosaceae, *Kelseya uniflora*, meets the requirements but it occurs to the North of our area with a disjunct distribution in Wyoming, Montana and Idaho. *Petrophytum caespitosum*, while qualifying in some respects, is a very widespread plant throughout the area, with a considerable variation in foliage and adapting to a wide range of habitats. Distinct though these are, they are but two out of many distinct rosaceous genera, like *Chamaebatiaria*, *Luetkea*, *Purpusia*, *Fallugia*, *Purshia* and the widespread *Cercocarpus*, which are centred on this area. The isolated colonies of *Primula* belonging to the *P. cusickiana* group might qualify as paleo-endemics though they are not very well differentiated species and can be regarded as disjunct representatives of a single species, distributed from north-west Oregon and Idaho (*P. cusickiana*) to Arizona and New Mexico (*P. ellisiae* and *P. rusbyi*). *P. maguirei* from quite low elevations on the shaded cliffs of Logan Canyon in northern Utah, *P. domensis* from Notch Peak in the House Range of western Utah and possibly *P. nevadensis* from the high limestones of the Grant and Snake Ranges in eastern Nevada could all be grouped together with the preceding ones. Tiny *P. capillaris* from high in the Ruby Mts of North-east Nevada is closer to *P. angustifolia* of the alpine-tundra in the southern Rocky Mts Three of these relic *Primula* species are endemic to the Great Basin, a depressingly vast area of cold desert but nevertheless a place of subtle diversity rich in endemic species.

SOME GREAT BASIN ENDEMICS

Beyond the Sierra Nevada, stretching to the foothills of the Rocky Mts, lies an enormous area, where more than two hundred lesser mountain ranges are strung out in more or less parallel lines running from north to south. The greater part of this area, occupying most of Nevada and western Utah, lies within the Great Basin. The first taste of the vegetation of this area, which a visitor to California might have, would be a visit to the White Mts along the eastern boundary of the state. While this range does possess several endemics, most are not of great relevance to the gardener. Its interest lies largely in the relationships of its flora to that of the surrounding area. For instance, the high altitude *Polemonium chartaceum* would be restricted to this range if it did not recur far to the north, on the top of Mt Eddy. The most horticulturally desirable of the endemics are *Penstemon scapoides* and *Eriogonum gracilipes*. The latter belongs to Section Capitata, a group of dwarf species, which can give us some understanding of plant distribution in this area. The most widespread species is the lower altitude, pulvinate *E. shockleyi*, a variable but always extremely beautiful, white-felted cushion with flowers varying from white to yellow, suffused with red. Alpine species include *E. kingii* in the Ruby Mts and *E. holmgrenii* in the Snake Range, Nevada, as well as *E. gracilipes* in the White Mts. The group extends into California with *E. kennedyi*, which attains the most compact development, *E.k.* var. *alpigenum* in the granite gravel on the top of Mt Pinos in Ventura County. Many of the numerous Great Basin ranges have one or more endemic species but the richest area is the region of eastern Nevada along the Utah line. Here there are a dozen or so high mountain ranges, capped with limestone. On these and, more particularly, in the foothills and valleys between them, grow several endemics to this area. Some, like *Lewisia maguirei*, very local indeed; others are more widespread or locally numerous, though always restricted to specialised habitats, such as little *Swertia* (*Frasera*) *gypsicola* on white, gypsum 'barrens'. Some are local developments allied to species in adjacent areas. *Castilleja barnebyana*, surely the most desirable of the genus for the rock-gardener, is a reduced, saxatile vesion of *C. scabrida* of the Colorada Plateau sandstones. Running along limestone crevices or insinuating its scarlet flower into a *Petrophytum* cushion, this can provide a stunning sight, if it has not been grazed by the local rodents. *Penstemon francisci-pennellii*, one of several endemic Penstemons, is a fine, compact race of *P. leiophyllus* of the Utah Plateaux. *Scutellaria nana* var. *sapphirina*, with rich azure-blue flowers instead of the dull purple of the type race, grows very locally on calcareous clay, a tiny plant running underground and almost impossible to find out of flower. Perhaps most remarkable of all are the hard pads of *Lepidium nanum*, an incredible development of this weedy genus looking more like a South American *Xerodraba*. In its very local, calcareous habitats, it is accompanied by other compacted cushions, notably *Oxytropis oreophila* var. *juniperina*, *Leptodactylon caespitosum*, a pulvinate race of *Astragalus calycosus* and *Erigeron compactus*. Distributed to the east of this area but also endemic to it, *Phlox tumulosa* rivals the *Lepidium* in the reduction of its compacted mounds. It appears to be derived from the somewhat looser *P. griseola*, distributed to the south-east but still a Great Basin endemic.

SOME COLORADO PLATEAU ENDEMICS

Although occupying less of the intermountain area than the Great Basin, the other large division of the area, the northern part of the plateau, drained by the Colorado River and its tributaries, is even richer in endemic species. A key area comprises the high plateaus of southern Utah, where spectacular scenery provides an unrivalled background to the vegetation. Pink Wasatch limestone, eroded into the wonders of Bryce Canyon, provides a home for several endemics in Garfield Co. Loose screes in the bristlecone pine communities are the place for tiny *Lesquerella rubicundula*, the most exquisite of dwarf *Penstemon*, *P. bracteatus*, *Silene petersonii* and pulvinate *Townsendia montana* var. *minima*, as well as more widespread species like *Linum kingii* and *Aquilegia scopulorum*. On the ridgetops are cushion-forming plants like *Cryptantha ochroleuca*, *Oxytropis oreophila jonesii* and, if you search long enough, *Eriogonum aretioides*, one of the tightest of the genus with hard, woolly mounds.

The Canyon Lands area of southeastern Utah, adjacent Colorado and Arizona, is unrivalled throughout the intermountain area both for its endemics and rock formations. The latter are often sandstones, which erode rapidly and provide an insecure foothold for plants. Few species have adapted to them but an extraordinary narrow endemic of the Navajo sandstone of Wayne County, Utah, makes an attempt. *Gilia caespitosa*, not really like anything else in the genus but possibly derived from its fellow Plateau endemic, *G. subnuda*, forms mounds of leathery rosettes, rather like *Saxifraga cochlearis*, from which long-tubed flowers of soft orange-scarlet appear on thready stems. Apart from the flowers, the whole plant is very sticky and becomes coated with the glistening, white, wind-blown sand of its surroundings. The most successful colonists of the sandstones occur in very different circumstances in the deep canyons of the Colorado River and its tributaries like the Dolores and San Juan. As the whole area has been uplifted, these rivers have cut more and more deeply into its surface, now flowing between sheer cliffs. For the most part these cliff-walls support little vegetation but where there is a steady seepage of water from the rock on a shaded cliff, a cool, moist habitat is available within this arid climate, enabling 'hanging gardens' to develop. Here, a diversity of relic populations survive. Such species as *Epipactis gigantea*, *Smilacina stellata* and *Cercis canadensis* occur here as well as new specialised species, such as several erigerons, *E. kachinensis*, *E. zothecinus* and *E. sionis*. There is even a rather odd form of *Petrophytum*. Outstanding among the endemics are *Aquilegia micrantha* with pale, long-spurred flowers and sticky leaves and, creeping through the algal mat, tiny *Mimulus eastwoodiae*, possibly a miniature derivative of *M. cardinalis*, which hangs out its glowing scarlet flowers in autumn. In earliest spring, dense colonies of the robust *Primula specuicola* come into flower in deep to pale rose-pink. This belongs to Section Aleuritia (Farinosae), which next occurs to the south in *P. magellanica*, at the southern tip of South America. It could be a paleo-endemic but it could also be a more recent, gorgeously inflated, development of tiny *P. incana*, now mainly Arctic in distribution but which has been collected in one or two bogs in southern Utah. A possibly parallel development occurs in *Dodecatheon*, where the most robust spectacular variation of *D. pulchellum*, *D.p.* var. *zionense*, is an endemic of these 'hanging gardens'.

NEO-ENDEMICS IN THE INTERMOUNTAIN AREA

So much mention of specialised endemics might give the impression that these species are obvious components of the vegetation. This is far from the case. The casual visitor from Europe would have the correct impression that, apart from a few familiar trees in the mountains, belonging to genera like *Pinus*, *Juniperus*, *Populus* and *Salix*, most of the area is covered with sagebrush, members of the genus *Artemisia*, which is distributed right round the northern hemisphere and down to the south of South America. It might be expected that most of our new endemics would be derived from genera of similar distribution and possible Arcto-Tertiary origin. This is indeed the case with two of the most important, *Astragalus* and *Erigeron*, which show the same pattern. The majority, however, are exclusively American with a North-South distribution. These are the large genera of *Castilleja* and *Oenothera* with the somewhat lesser ones of *Cryptantha*, *Mentzelia* and *Sphaeralcea*. All of these produce many narrow endemics in this area and also include species of great significance to the rock-gardener. The whole family Cactaceae should also be mentioned here, extending north into Canada and south to southern Chile and Argentina, it includes several local species, particularly in Utah, as well as extremely hardy and high altitude representatives. Its neglect by rock-gardeners in Europe is inexplicable except through ignorance or prejudice.

Two of the most significant genera in the area, *Penstemon* and *Eriogonum*, are almost exclusively North American in their distribution. The word 'almost' must be used as *Penstemon* has just entered Asia, presumably having had its progress halted by the Pleistocene glaciation, and there is an extraordinary disjunction in the distribution of an intermountain species of *Eriogonum*, the annual *E. divaricatum*, which occurs again in southern Argentina. The small genus, *Townsendia*, centred on the Rocky Mt area, includes a remarkable number of clearly defined, narrow endemics. The position of some genera with actively evolving members in the area is rather more debatable and depends on the view taken of their taxonomic treatment. *Phlox*, where more recent accounts have inclined towards the 'lumping' concept, appears to have very few narrow endemics whereas genera, like *Physaria* and *Lesquerella*, treated by a monographer inclined to 'splitting' give the impression that they include an unrivalled assemblage of restricted endemics. The reverse effect can be achieved by the generic 'splitter' when an important genus like *Gilia*, in the broad sense, is divided into segregates, like *Ipomopsis*. The overall impression, however, is that specialised species, meeting the criteria to qualify as neo-endemics, have evolved from resilient and adaptable ancestors of mainly American origins.

SOME ENDEMICS OF THE 'BARRENS' OF EASTERN UTAH, ADJACENT COLORADO AND WYOMING

Nowhere is this adaptability more evident than among the colonists of the inimical habitats exposed around the drainage system of the Green River, the northern tributary of the Colorado. This includes such key areas as the northern part of the Canyon Lands, the Uinta Basin and the Piceance Basin. Here there are ridges of ancient river deposits and shales laid down on the beds of lakes in the early Tertiary Period. Many are recently exposed and, in the present period of low rainfall, still heavily impregnated with salts or metals toxic to plant growth. Such an element is selenium, whose presence is often indicated by the yellow wands of *Stanleya*, a widespread genus of the Cruciferae with flower-stems reminiscent of *Eremurus*. The more local *Astragalus asclepiadoides* with broad grey-green leaves appears to mimic *Asclepias cryptoceras*, which often grows nearby, and the rush-like *A. saurinus*, with white-tipped purple flowers, is confined to Uintah Co., Utah. Some *Astragalus* go even further than these, which are merely selenium-tolerant, and actually absorb the element, giving them a distinctive and unpleasant odour. Of course, not all of this genus is so eccentric in its appearance as those nor in its habits. Widespread, though always local, throughout this area are several attractive, dwarf species, such as *A. musiniensis*, endemic to eastern Utah, and *A. chamaeleuce*, more northern in its distribution. These are as beautiful in their foliage and pods as in their flowers. Both belong to Section Argophylli, which includes many of the species likely to interest the rock-gardener. One of these, *A. utahensis*, a widespread species in Utah, was considered by Marcus Jones, the pioneer of Utah botany, to be the most beautiful flower in the state. Another desirable group is Section Sericoleuci. Its distribution is centred to the East of the Rocky Mts but two species extend to north-eastern Utah. These are white-flowered *A. gilviflorus* and *A. aretioides*, which with its hard, compacted mounds of silky white foliage, covered with magenta-pink flowers represents the ultimate reduction of the genus as well as the ultimate in desirability to many gardeners. While this grows on a variety of soils throughout its range, at the south-western end it seems restricted to eroded tufaceous outcrops.

The exposed shales can weather into low, rounded clay hills. The clay can be so dense and fine-textured that both the movement of water and the availability of oxygen are severely restricted. Often these hills support no plant-growth at all but a few, often extremely local, endemics are adapted to them. *Penstemon penlandii* is restricted to the alkaline, selenium-rich clays of the Troublesome Formation. The clays derived from the Mancos shales have several endemics: *P. retrorsus* in western Colorado, *Sclerocactus wrightiae* in Utah, *S. mesae-verdae* in southern Colorado and New Mexico, *Townsendia aprica* in Utah and *Abronia argillosa* in Utah and western Colorado are all beautiful, dwarf species.

One of the richest areas is the Uinta Basin of Utah and immediately adjacent Colorado and Wyoming. Here on barren and semi-barren habitats, often old river deposits, are such outstanding plants as *Townsendia mensana*, compact with cream or pinkish daisies, *Gilia stenothyrsa*, with exquisitely cut, grey basal rosettes erupting into a column of pale lavender-blue or white flowers, and *Penstemon acaulis*, tiniest of the genus with purple-blue flowers on pads of minute rosettes, along with a multitude of other penstemons. Within this area is one of the most extraordinary habitats in all the American West: the huge deposits of oil shale of the Green River Formation. On these barren hills and rounded ridges of flaking, white shale, grows an amazing collection of species confined to this habitat. Many are of no great attraction to the gardener: *Thalictrum heliophilum* is an insignificant little plant and *Lesquerella parviflora* lives up to its specific name. However, several are of considerable beauty or interest. Distinct, little *Astragalus lutosus* can be found on the tops of the 'barrens', often with such other endemics as *Haplopappus armerioides* var. *gramineus*, *Eriogonum brevicaule* var. *ephedroides* and *Cryptantha barnebyi*. The endemic penstemons are very local: *P. grahamii* is surely the most spectacular of the Section Cristati; *P. debilis*, thick-leaved with pale lavender flowers, has adapted to the shale scree with a habit similar to *P. bracteatus*. It is surprising to meet a species of *Aquilegia* in such inhospitable surroundings. *A. barnebyi* chooses shaded slopes and gulleys where there may be some seepage of moisture. Its glaucous foliage and pale orange-pink and cream flowers with long-exerted stamens distinguish it.

ENDEMICS OF THE ALPINE TUNDRA IN THE SOUTHERN ROCKY MOUNTAINS

The high altitudes have few narrow endemics compared to the lower elevations. The basic flora is derived from a variety of sources. Circumboreal species, like *Eritrichium nanum* and *Silene acaulis*, associate with those with links in eastern Asia, like *Saxifraga chrysantha* and *Gentiana algida*. Some with purely North American origins appear to be derived quite recently from lower altitude populations. Such are *Eriogonum flavum* var. *xanthum* and *Hymenoxys acaulis* var. *caespitosa*. The widespread, high alpine *Castilleja occidentalis* may be derived from the subalpine *C. rhexifolia* var. *sulphurea*. While there are a few fairly restricted species, like scree-dwelling *Penstemon harbourii*, even classic alpine endemics like *Primula angustifolia* are quite widely distributed. The area around Hoosier Pass and the Mosquito Range in the Colorado Rocky Mts provides some exceptions. Not only is this area noted for some remarkable disjunct populations of more northern species but it has its own endemics in little, woolly *Gilia globularis* with ice-blue scented flowers, the spectacular yellow *Physaria alpina*, the only alpine member of the genus, and a superlative snow-melt *Townsendia*. The last does not flower until late summer on patches of bare earth below the last snow patches. It would appear to be correctly named *T. rothrockii* but it seems improbable that it is the same taxon assigned to this species from pine woods on the Uncompahgre Plateau or the plant in cultivation under this name. Contrary to what might be expected the more isolated, outlying ranges are no richer in alpine endemics. The Uinta Mts have *Penstemon uintahensis* and *Parrya rydbergii*. The laccolithic range of the La Sal Mts has the pulvinate *Erigeron mancus*, which would be much desired by gardeners except for the fact that it has no ray florets. Standing only a little apart from the main range, Pike's Peak, above Colorado Springs, has the attractive alpine member of the Umbelliferae, brilliant yellow *Oreoxis humilis*, but this is essentially only a separate race of the widespread *O. alpina*. This mountain possesses an unrivalled flora and is most notable for its particularly fine local races of more widely distributed species, like *Primula angustifolia*, *Boykinia* (*Telesonix*) *jamesii*, *Mertensia alpina* and *Aquilegia saximontana*. The last is closely allied to *A. laramiensis*, narrowly endemic to the Laramie Range of central Wyoming. This grows over a considerable range of altitude, up through the coniferous woodland almost to the summit of Laramie Peak itself, tucking its dissected leaves and nodding, white columbines into the granite crevices. Almost on the summit, there is a large colony of *Polemonium brandegei* in a form with pure white trumpets. From there you can look South to where, beyond the Colorado Rockies, the same species grows, in a similar situation, on the crest of the Sandia Mts in New Mexico, but in a totally different form with honey-yellow flowers. You can also turn your back on the infinity of the Great Plains and gaze towards the setting sun. Between you and the Pacific Ocean lies the rich diversity of plants which inhabit the American West.

Micropropagation – A Nurseryman's View

PETER FOLEY

Here at Holden Clough Nursery we first became aware of micro-propagation in the 1970s when we read about the nurseries in the United States and France who had set up their own laboratories, but it was not until the early 1980s that we were first offered stock produced by this method from British firms. An initial reaction was that rare plants should be able to be produced and made freely available in large numbers. We also saw that another advantage would be the cleaning up of virus infected plants, especially some of the primulas of the Auricula Section, such as *P.* 'Beatrice Wooster'.

Another advantage that emerged is the even growth rate that is produced with this technique. With conventional propagation methods, such as cuttings, you get some slow-growing and some fast-growing plants, but with micropropagation the pattern is very even indeed. In addition, from the nurseryman's point of view, plants are easy to produce as they are all delivered as either plugs or cells and new varieties can now be introduced and made available very quickly through this mass-production method.

Of course, where there are advantages there are usually disadvantages and the first thing that springs to mind in this respect is that, no matter how well a rare plant can be propagated, there is only a limited market for it, usually as there is only a small number of people who are capable of growing it. This can be illustrated with sale of some show auriculas. These were over-produced and so were sold off cheaply to people who obviously had little experience of growing them. The result was failure and loss of the plants along with the ensuing disappointment.

Another disadvantage is that when plants are free from virus they are open to infection and disease. When we were offered *Primula allionii* 'Avalanche' in 1982, it grew very vigorously at first but soon became infected with botrytis, the result of which was that they all died in spite of fungicide treatments. In this paper I will be mentioning other growers as I asked for their opinions because, bearing in mind that micropropagation is such a new technique, I thought it only fair to find the views and experiences of others, instead of just giving my own, as these could easily be biased.

At the same time as the *Primula allionii* mention above, we were offered *P. aureata* which up to then had been an extremely rare petiolarid primula sold by only one nurseryman, at Hartside, Cumbria. As a result of microbpropagation this primula has been produced in quantity and the retail price has fallen by 50%, making it much more freely available. However, we have found that the plants have produced a lot of shoot proliferation and, indeed, when dividing some crowns, we have found them more akin to *Campanula cochleariifolia* than a primula. We have also noted that success with plants from this micropropagated stock has degenerated from the initial vigour, despite transplanting or re-potting and we now have no stock left produced by this method.

Another disadvantage can be the actual plant that results. *Jankaea heldreichii* has never been produced commercially by micropropagation but a few have been produced in a private laboratory. The resulting plants that I saw in Margaret and Henry Taylor's collection in autumn 1990 were very leafy, more like a *Ramonda*. There were very few silver hairs on the leaves and they were not in a typical prostrate rosette.

A point that has been made by several nurserymen is the fact that although plants were sent for culture, they have not received any back, nor even an acknowledgement, when the laboratory had failed to produce any young stock. We sent plants of *Shortia soldanelloides* 'Magna' and *Primula bhutanica* 'Branklyn' in February at which time they stated that they would not attempt micropropagation. We were then told that they had started taking cuttings in April and, of course, they only produced flowering offsets rather than the vegetative growth, which would have been avoided if they had waited until the flowering period was over.

The other main factor is that plants produced by this method must have a high level of value and those that discerning rock gardeners and alpine growers have in their collections are a very small percentage of the general number of alpine and rock garden plants that are produced each year. The greater percentage of sales is through wholesale nurseries and garden centres where micropropagated alpine material has no place whatsoever; here cheap value, high volume lines are the major requirement.

I will now give you some of the experiences that I personally have had over the past few years. A number of these are of a herbaceous perennial nature because few true alpines have been commercially propagated by micropropagation.

Already mentioned have been *Primula aureata* and *P. allionii* 'Avalanche' but one of the success stories has been another primula, the double primroses, which have been extremely rare plants, only available from a few nurseries. Many of the new varieties raised by Jared Sinclair's Barnhaven Nursery initially became available, as well as older varieties such as 'Marie Crousse' and 'Lilacina Plena'. The only point that we have noticed about these is that some varieties, such as 'Ethel M. Dell' and 'Belle Watling', produce little or no flower but a lot of foliage in their first year after potting and then, in their second, they produce less foliage and a marvellous

Corydalis turczaninovii (see page 194)

55   *Corydalis zetterlundii* (see page 195)

56   *Townsendia rothrockii* from Mosquito Range in the Colorado Rocky Mountains (see page 205)

57   *Calochortus coeruleus* var. *fimbriatus* grows in dry, coniferous woodlands (see page 198)

58   *Aquilegia laramiensis* is endemic to the Laramie Range of central Wyoming (see page 206)

amount of flower. All the other varieties made good crowns and flower within a matter of a few months from potting.

Another group of primulas that have come to the fore due to this technique is the show and alpine auriculas such as 'Neat and Tidy', 'Mojave' and 'Greta'. Other examples, suitable for a rock garden are 'Rufus' and 'Red Dusty Miller'.

Daphnes have a success story, with the exception, that is, of *D. cneorum* 'Eximia'. Although they can produce young plants of this very easily, the laboratory found them very difficult to grow on in plugs or cells but we did, however, receive a superb batch lined out in seed trays. As anyone who grows daphnes will know, they are one of the plants that resents root disturbance of any kind and when we came to pot these on, the roots were very much intertwined and, as a result, 90% of the plants failed.

One hybrid, *D.* × *houtteana* (*D. mezeruem* × *D. laureola*), has always been riddled with virus is now free of it and available much more freely than in the past. Other species from this method have been *DD. blagayana*, *napolitana*, and *tangutica*. This laboratory has now announced that it has ceased daphne production for economic reasons. To be a viable proposition many of these plants need to be produced not in thousands but tens of thousands.

Other plants received are the black-leaved *Ophiopogon planiscapus* 'Nigrescens' and hostas in many varieties but the disadvantage here is that variation from the type plant has occurred, with some reverting to the parent and others producing a new sport. A few varieties have to be grown on for two or three years to verify that they are staying true to type. *Aruncus dioicus* 'Knieffii', with its lovely cut leaves, is another success story, producing virgorous, well-balanced plants. *Heuchera micrantha* 'Palace Purple' and *H.* 'Snow Storm' have been other successes with the latter being widely available only a short time after it was discovered as a seedling.

Bergenia have done well, with good vigour, side shooting at the crown and flowering well in their second year. Varieties that we have grown include 'Baby Doll' and 'Wintermärchen'. Pieris are good, high-value plants and, again, have lent themselves well to micropropagation as have rhododendrons, especially the 'Yakushimanum' hybrids, which have produced superb, bushy, well-budded plants.

Lewisias are plants that grow freely from seed as can be seen in the lovely strains available, especially Sunset Strain raised by Jack Drake many years ago, and more recently John Lawson, who now owns the nursery, introduced the variety 'Sundance', which he sent for micropropagation. This has had great success, although he states that other plants that he has submitted have not followed in the same manner.

There are also a number of plants that you wonder why they have been micropropagated as they come readily from division or seed. Example of these are rhodohypoxis, astilbe, *Thalictrum aquilegifolium*, *Potentilla* 'Gibson's Scarlet'. However, we have found that the astilbe, for example, has had its vigour and the flower production much improved. *Doronicum* 'Spring Beauty' used to fail in the winter due to our high rainfall but the batch that we have grown in 1990 from micropropagated plants have overwintered very well indeed and have produced good flowers this spring.

David Walkey, at the end of his talk, said that private laboratories should play a greater role in micropropagation as during the last decade it appears that the larger commercial laboratories have selected the plants that are financially attractive to them and this does not cover the vast majority of alpine plants, due to their small market potential. Small laboratories ought, therefore, to contact growers with offers of their services.

There is also the possibility of several alpine nurserymen collectively ordering on a bulk basis, so as to keep the individual item prices as low as possible. Of course after listening to David Walkey's talk, the possibilities seem really endless and I would like to give a few examples of the plants that could be subjects for micropropagation: hepatica, corydalis, *Cyclamen africanum* (and other good forms), *Linum* 'Gemmel's Hybrid' (in the hope that there may be more vegetative growth produced instead of flowering itself to death), hellebores, *Paeonia cambessedesii*, *Juniperus communis* 'Echiniformis', *Celmisia sessiliflora*, *Trillium rivale* and *T. chloropetalum*.

I would hope that during the next ten years there will be further advances in micropropagation and by the time we come to 'Alpines 2001' many of these plants will be more widely grown and will be displayed by the exhibitors in the Show as well as being available from the trade stands.

Saxifrages – Twenty Years On

ADRIAN YOUNG

S axifraga are once again becoming popular alpine plants. During the
1930s they were grown in large numbers in Britain and many new
cultivars were introduced, particularly by Russell Vincent Prichard and
Franz Sundermann. They were taking a lead from Reginald Farrer who was
more than enthusiastic, especially about the Kabshias, his 'shining beauties'.

After the Second World War many of the plants were no longer available
and cultivation of the genus waned. In the 1960s Valerie Finnis built up a
remarkable collection at Waterperry Nursery and, with some help from
fellow enthusiasts like the late Miss Cecilia Christie Miller, popularised the
Kabschias. In 1971 Valerie Finnis married Sir David Scott and moved to
Boughton House and its superb gardens.

During the 1970s Winton Harding appeared to be a lone voice extolling
the virtues of saxifrages. His stimulating book *Saxifrages*, first published by
the AGS in 1970, was the only modern book available that mentioned the
new species and cultivars.

In 1974 I became interested in the Kabschias and started growing and
studying them at Waterperry. It rapidly became apparent that most of the
plants in cultivation in Britain were wrongly named. Brian Arundel and I
struggled for years trying to sort them out with a limited amount of success.

Then in the early eighties we discovered the Czechs, particularly Dr
Radvan Horny, who had spent the previous twenty years studying Kabschias. During the decline of popularity here, the level of interest in
Czechoslovakia had risen to new heights. Dr Horny had access to many of
the cultivars introduced into his own country before the war and generously
made material available to us. In 1986 his comprehensive book *Porophyllum
Saxifrages* was published in Britain by John S. Byam-Grounds. This was
remarkable for two reasons. The first was that it published a binomial
system of classification for the cultivars, a system that related each cultivar
of a particular cross to a group name. For example all the 18 cultivars
resulting from *S. aretioides* × *burseriana* were gathered together under the
group name *S.* × *boydii*. Dr Horny published 62 bi-nomial groups and
brought order out of the chaos of names. The second was that he gave a
botanical description and drawing of each plant, thereby allowing us to
identify positively many of our plants.

Other factors which helped to build interest were the introduction of

Lincoln Foster's exciting new American hybrids. He generously sent me most of his new crosses and we have been able to introduce many into cultivation in Britain. The arrival from the Himalayas of many fascinating species collected by George Smith, Ron McBeath, John Templer and others have also aroused great interest.

Richard Gornall's recent revision of the genus is also stimulating interest in the plants. Several interesting points have come out of Richard's work. Firstly, most of the Engler and Irmscher's 1916 classification in *Das Pflanzenreich* has been confirmed. Secondly he has combined the sections Kabschia and Porophyllum (*S. oppositifolia* etc) as recently found links between plants in each section has made it unnecessary to keep them separate. Thirdly, the grouping together of the three old sections that contain the mossy saxifrages. Fourthly the confirmation, with scientific evidence, that *S. caesia* and *S. squarrosa* do belong to the Kabschias. Finally this was the first serious look at some of the new Himalayan species and their placing in the appropriate sub-sections. Furthermore the publication of *The Saxifrages of Europe* by Professor Webb and Richard Gornall, containing much useful information is inspiring more people to search out saxifrages in the wild. All this is expanding our now considerable knowledge.

Last but not least has been the success of the Saxifraga Group, which really does seem to be meeting a need. Brian Arundel and I tentatively suggested the possibility of forming such a group two years ago and were staggered when sixty people turned up to a discussion meeting at Waterperry. We now have approximately 250 members and useful work is proceeding, including cultivar registration, national reference collections in partnership with the NCCPG, the compilation of registers of plants in (or that have been) cultivation, and, finally, the publication of a high-quality journal.

Saxifrages are back and will soon, once again, take their rightful place in the hearts and minds of alpine gardeners.

The Evolving Art of the Rock Garden

JOHN PAGE

In British gardens through the nineteenth century the use of rocks as an interesting and ornamental feature took many different forms. In the 1830s, the natural rock was unearthed to decorate the pleasure ground at Redleaf in Kent. In the following decade, Joseph Paxton piled up great boulders of millstone grit in the Duke of Devonshire's garden at Chatsworth to add a touch of wildness and surprise beyond the formal lawns and beds surrounding the great house. At Biddulph Grange in Staffordshire, James Bateman and his designer Edward Cooke made extensive use of rockwork to provide a congenial home for the excellent collection of plants and some attempt at geological realism was made. A less ambitious 'rockery' might be found in almost any garden during this period, the playful suffix '-ery' indicating that this was usually a haphazard help of stones, though anything else was likely to be incorporated, such as tree stumps, flints, waste from local foundries or a battered bust of Dante. Plants used in these rockeries were mainly ground coverers such as ivy or periwinkle, and the inevitable ferns. Some gardeners were clearly more enterprising as the following extract from a letter to the editor in the *Gardeners' Chronicle* in 1849 shows: 'Rockwork! Good Mr. Editor do tell me how to make rockwork. I am anxious to have rock plants, and a rockery, and all that − Ferns, and Mosses and Alpines'. In attempting to answer the lady's question about her rockwork, the editor frivolously suggested a trip to Chatsworth. In fact, little was known about the difficult art of combining alpines and rocks.

There was no shortage of suitable plants. The floral treasures of the great mountain ranges of the world were coming into the country thick and fast, and the increasing number of visitors to Switzerland were bringing back the delights they had found high in the Alps. In her remarkable garden at Hoole House near Chester, Lady Broughton had a huge 'rock-fence' built which reproduced a mountain scene and glacier in the Savoy Alps. Here she grew soldanellas, campanulas and many other interesting alpines such as *Cortusa matthioli*, each in its own little 'nidus' of seemingly appropriate soil, top-dressed with light-coloured chippings to reflect heat and dark to absorb it. Normally, however, alpines at this time were grown in pots and where rock gardens as we know them were built, they tended to consist of mounds terraced with concentric circles of stone, topped by a crest of vertical, angular pieces. The outstanding exception was the alpine nursery of James Backhouse at York, which was in full swing in the 1850s. Half a century ahead of its time, this nursery housed a rock garden where alpines grew in crevices and what appear from the illustrations to be scree conditions. The firm specialised in building millstone grit rock gardens where bold, angular lumps were assembled to form soil pockets. By far its most spectacular creation was the mock Alpine scene built for Sir Frank Crisp at Friar Park, Henley-on-Thames. Seven thousand tons of the favourite stone were carted from Yorkshire to form a fantasy garden, all 'colour, grassy ways and singing water-courses', with a snow field at the crown below a make-believe Matterhorn. The rocks were brought together in irregular mounds as if they had been dumped by a glacier. Not perhaps to our taste, but the vast number of alpines grew well if one is to judge by the reports and pictures of the day.

The task faced by botanic gardens of gathering together and displaying the alpines for which the public so enthused was tackled in a variety of ways. Around 1870, the Edinburgh curator, James McNab, built a striking bank consisting of hundreds of separate square enclosures, 'each filled with soils suited for the various plants to be put into them'. Unlovely though it may have been, (Dean Hole called it a 'Lilliputian cemetery', though he hastened to add that it was 'a grand commencement'), the display made scientific and horticultural sense and was a winner with the public. The alpine plantsmen of the twentieth century would undoubtedly have found it fascinating. Over the influence of McNab's boxes on domestic rock gardens of the day, however, we will draw a veil. The nation's rock garden at Kew was rebuilt in 1882. It was based on a long, winding path, representing a Pyrenean stream bed, flanked by rocks from which flowers cascaded. Birmingham Botanic Garden wisely left the construction of its rock garden to Backhouse, and we await the restoration it is undergoing with interest.

Looking back in the 1890s, Dean Hole recalled a 'dim, very dim pre-vision in Rock Gardening' in his youth, which had then faded. There had been such a spate of awful failures that, even after the fine pioneering work of the Backhouse nursery and all the excellent advice of William Robinson in his revolutionary work Alpine Flowers for Gardens (1870), Hole could still sense amongst the horticulturalists of his day a strange indifference towards rock gardens. Farrer too agreed that there had been 'an almost general slump' in the noble art of growing alpines during the period 1870–90. Around the turn of the century something happened. The incurable condition that we now know as alpine gardening took hold. There emerged a new breed of owner-gardeners with enquiring minds, who found the cultivation of alpines supremely satisfying. Spurred on by the Swiss Henri Correvon, Director of the Alpine Garden at Geneva who visited this country regularly to spread the word, they experimented to find the right atmospheric conditions for their alpines, to check on what happened when the plants were grown in sphagnum moss, to investigate whether elevation was really necessary when they placed their rocks, to learn more about the use of fertilisers and so on. The Reverend C. Wolley Dod was growing his high alpines on potato ridges and in raised beds where the soil mixture was clearly a forerunner of the modern scree. Another cleric, Canon Henry Ellacombe, who had been to the Alps to see for himself the conditions which plants chose in nature, commended 'dwarf walls' with soil in the interstices. 1900 saw the publication of *Alpine Plants* by W. A. Clark who had managed the very large collection at the Backhouse nursery. Chiefly concerned with the problem of growing the rare and difficult, the book gave sound advice on soil mixtures, drainage and aeration. In the same year the *Gardeners' Chronicle* commented upon the effect that all this technical support was having. 'Of late years, as the love for alpine plants has increased, so the desire to cultivate them has extended. The herbarium, all-important as it is, by no means satisfies either the lover of plants for their own sakes, nor the student who wishes to investigate the structure and habits of the plants in question. Just now the study of what is called Ecology is earnestly pursued. Intelligent observers are not contented with simply observing and admiring – they must know the "reason why?".'

All this then was going on in the years before Reginald Farrer burst onto the scene and the question must be asked whether he really added anything which was essentially new. In his day, he was associated with the development of the moraine, his version of the scree, though Ellen Willmott and E. A. Bowles had worked on this earlier. His fame sprang from his writings, which in turn derived from his joy at discovering and studying 'the children of the hills' in their native habitats and from the fascination of grappling with the problems raised by their cultivation. If he does deserve to be called the father of alpine gardening in our time, his claim must rest on the passionate love for the plants he grew which he managed to convey to others. His sense of the individual personalities of alpines was extraordinary and the energy he devoted to their culture in British gardens fanatical. Henceforth, the rocks for rocks' sake approach of the Victorian era would give way to an interest in the plants themselves which was so strong that the rockwork would come a poor second and at times be insignificant. Those who knew Farrer were not imprssed by his handling of rock. For him it was simply a means to an end – better cultivation – though he clearly did care about the overall impression a rock garden made, whilst not worrying too much about geological accuracy. The finished garden should be 'of a piece', seeking an effect of 'linked and unforced naturalness' and imparting 'a feeling of calm, of real inevitability and balance.' The gardener must realise that the rules for his chosen medium of self-expression were the same as for any other work of art. There should be a clear plan, of a rocky glen, for example, such as an architect might produce for a house. In the 'golden afternoon' of Edwardian England, rock gardening developed from being a fashion to a 'movement' and finally a mania. Many bad gardens were foisted upon the public by jobbing gardeners who had become 'rockwork masters' overnight. Farrer's witty denunciation of the worst excesses of the day, the Drunkard's Dreams and the Plum-Buns and so on, (see *The Rock Garden*, circa 1912) must have improved the appearance of thousands of villa gardens. The wave of suburban gardeners, and enthusiasts with more land at their disposal, certainly needed guidance, because there was no shortage of conflicting advice in print. The influential Wolley-Dod, for example, a plantsman first and foremost, viewed any attempt at stratification as likely to undermine growing conditions. He therefore recommended the use of large and unshapely stones, buried deeply and avoiding symmetry, the chief aim being to produce pockets of suitable soil which did not dry out and, where necessary, provided shade. Yet another approach was that of Gertrude Jekyll who urged her readers 'to set the stones more or less in courses or in lines of stratification, just as we see them in nature in a stone quarry or any mountain side where surface denudation has left them standing out clearly in nearly parallel lines'. For Miss Jekyll the rockwork was but one part of the garden, to be placed at some distance from the house and to be approached gradually in order to 'avoid that rude shock so often experienced when the rock-garden comes into view, from its appearance being so uncompromisingly sudden'.

Another variant arose when the owner was lucky enough to have natural rocks on site. Farrer had a high cliff on the family estate at Ingleborough, and enjoyed great sport sending his gardeners down on rope ladders to plant up the fissures and gullies with seedlings or pelt the walls in the rain with balls of soil packed with seed. Sometimes the earth was removed to expose the bedrock, as at Brockhurst, the home of F. J. Hanbury near East Grinstead, where half a meadow was stripped to bring to light spectacular crags and ravines. With thoughtful planting and constant attention, fine effects were achieved, but the difficulty of maintaining alpines under these conditions proved to be formidable and only a few natural rock gardens of this type have survived. The exposed stone at Muckross House is one splendid example which has come down to us and the glaciated rocks at Rowallane and Brodick still provide an attractive setting.

For over a century, sandstone in its various forms had been the most popular choice in the rock garden. A breakthrough came when a Mr. John Wood from Skipton exhibited a weathered limestone and turf garden at the Royal Horticultural Society's show at the Temple in 1912. The *Gardeners' Chronicle* reported that it was 'by general consent the most natural piece of rockwork ever exhibited'. It contained no plants. Another straw in the wind was a rock-garden one foot square and full of good alpines (a trough!) which

Clarence Elliott described in 1917. Two schools of thought were emerging, later to be called the 'rockers' and the 'plantists.'

Matters came to a head in 1923 when Capt. B. H. B. Symons-Jeune exhibited a Mendip limestone rock garden at the RHS Chelsea Show which so brilliantly replicated nature that it turned the heads of the Society's officials. They disregarded the verdict of the judges they themselves had appointed and awarded the Captain first prize. The originality in his approach lay in his study of what actually happened to bands of rock as they outcropped, how the stone fractured as the result of successive pressures from different directions and how the outlines were shaped and softened by erosion. The photographs of his exhibit which caused the furore show a beautifully authentic rocky knoll with strong vertical fissures. There was a small waterfall and pool, and the whole creation was fringed with turf.

Evidently what the judges who had been unmoved by the masterpiece had disapproved of was the low number of alpines amongst the rocks and the suitability of their placing. In this they were nearer in spirit to the other camp of rock garden designers of the day which included such outstanding nurserymen-plantsmen as Reginald Kaye, Walter Ingwersen and Clarence Elliott. They too of course were producing fine rock gardens. The difference was that they were at the same time highly experienced growers who had specialised in alpines. Providing the plants for the swelling band of Farrer disciples, many of whom were to become founder-members of the Alpine Garden Society, they popularised new ways of using alpines in the garden such as troughs, sinks, roof gardens, alpine meadows and alpine lawns. They also gave fresh impetus to alpine houses, cliffs, walls, pavements, different types of scree, bog gardens and peat beds. 'Rock gardening' as a term could hardly cover now the range of activities involved and from about this time, the more ambitious 'alpine gardening' became more common. In fact, it was beginning to dawn upon many growers that one might not need the rock after all. Some gardeners of course were quite happy to have only rock. Churchill at Chartwell amongst them.

It must be said that, despite the magnificence of Symons-Jeune's rockwork, it was only a passing phase. With more than two or three species of alpine amongst his rocks and rills the whole illusion was spoiled, and maybe a nurseryman out of business. In reality, his wide vertical fissures were not the easist places to cultivate alpines, and the turf posed maintenance problems. Perhaps nature thought he was getting a bit too close for comfort. In 1927, the Captain was brought in to improve the garden at Lingholm near Keswick overlooking Derwentwater. He introduced an immaculate promontory and a Borrowdale slate bridge, described the original site as wood and swamp on either side of a little stream, hidden with alder scrub and brambles. When the author, with the kind permission of Lord Rochdale, visited the site recently the bridge was disappearing under a mantle of moss and he found wood and swamp on either side of a little stream. One seeks to better the Lake District at one's peril.

Neverhtheless, Symons-Jeune's influence was considerable and a great many of the scenic gardens that adorned the rock bank at Chelsea before and after the Second World War stuck to his principles. When they were constructed by a man with an eye of an artist such as Geoffrey Chalk who worked for Gavin Jones, they could reach heights of perfection. By the end of the 1960s, however, they were no longer to be seen at Chelsea.

Their disappearance has gone hand-in-hand with the rise of the alpine gardener as an exceptionally skilful cultivator of plants as evidenced by the wonderful exhibition which accompanied the Sixth International Conference we have just experienced. Now, the expert grower's chief media are his screes and raised beds, when he can be coaxed away from his alpine house and frames. We can take Duncan Lowe's scree near Lancaster as an example of the state of the art. The soil mixture is relatively shallow, and perhaps the most interesting and vital feature is the surface dressing. Gone are the evenly graded chippings, neat as the gravel on a new tomb. Instead we find between the low strata emerging from the scree a layer of rock fragments varying in size. The effect is visually pleasing and utterly convincing. The health and vigour of the alpines growing there is clear proof that the system works. The holy grail of rock gardening, a garden which makes horticultural sense and is at the same time aesthetically satisfying, may be within our grasp. Others might find it in the exquisite alpine garden which the AGS staged at the 1989 Chelsea show, which demonstrated that it is possible to make a garden sufficiently versatile to accommodate the enormous range of plants our members wish to grow and still delight the eye.

Modern housing with its postage-stamp back gardens has led to a general scaling down and one has the impression that less and less rock is being used, not because of the cost and the problems of its transportation, but simply because we lack the room. The very smallness of alpines and the possibility of having a collection which provides interest all the year round has made them ideal plants for our time. It comes as no surprise to learn that they constitute the fastest growing sector of the horticultural trade.

Alpines remain popular with the public at large. We have long since had fine municipal rock gardens, particularly at seaside resorts. The excellent Preston Park at Brighton, built in the thirties, is still worth a visit and 'rox populi' throughout the country are generally in good shape. Betjeman's rockeried roundabouts continue to adorn our dual carriage-ways. At Solihull in the West Midlands a handsome limestone affair is being used to cloak a former Council refuse tip. It is very successful, give or take the occasional whiff of methane.

Finally, it is pleasing to report that though the scenic rockworks of the mid-twentieth century are now no more than phantoms, the natural rock garden in its purest form is not dead. Betty Kershaw's plantings on her lovely outcrops and exposed limestones at Silverdale have deservedly won the AGS Gold Medal.

The Evolving Techniques of Growing Alpines

VIC ASPLAND

The overall rock garden scene has been reviewed in the last paper, so let us consider a few methods of cultivation in detail.

My first tale begins just ten miles from Reginald Farrer's Craven Nursery, with the opportunity that, it would seem, he missed. Mrs Mary Saunders lived in the village of Wennington, and must already have been an accomplished gardener at the time that he was taking his first faltering steps in rock garden construction. She was astute enough to notice that self-sown seedlings grew extremely well in a path made of coarse sand taken from a local stream, and to explore the possibilities. A stone trough was filled with the same sand, planted, and the experiment began. Its success was complete, and forty years later she was tending an impressive array of troughs, querns and the like, planted with alpines introduced by Farrer's Kansu expedition, as well as plants collected in the Alps. The large number of troughs accumulated allowed Mrs. Saunders to allocate to each plant its own trough. Before you rush home to starve your plants, I should add that the initial spartan fare was subsequently modified by the addition of leaf mould.

That, strangely, might have been the end of the story. It is most unlikely that Farrer did not visit Mrs. Saunders' garden and see the new development (in 1907 he was growing *Primula farinosa alba* which she had found growing locally and given to him), yet incredibly he did not take up the idea. As far as I am aware there is not a single reference in any of his writings to trough gardens. This is highly unusual, for he was never indifferent to any feature of alpine gardening; he either loved something to distraction or reviled it with the utmost vitriol.

So, for lack of a publicist, one of our most valuable methods of cultivation was unknown in the country at large. The next name to enter the field is Clarence Elliott, who established Six Hills Nursery in 1907, after being apprenticed at Backhouses of York. Quite independently, he began experimenting with the smaller alpines in about 1913, making bowl gardens, in bowls up to about 12–18ins (30–45cm) across. One of the bowls happened to have been made by an English potter, whose work was being sold at the time by a shop in Bond Street. Contact was made, Clarence does not relate how, and he subsequently embellished further bowls with miniature rock gardens for sale there. He considered the prices 'terrifyingly high', but his first offerings were all sold within a day, and a brisk repeat trade ensued. Within a few weeks however, the bandwagon began to roll, and cheap and nasty imitations were appearing in florists shops all over London. He had had enough, and soon withdrew. Clarence had come to know Mary Saunders, visited her on a number of occasions and took her technique to heart. Soon he was planting sinks for himself, and was impressed by the results! The plants flourished, even difficult ones. The explanation, he reasoned, was that 'one could concoct the most perfect soil confections and the drainage was faultless'.

Knowing he was on to a good thing, he obtained more sinks and made more gardens, and even supplemented the supply with stone pig-troughs. A selection of troughs featured in his exhibit at the Chelsea Flower Show in 1923 and were an immediate success; so much so that in subsequent years sinks began to appear in other exhibits. The public appetite had been whetted and soon he was writing articles for the gardening press to spread the gospel. By 1930 a trough famine had developed. Ever resourceful, he arranged for a supply of new troughs to be made, and first exhibited them at Chelsea in 1932. In a publicity handout produced a little later he observed that 'the stone shows a rugged craftsmanship without affectation or tiresome "rustic" effect'. You may be interested in the prices. A trough 30 × 18 × 6in (76 × 45 × 15cm) cost fifteen shillings (75p), and a stone pedestal to support it twelve shillings and sixpence (62.5p). In 1939 an exhibition of flower paintings at a London art gallery prompted the proprietor to invite him to exhibit some sink gardens in the principal room. With puckish humour Clarence took along three: in a stone sink, in a stone pig-trough and in a Nankin blue and white bidet. The comments of the art connoisseurs are not recorded, but it seems that the exploit did not seriously damage the progress of this method of cultivation which continues to increase in popularity. The photograph shows an example planted by Clarence's son Joe.

The development of the peat garden as we know it today did not have the same explosive quality as that of the trough, but we can identify its conception with a fair degree of certainty. The use of peat to enhance the moisture-retaining ability of soils, in particular to permit the growing of American ericaceae, was widely practised in the mid-19th century. Reginald Farrer used peat in the construction of his 'big bog', but had nothing to say about the peat garden; it had not yet arrived in Britain.

The first development was driven by necessity. Creating a garden in Abbeyleix in Ireland, Murray Hornibrook was faced with a total absence of stone, so he improvised. Retaining walls were built up using large blocks of top-spit peat cut from the nearby bogs. Infilling with peaty composts formed terraces in which a host of moisture-loving plans flourished: *Shortia*,

Trillium, *Ramonda*, *Primula*. The successful venture was featured in *The Garden* in 1914, and the seeds of the idea sown.

In the mid-1920s a pair of accomplished cultivators, Kenneth and Douglas McDougall were faced with a slightly different problem. Developing the garden at Logan on the Mull of Galloway, they had a host of seedling Chinese rhododendrons raised from seed collected by Farrer and Forrest for which planting space had to be found. A sloping site facing south-west seemed to offer the best prospects, and soon walls some 18in (45cm) high were being built across the slope, using peat slabs cut from a local bog, to form terraces some twelve feet (3.7m) wide. The peat used was not the top-spit material used by Hornibrook, but the deeper, less fibrous material such as is cut for fuel. (It proved to be sufficiently durable to still be in place after forty years, in spite of the many plants growing in and through it). Whether the brothers had seen Hornibrook's article is unknown. Was this an independent development along similar lines, or was it evolved from the original idea?

The south-west aspect was not a problem in an area with an annual rainfall of 40in (102cm) and so close to the sea. Indeed, the rhododendrons flowered all the better for the ample exposure to sunlight. The grape-black flowers of *R. tapienum* and the pink of *R. myrtilloides* were particularly impressive. *Nomocharis pardanthina* also flourished and was soon happily self-seeding into the peat. By the late 1930s the success of the project was abundantly obvious, the rhododendrons prospering to the point that they were growing into each other.

A visit to Logan by staff from the Edinburgh Royal Botanic Garden fired them with enthusiasm, and construction of a similar feature began at the RBG in 1938. The softer, more fibrous top-spit peat was used, with the intention of providing blocks which would be penetrated by plant roots almost at once. From the point of view of cultivation this choice was perfect, but by the end of the war many of the walls had collapsed, and had to be reconstructed to a somewhat reduced height. From that point on success was assured, and present-day visitors cannot fail to be impressed by the many ericaceous genera flourishing there, and in addition the mecanopsis and asiatic primulas (*P. flaccida* is my favourite at Edinburgh!). Following the example of Edinburgh, construction of peat gardens spread south, to Savill, Wisley, Kew, Ness, Harrogate etc. from where the alpine-growing public at large adopted the idea for themselves. Now all good garden centres offer peat blocks, and even a small garden can have a peat bed. Moving south and east brings, of course, the need for a more north-facing aspect, or irrigation, or both, but the plants *do* grow well. In 1981 a peat bed was built at Kew to house plants brought to 'Alpines '81' by Japanese delegates, and this was supported by low stone walls. This leads me on to the subject of raised beds in general. Supported by stone and usually containing a coarse, gritty and free-draining compost, they provide a range of habitats. The base of a raised bed facing west is ideal for ramondas, while the top of the bed will keep happy such sun-lovers as *Campanula allionii*. Ideal for a garden centrepiece, the raised bed can now be located close to the house, a location the Victorians would never have contemplated, even though they were probably developed by Shirley Hibberd around 1868.

Compared with the above developments, the tale of the scree is, to put it mildly, confused. It would seem that those involved in its development could not agree precisely what it was, how to make it, or what to call it. The first artificial screes were made in Austria in the late 1850s, but the transfer of the principle to Britain was very slow. By 1891 the Rev. Wolley-Dodd was discussing the principle, but there is no firm evidence that he actually built a scree until the very late 1890s. We do not know if Farrer read of the early efforts or discovered the principle independantly, but by 1909 he was writing of his first scree. He had brought four large and handsomely weathered limestone blocks together and filled the cavity between them with 'some sharp large rubbish for drainage' followed by 'chips of blue limestone, such as they use in these parts for mending roads. And, with this a faint adulteration only, of soil'. The plants were installed, and flourished, even difficult specimens like *Campanula zoysii*. Farrer was beside himself with pleasure, and longed to take it with him on his travels (a somewhat impractical proposition). Thus was made possibly the first scree in Britain. Unfortunately Farrer called it the Old Moraine, and helped to sow the seeds of confusion for the next twenty years.

Clapham, the village in which the Farrer's Nursery lay, has an annual rainfall of over 47in (120cm), so not unnaturally the benefits of the scree which he most extolled were open texture and free drainage. In the more arid south the sparse conditions of his moraine were considered unsatisfactory, and Reginald Malby was attempting to model more closely the conditions in a natural glacial moraine, with copious supplies of underground water. He dug hollows in the garden and lined them with concrete, building in water feeds and drains, and then filling them with coarse scree mixture. In summer the drains were closed, and the concrete basin filled with water, while in winter the drains were opened to allow the water to escape. These constructions were also called moraines, and Malby cited among the plants flourishing in his *Campanula zoysii*. J. H. Jenkins published a plan for a concrete moraine in 1913. The debate between the factions had the benefit of spreading the gospel, and in *The English Rock Garden* (1913) the dogmatic Farrer also felt obliged to offer a diagram of a concrete moraine trough 'while at the same time preferring . . . to abstain from such unnecessary expense', a neat rearguard action.

By 1928 Clarence Elliott was building all kinds of scree: acid, limestone, rich, poor, all with equal success, and with not an ounce of concrete laid. He referred to this time as a sort of Heath Robinson period in rock gardening and confessed: 'being a simple gardener with no gift for sanitary engineering I never fell for such refinements; good results were reported from such contraptions at the time, but one hears little of them now'. The AGS was born shortly afterward, and the fourteenth *Bulletin* was devoted to the scree. It shows that by 1933 writers could still not agree on how to build one, what the ideal mixture was, and still, what to call it. Will Ingwersen's article was titled 'Experiments in My Moraine' and he used the terms scree and moraine interchangeably, remarking finally that for horticultural purposes there was no difference. In spite of the lack of agreement on detail, all were agreed that the scree was a very good thing. There was no mention of concrete, for that battle had been decisively won. There are fine examples of screes at Edinburgh and St. Andrews, but possibly the finest modern example is at Würzburg Botanic Garden, for the size distribution of the rock fragments has been carefully graded to give a most natural appearance. In the Mediterranean area *Edraianthus graminifolius* creeps about and smothers itself with flowers, while *Erinacea anthyllis* and *Astragalus angustifolius* make large flower-covered mounds.

In 1985 however, the moraine was triumphantly brought up to high-tech date by Ray Radebaugh of Louisville, Colorado, an area renowned for its very drying winds. Using modern materials and equipment he has reproduced the structure of a natural moraine: an impervious sloping foundation overlain by a free-draining deposit of rock particles, and a continuous underground flow of glacier meltwater. His site was carefully graded and the waterproof foundation provided not by concrete, but by 6mm polythene sheeting. Unlike the early structures, this one leads into a drainage trench at low level, so there can be no outlet blockages and no flooding even in wet weather. Water distribution at the top of the moraine was arranged by forming a shallow channel up to 6in (15cm) wide and 2in (5cm) deep. The polythene sheet covers the whole area and was then covered with gravel of about ³⁄₈in (1cm) diameter to a depth of up to 2in (5cm). With water supplied to the feed channel, capillary action should draw water down the slope and up to the surface of the gravel layer. Any dry spots were thinned until this was so. An open gritty compost and a garnish of rocks completed the construction. Water is supplied by ¹⁄₄in (0.6cm) copper pipe controlled by a stainless steel needle valve. Ray's 60 square foot (5.6m² moraine consumes a moderate five to ten gallons (23–45 litres) of water per day. Is it worth the effort? Be assured that it is, for here grow *Raoulia monroi* and *R. lutescens*. *Cassiope lycopodioides* and *Calceolaria darwinii* flower well, and *Dicentra eximia* is seeding down! Anyone eager to have a go should consult the *Bulletin* of the American Rock Garden Society Vol. 48 No. 4 (Fall 1990).

In 1911 the Swiss nurseryman Henri Correvon gave a lecture on alpine gardens to the Royal Horticultural Society. Paradoxically he reviewed mostly English gardens, such as Sir Frank Crisp's Friar Park situated at

59   *Saxifraga lolaensis* from Tibet (see page 211)

60   *Saxifraga aristulata* from the Himalayas (see page 211)

61   One of the earliest rock gardens at Hoole House (see page 213)

62   A modern AGS Gold Medal rock garden belonging to Betty Kershaw (see page 219)

63   One of Joe Elliott's troughs (see page 221)

64   The scree at Würzburg Botanic Garden, with *Edraianthus graminifolius* (see page 225)

65   This *Rhodothamnus chamaecistus* won Best of Show at Warwick (see page 228)

66   *Crocus scardicus* at the Warwick Show (see page 230)

Henley on Thames. It had a rock garden constructed from ten thousand tons of millstone grit transported from Bradford and was completed by a scale model Matterhorn with tinplate Chamois. He also mentioned the prowess of Mary Saunders as a cultivator and seeing at Wennington *Eritrichium nanum* and *Androsace helvetica* 'flowering wonderfully'. He stated that the maritime English climate suited alpine plants better than the continental climate of Switzerland. He praised the artistry of British rock gardens and described the Swiss garden Linnaea situated at Bourg St. Pierre in the Valais as 'constructed very unaesthetically and with the most deplorable artistic effect'. He did, however, claim for the Swiss superiority in the matter of wall culture. In his garden at Floraire he built a wall of roughly squared tufa blocks and on the south face planted saxifrages, androsace, dianthus, draba and campanula. Acantholimons went on top, and *Saxifraga florulenta*, ramondas and primulas to the north. A contemporary photograph by Ellen Willmott shows his enviable results. He told his audience that several hundred alpine plants had been set in the old fortifications below the Promenade St. Antoine in Geneva, and that several mountain railway companies had made similar plantings in trackside walls. As many of you know, Roy Elliott built a tufa cliff in 1961, sheltered below a cantilevered roof. Here for many years flourished *Jankaea heldreichii*, sharing the cliff with *Erinacea anthyllis*, *Saxifraga* 'Tumbling Waters' and plebian *Erinus alpinus*. The principle has now been developed in a highly sophisticated way by Michael Kammerlander at Würzburg, with outstanding results. In a specially constructed glasshouse plates of tufa 2.5–4in (6–10cm) thick are supported on a steel framework and supplied with water from behind by way of a thick bed of sand. Embedded pipes provide water input and drainage. The water content of the sand is monitored by electronic sensors, and the water supply is controlled by electronic instruments. Even with this level of sophistication it is still necessary to determine the optimum water levels suitable for a particular group of plants, but thereafter this level can be maintained automatically. *Primula gaubeana* does well in the present regime, chosen particularly to suit dionysias, for example *DD. involucrata*, *tapetodes*, *imbricata* and *curviflora*.

Possibly the most innovative centre for the outdoor cultivation of alpines today is the Botanic Garden of Brno, Czechoslovakia. Josef Holzbecher and his collaborators have taken a keen interest in the provision of fissures for the roots of alpine plants to explore. Sinks are filled with closely-packed layers of slate – a technique examined in England some years ago by Ralph Haywood, Joe Elliott's nursery foreman – and have proved to be particularly good homes for saxifrages. Totally new however are the 'slate stacks'. Parallel concrete slabs are erected to stand 3–4ft (90–120cm) high and about one foot (30cm) apart, and the space between is packed with slate slabs, stacked on edge. Androsaces and other cushion plants find this environment satisfactory as any excess moisture is rapidly shed from the neck of the plant. Replacing the slate with tufa and choosing a more shady site has provided a congenial vertical habitat for ramondas. Elsewhere horizontal crevices have been tested, and found to be better suited to the needs of *Vitaliana primuliflora* for example. The crevice life will, it appears, suit the most unexpected plants for in a moist vertical wall of loosely-stacked blocks *Rhododendron camtschaticum* occupies this unlikely niche, and flowers prolifically to show that all is well.

Probably unique to Brno are the 'saxifrage staircases'. These are best described simply as shallow-sided troughs mounted at an angle of about $30°$ to the horizontal. The lower ends dip into a water channel from which the tufa-rich filling is able to draw up water. The overall appearance may not be to the taste of the conventional alpine gardener, but the results obtained should give him pause for thought.

This brings to a close my review of this century of alpine gardening, for which the outlook is optimistic. Modern enthusiasts are still using some of the old faithful methods in their original forms, updating others, and still pushing back the boundaries of the possible in the search for new techniques. As this conference shows, rock gardening is alive and well!

The Conference Show

ROBERT ROLFE

In ten years the venue had only shifted an hour's drive from the Nottingham location of 'Alpines '81', the date was much the same, so too the number of entries, and a heartening number of exhibitors had kept the faith, even if some took one look at the flight of stairs leading to the show-hall, another at the array of heavy pots in their carboot, and felt the full impact of the intervening years.

A fundamental difference, however, was apparent in the plants on display; it would be instructive simply to list them all in the manner of a classroom register (the only way that an article of this size could hope to be comprehensive) but by identifying certain trends and highlighting a few of the plants, easy and challenging, familiar and obscure, some indication of the overall display may emerge. If you expected a cogent recital of the awards and their winners, apologies are in order.

Last time around notebooks were optimistically scribbled in when a slide of *Clematis marmoraria* appeared on the lecture screen; delegates mulled over the scarcity of certain dionysias; and wished they had brought along their copies of Sampson Clay as mention was made of *Oreopolus glacialis* and Jim Archibald spirited up visions of nototriches. At Warwick the clematis, along with a spectacular example of the first in a burgeoning line of hybrids, *C. × cartmannii* 'Joe', attracted admiration but no great surprise, nor were the vigorous young plants of *Dionysia bryoides* and *D. lamingtonii* that lined one nursery's stand sold out scarcely before delegates had unpacked their suitcases — a consequence, perhaps, of the labyrinthine routeways along which an astonishing variety of alpines were being offered for sale. A small plant of the oreopolus revealed the first of its creamy yellow flowers to a suitably impressed audience (notwithstanding a cavalier reception from the set of judges responsible for its fate on the bench), whilst *Nototriche compacta* put in a discreet appearance . . . plants have now been in cultivation for three years and a few have yielded the occasional flower.

That the show brought together some remarkable plants will surprise no-one: picking at random one might give special mention to *Fritillaria pluriflora*, a group of half a dozen several flowered spikes, to see the equal of which a journey to California would be necessary; a hearty mound of *Nassauvia gaudichaudii* where a very tentative examination with a diary pencil (for heavens sake, do not emulate this practice when the plant next appears) revealed a dependance upon a thick central stock, with just a few of the lower branches rooting along their length; *Cypripedium japonicum* up to a total of seventeen pink, inflated flowers after an unpromising start in life – a single crown of the withered sort that required resuscitation long before any thoughts of future triumph could be entertained; and an abundantly flowered *Epigaea repens*, covered in waxy white clusters of blossom like some dwarfed, procumbent stephanotis, devoid of the excessive and frosted leafiness that is its general lot in the garden.

Determining the premier award posed difficulties of both logic and logistics: the ability to argue the merits of a particular plant could reasonably be left to its sponsoring judge, but who would wish to be Mary Randall, directing some 40 such individuals and trying to convert the babble of opinion into a generally-felt preference? There was also the task of heaving a beautifully planted trio of *Paraquilegia anemonoides*, a ferny-based mass of rich violet, quivering cups, onto the assessment table; the absence of a pot size limit had enabled Henry and Margaret Taylor to enter their stone-layered trough tenanted by this species, and as one of the removal men, it was a relief *not* to be advising the owners of damage in transit.

Selecting not merely a country-wide but an international judging panel revealed interesting differences in the criteria used to evaluate a plant. Virtually everyone has some plant or other that grows unusually well in their locality, but this is surely no good reason for denigrating it on the showbench. It is the best plant in the show (not the most difficult or unusual) that is sought, and if *Narcissus bulbocodium* is counted as a reliable plant – there was a prodigiously flowered potful in immaculate condition up for consideration, or *Primula elatior* is known to flood some East Anglian woodlands with its jangling lemon flowers (an especially fine clump was adjudged the best plant in Section C), then these qualities should not in themselves be used as a lever for downpointing. Less familiar plants from more exotic locations can be every bit as rampant: after all, *Viola diversifolia* will on occasion carpet the higher screes of the eastern Pyrenees in a colour range from lilac to near purple, and was dominant in one nursery's greenhouse only three years after being introduced, but few would find fault with the elegantly poised specimen staged at the Conference.

The counter argument runs that some plants are unwilling to submit to cultivation just about *anywhere* and it was one of these, a fifteen year old *Rhodothamnus chamaecistus* lifted from the peatbed in preparation for a housemove, that gained the accolade Best in Show. Obtained from the Lancashire nursery of Reginald Kaye in the days when his catalogue offered it in two sizes . . . where other than the seedlists does it appear nowadays . . . it had formed an unblemished 20cm mound profusely decked with pale rose pink flowers, fluttering its eyelash-like exserted stamens at the judges with devastating effect. One accepts that it is possible to instance examples of the species with larger and more intensely coloured flowers but hesitates to label them automatically superior.

If you really want to bestow 'missing' components on a given species then raising plants from seed is one option, although it is of course possible to go the whole hog and entertain the idea of garden hybrids. Barry Starling's work with Ericaceae continues apace, and in the class intended to demonstrate 'the relationships and differences between species within a genus', *Kalmiopsis leachiana* lent its qualities to both the rhodothamnus (several clones proving to be excellent garden plants) and every species of *Phyllodoce* bar *P. nipponica*. Of the four plants representing the latter bigeneric cross, there was widespread admiration for a plant simply labelled as a sister seedling to × *Phylliopsis* 'Sugar Plum', a combination involving in this case *P. caerulea*, with a dwarf, compact habit and indications of notably generous blooming, the upper portion of every shoot wreathed with capacious bonnets of the colour implied by the cultivar name.

Such plants do not necessarily mix well on the showbench, and the segregation of the primula classes into naturally occurring and artificially engineered plants is a worthwhile development.

Hence the purist could enjoy the restrained perfection of *Primula amoena*, the firm hirsute stems cascading with large wine-coloured flowers, and of the little-seen *P. hazarica*, a Kashmiri representative of the Farinosae section showing a well filled, lilac pink umbel, which had been reared from the exhibitor's own seed – so often the Himalayan species do not progress beyond a first (and last) blooming from wild collected seed. Those who attended the Showing symposium heard that well-rotted manure was a boon in growing these plants; possibly living close to the stables at Newmarket had something to do with the reason for success?

On the other hand there was little doubting the popularity of the more recent European primula hybrids: in particular, *P. allionii* has shown a markedly improving influence on the rather over hearty *P.* 'Linda Pope', and elsewhere could be seen contributing to a pure white *P. hirsuta* (= *P.* × 'Snowcap') and to the various manifestations of *P.* × *pubescens*. This last marriage has produced what several overseas visitors deemed one of the highlights of the show, a plant with clusters of up to five, 1.2in (3cm) wide white flowers, stained blue/pink around the petal notch. Brian Burrow, whose efforts have produced so many of these plants, has kindly released a list documenting details of parentage, and in view of the confusion in naming evident at the show, it is worth noting that the plant has the reference number p79/7, is a result of *P. allionii* 'Crowsley Var.' × *pubescens* 'Harlow Car', and has the proposed sobriquet *P.* 'Pink Ice'.

Startling in a different way was the sheer number of exhibits owing their presence to the collecting activities of just three men, all of them present for the occasion, though lecturing on current endeavours as much as past achievement. From the MacPhail and Watson 1977 expedition to Turkey there was the dramatic *Tulipa undulatifolia*, scarlet red in that dusky manner peculiar to the genus (one of several dwarf species gaining popularity now that we appreciate not every tulip comes from Amsterdam or in a bunch via Interflora) and that most concise of linums, *L. aretioides*, whilst the Pern & Watson Andean seedpackets have yielded among others *Lithodraba mendocinensis*, a neat cushion of slightly flexed linear leaves that has yet to bear the relatively large white flowers mentioned in the relevant Flora. One of Jim Archibald's earlier finds, *Crocus scardicus* JCA 760, delighted those able to attend on the first day with a short-lived display of its rich yellow chalices . . . the irrefutable reply to anyone querying the wisdom of a class for the genus so late in the season, and coming up to date there was a well-budded group of *Cryptantha ochroleuca*, showing little sign of missing the high limestone screes of Utah apart from a susceptibility to botrytis. Finally, we had Ron McBeath to thank for the presence of *Saxifraga rhodopetala*, a promising species with delicate cymes of rich pink flowers (its owner was handed a box of material originating in Nepal and described as *S. andersonii* forms which was found to contain no less than four different species), and for the yet scarcer *Saussurea tridactyla*, germinating well from a collection made on Kanchenjunga but needing a cool, dry atmosphere to develop into the 4in (10cm) rosette swathed in white wool that triumphed in the class for new or rare plants. Other plants from this source have flowered in cultivation but the semi-obscured purple florets are more an achievement for the grower than an adornment for the plant.

It was one of the strengths of the Conference that at every corner people with direct experience of the plants in their natural state could be found to interpret the exhibits. Studying a deep pink *Trillium hibbersonii* that had thrown a four-petalled flower among its standard issue colleagues, we were told that the white-flowered plant dominant in garden stocks is not particularly representative of wild populations (another site is now known but access is difficult at blooming time due to torrential rain: no wonder it grows so well in the open garden, despite a residual reluctance to 'risk' it there). The precise status of this plant is currently under investigation at the University of British Columbia Botanical Garden.

Some of the observations made were rather less helpful; it might have been illuminating to follow – at a discreet distance – the man who gazed upon a healthy *Primula aureata* and its neighbour, the decorative *P. × kewensis*,* pronounced them one and the same plant, and said he preferred the second of the two because the flowers had assumed their proper colour and the scape its full size instead of remaining squashed in the rosette.

Faced with that sort of advice, it was decided to examine the displays of

---

* In England, at least, often exhibited incorrectly as *P. gaubeana*, a somewhat scarce species in our gardens at present and wholly distinct from its changeling.

photographs and paintings, covering every spare metre of available space around the periphery of the hall, and gaining by their position adjacent to the plants instead of some darkened room down-the-corridor-second-on-the-left-then-first-right-you-can't-miss-it. Repeatedly they proved complementary in relation to the showbench exhibits, so that a memorable print of *Raoulia eximia* in a flock clinging to a ridge with a geometric geology like some replica of the Giant's Causeway had its counterpart in a perfectly even, pot grown mound, humped like the business part of a bowler hat: the seamless silvery green rosettes gave off a sheen as if made from crushed velvet. Similarly a restrained watercolour depicting a single shoot of *Erythronium revolutum* passed the test for verisimilitude when compared with Kath Dryden's large panful of this species. Having now raised literally thousands of this and other species from seed, she presently keeps the densely packed young plants in an open wooden frame, protected by a holly hedge from scorching sunlight and buffeting winds, which account for the majority of setbacks in early life.

Combining the best of both worlds, Edinburgh Royal Botanic Garden brought down a storyboard demonstrating the diversity of alpine climates and habitats, fronted by two modernistic hexagonal containers, one chiefly housing New Zealand cushion plants, the other colourfully crammed with the diversity of bulbous plants – the perfect setting for the otherwise rather tall *Fritillaria elwesii*, rising through the understory of its brightly painted cohabitants to display twinned or tripleted dusky purple bells, and for the creamy yellow spikes of *Muscari macrocarpum*, whose sweet cinnamon scent pervaded the entire exhibit.

Nearby, the University of Liverpool Botanic Gardens at Ness assembled a wide-ranging collection that included a covetable clump of *Iris melitta* (the crimson pink flowers holding up well in the warmth of the Hall) and several mature examples of plants grown for foliage and form . . . a fastigiate huddle of *Santolina chamaecyparissus* 'Small-ness' drew attention, though its christening suggested an advanced case of 'tin ear'.

It was, in the best sense of the words, a colourful show, whether your eye fell on the duplicate yellow domes of *Dionysia aretioides* or focused on individual delights such as Dr. Tom Norman's navy and lilac *Orchis longicornu*. It was also one that combined mass appeal and covert elitism; if you had that 'seen it all before' feeling when confronted by immaculate hybrid rhododendrons there was always refuge in the diminutive appeal of *Primula caveana*, the peeping white buds of *Chionohebe densifolia* (cf. its widely-feted Australian sibling) or perhaps *Fritillaria striata*, intricately striped within and, like the soldanellas opposite, repaying examination of this uncanvassed asset. It was the show that gave the lie to the notion of some wait 'till you're asked plant distribution scheme for the advanced exhibitor; where you could buy seed of *Viola cotyledon* when the unflowered but alluring clump on the showbench had worked its charm, or join the plant sales throng to pick out plants habitually saddled with the adjective unobtainable.

Above all it was enjoyable – not for the iris, etiolating progressively after five days of unsuitable accommodation, nor for plants from areas of high rainfall, however mollifying the dedicated efforts of the watering team – but for the continuous round of people who went through the door and witnessed a truly representative range of alpine plants.

Index